PROTEIN BIOCHEMISTRY, SYNTHESIS, STRUCTURE AND CELLULAR FUNCTIONS

CYTOCHROMES *b* AND *c*

BIOCHEMICAL PROPERTIES, BIOLOGICAL FUNCTIONS AND ELECTROCHEMICAL ANALYSIS

PROTEIN BIOCHEMISTRY, SYNTHESIS, STRUCTURE AND CELLULAR FUNCTIONS

Additional books in this series can be found on Nova's website under the Series tab.

Additional e-books in this series can be found on Nova's website under the e-book tab.

CYTOCHROMES *b* AND *c*

BIOCHEMICAL PROPERTIES, BIOLOGICAL FUNCTIONS AND ELECTROCHEMICAL ANALYSIS

RURIK THOM
EDITOR

New York

For permission to use material from this book please contact us:
Telephone 631-231-7269; Fax 631-231-8175
Web Site: http://www.novapublishers.com

NOTICE TO THE READER

The Publisher has taken reasonable care in the preparation of this book, but makes no expressed or implied warranty of any kind and assumes no responsibility for any errors or omissions. No liability is assumed for incidental or consequential damages in connection with or arising out of information contained in this book. The Publisher shall not be liable for any special, consequential, or exemplary damages resulting, in whole or in part, from the readers' use of, or reliance upon, this material. Any parts of this book based on government reports are so indicated and copyright is claimed for those parts to the extent applicable to compilations of such works.

Independent verification should be sought for any data, advice or recommendations contained in this book. In addition, no responsibility is assumed by the publisher for any injury and/or damage to persons or property arising from any methods, products, instructions, ideas or otherwise contained in this publication.

This publication is designed to provide accurate and authoritative information with regard to the subject matter covered herein. It is sold with the clear understanding that the Publisher is not engaged in rendering legal or any other professional services. If legal or any other expert assistance is required, the services of a competent person should be sought. FROM A DECLARATION OF PARTICIPANTS JOINTLY ADOPTED BY A COMMITTEE OF THE AMERICAN BAR ASSOCIATION AND A COMMITTEE OF PUBLISHERS.

Additional color graphics may be available in the e-book version of this book.

Library of Congress Cataloging-in-Publication Data

ISBN: 978-1-63117-467-4

Library of Congress Control Number: 2014933509

Published by Nova Science Publishers, Inc. † *New York*

CONTENTS

PREFACE

In this book the authors present further research on the study of cytochrome C as well as cytochrome B. Some of the topics discussed in the book include the regulation of cytochrome C in respiration as well as its role in apoptosis. It also focuses on the structural aspects and touches base on cytochrome B5 as a pleiotropic metabolic modulator.

Chapter 1 - Despite the fact that over 200 phosphorylation sites have been mapped on the mitochondrial oxidative phosphorylation (OxPhos) complexes, very little is known about the relevant cell signaling pathways and the terminal kinases and phosphatases that control these phosphorylations. Within OxPhos, cytochrome c (Cyt$c$) plays a special role because it is not only involved in electron transport but is also a key executer of apoptosis when it is released from the mitochondria. It is therefore not surprising that Cyt$c$ is regulated by phosphorylation. Four phosphorylation sites have been mapped on mammalian Cyt$c$, two of which have been studied functionally, demonstrating that both respiration and apoptosis are under the control of signaling pathways that have yet to be identified. A review begins here of the regulation and multiple functions of mammalian Cyt$c$, including respiration, reactive oxygen species (ROS) scavenging under healthy conditions, ROS production via p66[Shc], and cardiolipin oxidation during apoptosis. Then, targeting Cyt$c$ by manipulation of signaling cascades as a therapeutic avenue in conditions including neurodegeneration and cancer.

Chapter 2 – Cytochrome b_5 (Cb_5) acts within the cells as a pleiotropic co-factor of multiple enzymes and redox chains that play critical roles for normal function of healthy mammalian organisms. It is maintained in the reduced form largely by the NADH-dependent cytochrome b_5 reductase activity which catalyzes electron transfer to Cb_5 in mammalian cells. The enzyme system cytochrome b_5 reductase/cytochrome b_5 has been shown to be associated with the endoplasmic reticulum, mitochondria and plasma membrane of mammalian cells, where it is involved in multiple metabolic pathways, such as cholesterol biosynthesis, desaturation and elongation of fatty acids, methemoglobin reduction and steroids and xenobiotics metabolism catalyzed by cytochrome P450s. More recently, this system has been shown to be a component of the 'so-called' redox-chain of the plasma membrane present in mammalian cells, where it clusters within cholesterol-rich and caveolins-rich lipid rafts-associated sub-microdomains of the plasma membrane. The cytochrome b_5 reductase/cytochrome b_5 is also a relevant system in the redox biology of cell death, as it forms a stable complex with cytochrome c, a pro-apoptotic signalling molecules, and it is involved in the modulation of superoxide generation in mammalian cells, playing a major role in the NADH-dependent superoxide anion production of the neuronal plasma membrane accounting for most of the superoxide anion overshot that is observed in an early stage of the neuronal apoptosis. In addition, an expanding family of proteins containing a Cb_5-like domain is also present in mammalian cells. Both, the novel cellular functions described for Cb_5 and for novel proteins containing a Cb_5-like domain point out that Cb_5 can be seen as an intracellular signaling molecule in redox biology and as a potential cellular biomarker of health and disease.

Chapter 3 – Cytochrome c (cyt c) functions as a mobile electron carrier in the respiratory chain anchored to the external side of the inner mitochondrial membrane and shuttling electrons from cyt c reductase to cyt c oxidase. A further function of cyt c, beyond respiration, is realized outside mitochondria in the apoptotic program. Cyt c may respond to different environments by changing its fold, thus favouring the exertion of different biological functions in different pathophysiological cell conditions. The binding of lipids (free fatty acids as well as acidic phospholipids) to cyt c induces conformational changes and partial unfolding of the protein, strongly influencing cyt c oxidase/peroxidase activity. In the early events of apoptosis, the interaction of cyt c with a mitochondrion-specific phospholipid, cardiolipin (CL), brings about a conformational transition of the protein and acquirement of peroxidase activity. Transitions among different conformations are regulated by endogenous molecules such as ATP. Apoptosis is strictly connected to the pathogenesis of many human diseases, including neoplastic, neuro-degenerative and cardiovascular diseases, and derangements of cardiolipin biosynthesis and remodeling are crucial in regulation of apoptosis. So as the role of cyt c in respiration and apoptosis rely on its interaction with CL, the present book chapter reviews the structural features of this complex. Then a description of how perturbations in CL amount, acyl composition and CL-driven allosteric modulation of the cyt c properties, may contribute to cell fate.

Chapter 4 – For many decades mitochondrial cytochrome c was assumed to have a single biological role, namely the transfer of electrons from Q-cytochrome c oxido-reductase (cytochrome bc_1) to cytochrome c oxidase in the electron transfer chain responsible for the production of the mitochondrial proton motive gradient. Chapter 4 explores the growing range of functions which have been identified for cytochrome c. For example, cytochrome c has been shown to interact with specific lipid molecules which induce peroxidase enzymic activity in the protein. More recently cytochrome c has been shown to have a major role in apoptosis, following its stimulated release from mitochondria into the cytosol, where it provides a 'feed forward' amplification cascade. Evidence is also now emerging that the pro-apoptotic action of cytosolic cytochrome c, at least in some cells, can be further modulated by its reactions with other heme proteins.

Chapter 5 – Novel redox-active metallotherapeutic agents were used to develop effective antimicrobial remedies differing from standard antibiotics in their mechanism of action with participation of free-radical intermediates. For this purpose redox-active compounds carrying sterically hindered 1,2-dihydroxybenzene moieties along with metal ions in a single scaffold have been synthesized and characterized by means of chemical and physic chemical methods as well as screened for their antimicrobial activity against Gram-negative bacteria (*Escherichia coli, Pseudomonas aeruginosa, Serratia marcescens*), Gram-positive bacteria (*Bacillus subtilis, Sarcina lutea, Staphylococcus aureus, Mycobacterium smegmatis*), yeasts (*Cryptococcus laurentii, Lipomyces lipofer, Candida albicans, Candida boidinii, Candida utilis, Saccharomyces cerevisiae*) and fungi (*Aspergillus niger, Alternaria alternata, Mucor spp., Botrytis cinerea, Monilia spp, Fusarium spp., Penicillium lividum, Sclerotinia sclerotiorum*). This screening revealed silver(I) complexes that may be considered as potential chemotherapeutic agents with activity higher than or comparable to that of some standard drugs such as tetracycline, streptomycin, chloramphenicol, isoniazid, amphotericin B, fluconazole, terbinafine. Using the method of cyclic voltammetry, it shows some phenolic ligands as well as their silver (I) complexes to be also of a pronounced reducing ability. Bacterial cytochrome c-like enzymes being among the first targets for redox-active antimicrobials on their way into the cell, spectrophotometric investigation was carried out in order to estimate the rate of bovine heart cytochrome c reduction with the compounds synthesized.

Oxidation of 1, 2-dihydroxybenzene derivatives and their silver (I) complexes *in vitro* under anaerobic conditions can include two successive one-electron steps of oxidation of their ionic forms to yield *o*-benzoquinones on interaction with cytochrome *c* *via* intermediate *o*-benzosemiquinone formation. The results obtained are discussed in view of presumed correlation between the capability of the compounds synthesized for reducing cytochrome *c*, antimicrobial activity, and physico-chemical characteristics (redox properties determined electrochemically, lipophilicity, ionization constants of the ligands and stability constants of the metal complexes).

Chapter 6 – Cytochrome *c* (cyt *c*) is a mitochondrial membrane hemoprotein of high physiological importance. First, cyt *c* is one of the key elements of respiration chain transferring electrons from cyt *c* reductase (*bc*1 complex) to cyt *c* oxidase. Second, release of cyt c from the intermembrane space of mitochondria into the cytosol triggers the apoptotic pathway. The idea that specific interactions between cyt *c* and cardiolipin (CL), the main lipid component of mitochondrial membrane, are crucial to the protein biological activities, constantly receives further corroboration from both theoretical and experimental studies. Despite considerable progress achieved in the field of cyt *c* – CL biophysics, the detailed structural description of protein-lipid complexation is still lacking. The present study applies Förster resonance energy transfer (RET) technique to give comprehensive characterization of cyt *c* binding to the model lipid membranes composed of the mixtures of zwitterionic lipid phosphatidylcholine (PC) with anionic lipids phos-phatidylglycerol (PG), phosphatidylserine (PS) or cardiolipin (CL) in different molar ratios. The donor-acceptor pairs were represented by either anthrylvinyl-labeled PC (AV-PC) or anthrylvinyl-labeled CL (AV-CL) incorporated in trace amounts in lipid vesicles, and heme moiety of cyt *c*. Association of the protein with the lipid bilayers led to the decrease in donor fluorescence reflecting energy transfer from AV fluorophore to heme. The most effective RET was found for CL-containing membranes. This observation has been interpreted in terms of higher affinity of cyt *c* to CL as compared to other anionic lipids. In order to get understanding of protein specificity to CL, RET was measured as a function of CL content and ionic strength. Monte Carlo analysis of multiple datasets revealed a complex interplay between several processes, namely i) lipid demixing; ii) CL transition into extended conformation; iii) formation of hexagonal phase. The switch between these states was found to be controlled by CL content and salt concentration. These characteristics of cyt *c* – CL interaction are of great interest not only in the context of regulating cyt c electron transfer and apoptotic propensities, but also from the viewpoint of the protein biogenesis.

Chapter 7 – The initial stage of a number of neurodegenerative diseases, including Alzheimer's disease (AD), is characterized by oxido-reductive imbalance leading towards free radicals production as well as towards the impaired respiration in mitochondria. Both the decreased activity of cytochrome c oxidase (COX), i.e. the Complex IV of the respiratory chain, and the altered cholinergic transmission are found in AD patients brain.

Aluminium is a metal whose role in the etiology and/or pathogenesis of AD could not be rejected. It has multiple effects, such as cellular respiration damage and oxidative stress induction. In the experimental model the study, uses aluminium chloride was applied intrahippocampally (i.h.) to the adult male Wistar rats. That was followed by the decreased activity of three enzymes in the brain regions that are most affected in AD, such as the forebrain cortex, hippocampus and basal forebrain. The activity of glucose-6-phosphate dehydrogenase (G6PDH) was more than halved, while the activity of COX and acetylcholinesterase (AChE) was almost exhausted. All this was accompanied by deteriorated learning and memory established by a two-way active avoidance test.

The intrahippocampal application of G6PDH, the enzyme of the pentose monophosphate pathway, just before aluminium, reverted the activity of COX to the control values. The rats were also i.h. pretreateated with fresh prepared green tea leaf extract, which primarily has strong antioxidant effects. Such pretreatment resulted in statistically significant improvement of the activity of COX and AChE in comparison with the aluminium treated rats, although these values did not achieve the levels of controls. Besides that, green tea leaf extract reverted the decreased learning and memory to control values, as well.

Conclusion: Neurotoxicity of aluminium was demonstrated through the decreased activity of G6PDH, COX and AChE, that was clinically expressed as impaired learning and memory. G6PDH and green tea leaf extract showed protective effects against this toxicity.

In: Cytochromes *b* and *c*
Editor: Rurik Thom

ISBN: 978-1-63117-467-4
© 2014 Nova Science Publishers, Inc.

Chapter 1

REGULATION OF CYTOCHROME *C* IN RESPIRATION, APOPTOSIS, NEURODEGENERATION AND CANCER: THE GOOD, THE BAD AND THE UGLY

Maik Hüttemann[1,2,3,8,*], Jeffrey W. Doan[1],
Anton-Scott Goustin[1], Christopher Sinkler[1],
Gargi Mahapatra[1,2], Joseph Shay[1,8], Jenney Liu[1],
Hosam Elbaz[1,4], Siddhesh Aras[1],
Lawrence I. Grossman[1], Yuchuan Ding[5],
Steven P. Zielske[4], Moh H. Malek[6],
Thomas H. Sanderson[3,7] and Icksoo Lee[9]

[1]Center for Molecular Medicine and Genetics,
Wayne State University, Detroit, MI, US
[2]Department of Biochemistry and Molecular Biology,
Wayne State University, Detroit, MI, US
[3]Cardiovascular Research Institute, Wayne State University,
Detroit, MI, US
[4]Department of Radiation Oncology, Wayne State University,
Detroit, MI, US

---

* Corresponding author: Maik Hüttemann. Tel.: +1 313 577-9150, fax: +1 313 577 5218, E-mail address: mhuttema@med.wayne.edu.

[5]Department of Neurosurgery, Wayne State University, Detroit, MI, US
[6]Integrative Physiology of Exercise Laboratory,
Department of Health Care Sciences,
Wayne State University, Detroit, MI, US
[7]Department of Emergency Medicine,
Wayne State University, Detroit, MI, US
[8]Karmanos Cancer Institute, Detroit, MI, US
[9]College of Medicine, Dankook University,
Cheonan-si, Chungcheongnam-do, Republic of Korea

ABSTRACT

Despite the fact that over 200 phosphorylation sites have been mapped on the mitochondrial oxidative phosphorylation (OxPhos) complexes, very little is known about the relevant cell signaling pathways and the terminal kinases and phosphatases that control these phosphorylations. Within OxPhos, cytochrome c (Cyt$c$) plays a special role because it is not only involved in electron transport but is also a key executer of apoptosis when it is released from the mitochondria. It is therefore not surprising that Cyt$c$ is regulated by phosphorylation. Four phosphorylation sites have been mapped on mammalian Cyt$c$, two of which have been studied functionally, demonstrating that both respiration and apoptosis are under the control of signaling pathways that have yet to be identified. We here review the regulation and multiple functions of mammalian Cyt$c$, including respiration, reactive oxygen species (ROS) scavenging under healthy conditions, ROS production via p66^{Shc}, and cardiolipin oxidation during apoptosis. We propose targeting Cyt$c$ by manipulation of signaling cascades as a therapeutic avenue in conditions including neurodegeneration and cancer.

ABBREVIATIONS

Apaf-1	apoptotic protease-activating factor 1
CPP	cell-penetrating peptide
COX	cytochrome c oxidase
Cyt$c$	cytochrome c
Cyt$c$-T	testes cytochrome c
$\Delta\Psi_m$	mitochondrial membrane potential

ETC   electron transport chain
OxPhos   oxidative phosphorylation
ROS   reactive oxygen species

1. INTRODUCTION

Mitochondria are increasingly recognized not only as essential for human health but also as active players and executers of cell destiny. They are not only the production sites of more than 90% of the cell's energy but also integrate numerous signals, allowing responses from within the cell via retrograde regulation that have consequences far beyond the cell's borders. They are a major site of redox signaling and reactive oxygen species (ROS) production [1]. Earlier studies proposed that 1-2% of consumed oxygen is converted into superoxide [2], whereas another study reported significantly lower values of 0.15% with palmitoyl carnitine as substrate and even lower levels with other substrates [3]. ROS are mainly generated at electron transport chain (ETC) complexes I and III, which release superoxide towards the matrix and the intermembrane space, respectively, at high membrane potentials [4-6]. Since superoxide generated by complex III can easily leave the mitochondria it can directly signal to other components of the cell. The earlier view that ROS are merely damaging byproducts of the ETC has more recently changed towards the emerging picture that ROS play an important physiological role in cell signaling [7].

A disturbance of the balance between efficient generation of ATP and basal levels of ROS production is seen not only in traditional mitochondrial diseases, but also in numerous common pathologies, which are increasingly associated with mitochondrial dysfunction.

Both decreased energy levels and/or increased ROS have been associated with diabetes, cancer, acute inflammation (as in sepsis), neurodegenerative diseases, and ischemia reperfusion injury (as seen in stroke and myocardial infarction) [8-13].

Mitochondria are also key players in aging and show decreased capacity to produce ATP over time in combination with increased mitochondrial damage including mutations in mitochondrial DNA [14, 15]. During conditions of stress, various signals can initiate the intrinsic programmed cell death process through mitochondrial type II apoptosis.

Interestingly, life-sustaining and life-threatening functions, via OxPhos and apoptosis, converge on the small electron carrier cytochrome *c* (Cyt*c*).

Cyt*c* is one out of an estimated 1000-1500 nuclear encoded mitochondrial proteins [16] that, in addition to the 13 OxPhos proteins that are encoded by the mitochondrial DNA, constitute the mitochondrial proteome. Of those nuclear encoded mitochondrial proteins about half are expressed across all tissues with the remainder being expressed in a tissue-specific manner [17].

The existence of Cyt*c* as a part of respiration was first suggested by McMunn in 1884 [18] and rediscovered 40 years later by Keilin [19], whereas it took another 70 years to demonstrate that it is required for the execution of type II apoptosis [20]. Recently there has been a flurry of discoveries related to the regulation of Cyt*c*, and new functions have been described. A molecule that is essential in energy production and in apoptosis, as well as other functions, is likely to be subject to various regulatory signals. In what follows, we describe the structure and function of mammalian Cyt*c* and its regulation, focusing on recent advances in the understanding of cell signaling. We then propose a model according to which phosphorylation of Cyt*c* provides an overarching means of regulation of Cyt*c* in its most important roles.

2. CYTOCHROME *C* STRUCTURE

Under healthy conditions Cyt*c* is located in the mitochondrial intermembrane space and transfers packages of single electrons from the bc_1 complex to cytochrome *c* oxidase (COX).

Import of Cyt*c* into the mitochondrial intermembrane space occurs through the heme-lacking apo-Cyt*c* form of the protein. Protein import does not require the mitochondrial membrane potential ($\Delta\Psi_m$), ATP, or the Mia40-dependent pathway [21].

Mature Cyt*c* is then formed by the covalent attachment of a heme group, a process catalyzed by the enzyme Cyt*c* heme lyase [22].

In all eukaryotes, Cyt*c* folds into a tight, nearly spherical ball with a diameter of ~32Å, studded with 13-18 lysine side chains that contribute to its high isoelectric point, and an additional 10-11 aspartate and glutamate residues. The position and surface distribution of these charged amino acids is highly conserved from fungi to vertebrates.

Mature mammalian Cyt*c* contains 104 amino acids (~12 kDa), lacking the start-methionine (Figure 1A). It is evolutionarily conserved and highly positively charged with a pI of about ~9.6.

Cyt*c* was one of the earliest mammalian proteins successfully analyzed by X-ray crystallography, with the first structure of oxidized horse heart Cyt*c* published in 1967 [23]. Later higher resolution structures of Cyt*c* allowed a more detailed view of its structural properties.

The heme group is covalently attached to the protein through thioether bonds with cysteines 14 and 17 (numbering is based on the mature peptide lacking the N-terminal methionine). The heme iron is in a hexacoordinate configuration with amino acid ligands His18 and Met80. The Met80-heme iron bond causes a weak absorption band at 695 nm in the spectrum of oxidized Cyt*c*, which is an indicator of correct folding. The heme group is only 7.5% solvent-exposed on one corner (Figure 1C), where electrons enter and leave the protein, and it is otherwise surrounded by a hydrophobic environment composed of aliphatic and aromatic amino acid side chains. [24

This environment, together with the heme iron ligands His18 and Met80, was proposed to account for the high redox potential (about 260 mV) of mammalian Cyt*c*. [25.

3. PRO-LIFE FUNCTIONS OF CYTOCHROME *C*: ELECTRON TRANSPORT, ROS SCAVENGING, AND REDOX-COUPLED PROTEIN IMPORT

Cyt*c* is an essential component of aerobic energy metabolism, shuttling electrons from the bc_1 complex to COX. COX transfers these electrons to oxygen, and water is formed. Mice null for Cyt*c* die around midgestation [26], when energy metabolism switches from mainly glycolytic to mainly aerobic [27].

Electrostatic interactions between Cyt*c* and a binding pocket in its electron acceptor cytochrome *c* oxidase (COX) are the chief forces that drive its interaction with COX, including both the associative docking of reduced (Fe^{2+}) Cyt*c* to COX and its dissociative release as oxidized Fe^{3+} Cyt*c*. Heteronuclear single quantum coherence spectral analysis using ^1H-^{15}N Cyt*c*, revealed that the overall affinity of oxidized Cyt*c* for COX is only slightly, but still significantly, weaker than that of reduced Cyt*c* [28]. These studies suggest that these on and off interactions are driven chiefly by a relatively small number of charged lysines in the N-terminal (αA) and long C-terminal (αE) α-helices of Cyt*c*, as seen in Figure 1A and B. These two helices pack onto each other in the folded structure, situated 180° opposite from the 50s helix αB.

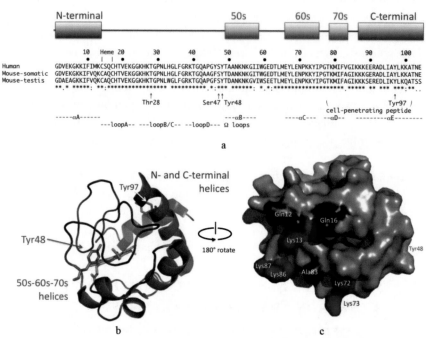

a

b   c

Figure 1. Cytochrome *c* sequence, domain structure, and phosphorylation sites. A, Human (NM_018947), mouse somatic (CAA25899) and testis (NP_034119) Cyt*c* show 91% (human-mouse somatic), 82% (human-mouse testis), and 86% (mouse somatic-mouse testis) conservation. Helical regions are depicted as boxes (top). Residues that have been identified as phosphorylation sites (Thr28, Ser47, Tyr48, and Tyr97) are designated with arrows, and the cell penetrating peptide region comprised of amino acids 77-101 is indicated below the alignment. B, Ribbon structure of horse heart Cyt*c* with highlighted helical regions (magenta) implicated in binding to COX by the Sakamoto model. [28 Crystal structure data of horse heart Cyt*c* (PDB ID: 1HRC; [24]) were processed with the program MacPyMOL 1.2. Tyr48 and 97, which can be phosphorylated and for which functional data are available, are highlighted. C, Space-fill model highlighting charged residues predicted to be crucial for Cyt*c*-COX binding based on the Roberts model [29]. In this model Cyt*c* and COX are positioned for efficient electron transfer between the heme crevice of Cyt*c* and the Trp104 electron entry point in COX subunit II with a distance of <4Å. Cyt*c* residues involved in binding with polar interactions are Gln12, Lys13, Gln16, Lys72, Lys73, Ala83, Lys86, and Lys87 with residues on COX at distances <6Å. Interestingly, all but 2 (Lys16 and 72) of these Cyt*c* residues that bind with COX [29] have undergone evolutionary selection in the primate lineage to reduce the electrostatic nature of the interaction. [155]

Upon Cyt*c* binding to COX, NMR signals from residues in the three Ω loops and helices αB, αC, αD (50s, 60s, 70s) show little or no chemical shift. These studies suggest that structural changes on Cyt*c* during binding and dissociation are mainly confined to Cyt*c*'s αA and αE helices, colored purple in Figure 1A and B. One interpretation would be that this area of the protein is the face of Cyt*c* with which it interacts with COX most intimately. It should be noted, however, that other convincing models exist, based on computer predictions [29] that align Cyt*c* on COX for efficient electron transfer between the heme crevice of Cyt*c* and the Trp104 electron entry point in COX subunit II with a distance of <4Å. This model involves Cyt*c* residues Gln12, Lys13, Gln16, Lys72, Lys73, Ala83, Lys86, and Lys87 for polar interactions with residues on COX at distances <6Å, thus extending the interaction area into the αD domain and beyond but questioning the importance of the αE region for binding (Figure 1C).

A second 'pro-life' function of Cyt*c* is redox-coupled protein import. Proteins that localize to the mitochondrial intermembrane space and the inner membrane and contain twin CX_3C or CX_9C motifs are imported by the Mia40/Erv1 pathway [30-32]. Here, protein import is coupled to Mia40/Erv1-mediated disulfide bond formation, which locks the proteins in their mature tertiary structure and in the mitochondria. The electrons derived from the disulfide reaction are transferred from Mia40 to Erv1 and finally Cyt*c* [33], thus feeding additional electrons into the ETC.

In its third 'pro-life' function Cyt*c* acts as a ROS scavenger. Among the most common ROS are superoxide ($O_2^{\bullet -}$), hydrogen peroxide (H_2O_2), and hydroxyl radicals ($^{\bullet}OH$); their buildup, if unregulated, will trigger apoptosis [34]. Several cellular lines of defense exist to protect the cell from ROS. These include enzymatic ROS scavengers such as superoxide dismutatases and catalase, as well as non-enzymatic scavengers such as glutathione. Cyt*c* is yet another enzyme that can detoxify superoxide [35, 36]. Since Cyt*c* accepts single electrons it can accept an electron from superoxide, generating oxygen. This reaction requires Cyt*c* to be in the oxidized form. Furthermore, it was demonstrated that Cyt*c* operates as an H_2O_2 scavenger [37]. In contrast to the detoxification of superoxide, conversion of H_2O_2 is catalyzed by both reduced and oxidized Cyt*c*. Cyt*c* constantly switches between reduced and oxidized states in a respiring cell. Therefore the detoxification reactions of both superoxide and H_2O_2 can take place. In conclusion, the redox capabilities of Cyt*c* make it an ideal antioxidant for the cell, especially given its location at a site within the mitochondria where the ROS load is very high. The pro-life functions of Cyt*c* are summarized on the left side of Figure 2.

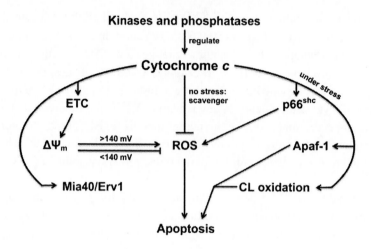

Figure 2. Model that the main functions of cytochrome *c* are regulated by Cyt*c* phosphorylation. Cyt*c* is essential for electron transfer as part of the electron transport chain (ETC), redox-mediated protein import, and as a ROS scavenger under healthy conditions. This is mediated by phosphorylation of Cyt*c*, which partially inhibits ETC flux and prevents mitochondrial membrane potential ($\Delta\Psi_m$) hyperpolarization, which would otherwise cause ROS production at ETC complexes I and III. Under conditions of stress, dephosphorylation of Cyt*c* increases ETC flux leading to $\Delta\Psi_m$ hyperpolarization and thus production of ROS, which can trigger apoptosis. Additional mechanisms involving Cyt*c* operate during conditions of stress including ROS production through the p66[shc] pathway and cardiolipin (CL) peroxidation catalyzed by Cyt*c*, which allows it to dissociate from CL and to be released into the cytosol, where the unphosphorylated form of Cyt*c* can bind to Apaf-1, triggering apoptosis.

4. THE APOPTOSOME: CYTOCHROME *C* RELEASE AND BINDING TO APAF-1 IS REQUIRED TO TRIGGER APOPTOSIS

The number of published studies of the role of Cyt*c* in apoptosis has increased exponentially since 1996 when Liu and colleagues first demonstrated in a cell free apoptotic system that Cyt*c*, in addition to other components including dATP, is required to execute the program [20]. It is now textbook knowledge that release of Cyt*c* from the mitochondria into the cytosol and its binding to apoptotic protease-activating factor 1 (Apaf-1) are key steps for triggering apoptosis. Cyt*c* binding to Apaf-1, the latter of which contains a dATP cofactor, induces hydrolysis of the dATP, which is subsequently replaced by exogenous dATP to form the apoptosome [38].

The apoptosome then recruits several pro-caspase-9 molecules and promotes cleavage to their active form.

Apoptosome-bound caspase-9 mediates cleavage and activation of caspase-3, a major committer and executor of apoptosis. [39, 40] Apoptosis involving the release of Cyt*c* is a process well established and conserved in mammals but more controversial in lower organisms. It was recently suggested that the intrinsic (type II) apoptotic pathway arose once, before the emergence of the deuterostomes, and that portions of the pathway have been lost in some lineages [41]. Several studies have indicated that it is also operates in organisms such as the protostome *Drosophila* [42], the very primitive metazoan *Nematostella* [43], and apparently even yeast [44], but seems to be absent in *C. elegans*.

4.1. Release of Cytochrome *C* Precedes Apoptosome Formation

The formation of the apoptosome requires the release of Cyt*c* from the mitochondria, which is an interesting and controversial topic. Although the release process is often considered to be the consequence of mitochondrial membrane rupture or mitochondrial permeability transition pore (PTP) formation, there are studies suggesting a different modus operandi. First, there is evidence that release of Cyt*c* is independent of PTP formation and that it precedes it [45, 46]. Second, mitochondria have the capability to reversibly release and take up Cyt*c*, with the latter restoring ETC function [47]. This may involve a special feature of Cyt*c*; it contains cell-penetrating peptide (CPP) sequences [48], allowing it to cross membranes in a non-traditional fashion (see also section 6.2). The region of Cyt*c* facilitating membrane translocation most efficiently is composed of amino acids 77 through 101 (Figure 1A).

4.2. Regulation of Apoptosis at the Level of Cytochrome *C*

If CPP-mediated transition pore-independent release of Cyt*c* is the preferred mechanism it may be subject to regulation, including by phosphorylation. Preliminary support for this idea is provided by a study showing that neuroprotective insulin treatment leads to Tyr97 phosphorylation of brain Cyt*c* [49]. Furthermore, phosphorylation of Tyr97, which is located within the 77-101 CPP (Figure 1A), leads to a suppression of Cyt*c* release from the mitochondria, as discussed in section 5.3.

When Cyt$c$ is released into the cytosol, it binds to Apaf-1, and Apaf-1 assembles into the heptameric apoptosome (Figure 3). Little is known about the possible regulation of Cyt$c$'s interaction with Apaf-1 and the formation of the apoptosome. The binding of Cyt$c$ to Apaf-1 is known to be electrostatic in nature, and mutagenesis studies suggest that lysines 7, 8, 13, 25, 39, 72, 86, 87, and 88 participate in binding to negatively-charged aspartate residues in the WD-40 domain of Apaf-1 [50, 51]. Binding of nucleotides, especially ATP, to several of these lysine residues prevents the interaction between Cyt$c$ and Apaf-1, thus presenting a means of regulating apoptosome formation [51]. The heptameric structure of the apoptosome (Figure 3A) suggests regulation by Cyt$c$ concentration, and mathematical modeling suggests that the optimal Cyt$c$/Apaf-1 ratio for apoptosome formation is one-to-one. Higher relative amounts of Cyt$c$ lead to preferential formation of tetrameric and larger oligomers, which by themselves are unable to form heptamers [52]. Another study also supports the concept that concentration of free Cyt$c$ is a regulating factor. tRNAs are thought to inhibit the reaction of Cyt$c$ with Apaf-1. Mei et al. found that Cyt$c$ binds to mitochondrial and cytosolic tRNAs, inhibiting Cyt$c$-induced apoptosome formation [53]. The authors speculated that since tumor cells synthesize tRNA at high rates, the suppression of apoptosis as seen in cancer could be caused by tRNA binding to Cyt$c$. Such a mechanism could be implicated in tumorigenesis and be a target for therapy in the future. In addition, various studies have shown that oxidized Cyt$c$ is more competent than reduced Cyt$c$ to form the apoptosome and to activate caspases (reviewed in [54]). Therefore redox signaling may be an important regulatory component of apoptosome-formation.

Another possible mechanism to regulate apoptosis is through Cyt$c$ phosphorylation, which may interfere with Cyt$c$-Apaf-1 binding. A recent model of the apoptosome based on electron density maps at 9.5Å shows the sevenfold symmetry (Figure 3A) [55]. In the model the four amino acids of Cyt$c$ that can be phosphorylated show various distances to the nearest residues of Apaf-1: Cyt$c$ Thr28 is within 6Å of Apaf-1 Trp884; Cyt$c$ Ser47 is within 5Å of Apaf-1 Ala763 and within 6Å of Ile800; Cyt$c$ Tyr48 is within 6Å of Apaf-1 Ile800; and Cyt$c$ Tyr97 is the most distant residue of the four, with the closest amino acids of Apaf-1 (Asp1106 and Glu659) within 14Å (Figure 3B). Further structural analyses and refinements are necessary to strengthen the model. Type II apoptosis is a multi-faceted process that involves additional important reactions in which Cyt$c$ is directly or indirectly involved, including ROS generation by the ETC and the Cyt$c$-p66^{shc} pathway, and oxidation of Cyt$c$-bound cardiolipin, which precedes Cyt$c$ release from the mitochondria.

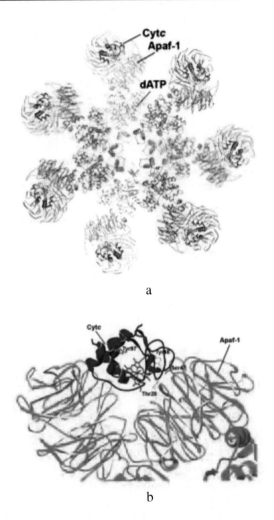

Figure 3. Interaction of cytochrome *c* with Apaf-1 based on the Akey model of the apoptosome [55]. Crystal structure data of the model (PDB ID: 3J2T) were used and processed with the program Swiss-PDBViewer 3.7. A, Overview depicting the sevenfold symmetrical structure of the apoptosome, highlighting Cyt*c* and co-factor dATP. B, Center-side view of the Cyt*c*-Apaf-1 interaction. Cyt*c* residue Thr28 is located within 6Å of Apaf-1 Trp884; Cyt*c* Ser47 is within 5Å of Apaf-1 Ala763 and within 6Å of Ile800; Cyt*c* Tyr48 is within 6Å of Apaf-1 Ile800; and Cyt*c* Tyr97 is within 14Å of Apaf-1 Asp1106 and Glu659. In the model, Cyt*c* docks to the WD40 domain of Apaf-1 (green) where the largely β-sheet structure is evident.

These topics are discussed in section 6 below and summarized in Figure 2 (right side). All these mechanisms work hand in hand and all have to be considered simultaneously to get a comprehensive picture of the role of Cytc in apoptosis.

5. REGULATION OF CYTOCHROME *C*

The last step of the ETC, the transfer of electrons from Cytc via COX to oxygen, is the proposed rate-limiting step of the ETC in mammals in intact cells [56-61].

It is therefore not surprising that all major forms of regulation have been identified for both Cytc and COX (for a review of COX regulation see [62]).

These include expression of tissue-specific isoforms only found in COX and Cytc among OxPhos complexes, allosteric regulation, and regulation via posttranscriptional modification, in particular by phosphorylations, the latter of which have been mapped on all OxPhos complexes (reviewed in [63]).

5.1. Isoforms

In mammals, two Cytc isoforms exist, the so-called somatic isoform found in almost all tissues and cell types, and a testes-specific isoform (Cytc-T). Cytc-T was first discovered in the testicular germinal epithelial cells of rodents [64]. It is the predominant isoform found in sperm. Mouse somatic and testes Cytc share 86% sequence identity (Figure 1A).

Although their overall functions are similar there are a few interesting differences between the isoform pair. Cytc-T has a threefold higher activity to reduce H_2O_2 but a fourfold higher apoptotic activity [65]. It was proposed that these Cytc-T-specific differences reduce ROS damage in sperm cells but are at the same time a selection tool to eliminate damaged sperm to ensure efficient DNA transmission by intact sperm.

Interestingly, Cytc-T can induce apoptosis through both the intrinsic and extrinsic pathways, suggesting that both death pathways converge at Cytc [66].

Cytc-T is absent in primates and the gene mutated to a non-transcribed pseudogene [67], implying that human Cytc has to carry out testis- and non-testis-specific functions.

5.2. Allosteric Regulation

Due to its high positive charge it is not surprising that Cyt*c* binds anions that are known to affect the interaction and thus the kinetics of Cyt*c* and COX. One such anion, ATP, binds to both enzymes [68-70] and this binding inhibits the electron transfer kinetics [71, 72] by altering the high-affinity Cyt*c*-COX binding site to a low-affinity site. [68] Since ATP is the ultimate product of OxPhos, it leads to an inhibition under conditions when energy is plentiful, thus working as an energy sensor. This regulation is also important in light of ROS production. Under conditions when almost all cellular ADP has been converted into ATP, and ATP synthase does not utilize $\Delta\Psi_m$, further pumping of protons by the ETC would lead to a buildup or hyperpolarization of $\Delta\Psi_m$, a condition known to lead to excessive ROS production. [73] ATP-dependent allosteric regulation requires phosphorylations on COX because no inhibitory effect of ATP was observed after *in vitro* dephosphorylation of cow liver COX [62]. Several 'enabling' sites have been proposed, including on COX subunits I, IV, and Vb [74-76]. Therefore, regulation by adenine nucleotides should be viewed and interpreted in combination with phosphorylations of COX and Cyt*c*.

5.3. Phosphorylation of Cytochrome C

In the past few years over 200 phosphorylation sites have been reported for the entire OxPhos system [63]. This finding was made possible by increasingly sensitive mass spectrometry methodology. For almost all of these mapped sites, the corresponding signaling pathways including the kinases and phosphatases are unknown.

In addition, some authors questioned how biologically relevant some of those phosphorylations are due to low stoichiometry and the possibility of unspecific auto-phosphorylations at sites with a higher affinity to ATP [77]. However, there is now clear evidence for the biological significance of at least a small number of phosphorylations including those on Cyt*c* and COX, which have been studied in more detail (for a review of COX phosphorylations see [78]). Here we will focus on Cyt*c*.

It is perhaps not surprising that the first phosphorylation site on Cyt*c*, Tyr97 in cow heart, was only recently reported, in 2006 [79], likely because most traditional protocols to purify mitochondrial proteins do not consider and thus do not maintain such phosphorylations.

We have therefore modified these protocols and added unspecific phosphatase inhibitors, such as fluoride for Ser/Thr phosphatases and activated vanadate for Tyr phosphatases, which we use for the purification of Cytc and COX [80]. For the purification of Cytc we initially purified mitochondria [79]; we now omit this isolation step and directly extract Cytc from cells or tissues under conditions preserving phosphorylations in all steps [81].

Mass spectrometry showed that Cytc from cow heart is Tyr97 phosphorylated under normal conditions [79], i.e., without external stimulation or inhibition of signaling pathways.

Spectral analysis of oxidized Tyr97-phosphorylated Cytc revealed a small shift of the 695 nm absorption band. Since this absorption is due to the Met80-heme iron bond, phosphorylation of Cytc in the periphery (i.e., an area not involved in binding to COX based on the Roberts model [29]; see Figure 1C) apparently affects the heme environment. Tyr97-phosphorylation leads to an inhibition of the Cytc-COX reaction as seen by enhanced sigmoidal kinetics with K_M values of COX for Cytc of 5.5 μM Cytc substrate concentration compared to 2.5 μM for unphosphorylated Cytc.

Analysis of liver Cytc also revealed tyrosine phosphorylation but, surprisingly, on a different site, Tyr48, located in the frontal area of the protein (Figure 1C), closer to the site at which Cytc binds to COX [81]. Interestingly, the spectrum of Tyr48 phosphorylated Cytc was not altered but the kinetics were distinct compared to both unphosphorylated and Tyr97-phosphorylated Cytc. In the reaction with COX, phospho-Tyr48 Cytc showed hyperbolic kinetics similar to unphosphorylated Cytc. Importantly, maximal turnover was more than 50% reduced for the phosphorylated form.

Both heart and liver-specific phosphorylations of Cytc occur on residues that are highly conserved in eukaryotes (Figure 1A).

Interesting, both Tyr48 and 97 phosphorylations lead to an inhibition in the reaction with COX via a reduction of maximal turnover and a shift from hyperbolic to sigmoidal kinetics, respectively, suggesting tissue-specific adaptations of Cytc regulation.

Our findings of partial inhibition of respiration as a consequence of Cytc Tyr48 and 97 phosphorylation fits our working model (Figure 2). We propose that under healthy conditions mammalian OxPhos does not operate at maximal capacity, thus avoiding high mitochondrial membrane potentials, which lead to an exponential increase of ROS production at $\Delta\Psi_m > 140$ mV [73].

In addition to changes in mitochondrial respiration, phosphorylation of Cytc may also impact its other functions including apoptosis, a life and death decision process in which Cytc plays a crucial role.

As discussed above, the role of Cyt*c* in apoptosis is several-fold and includes multiple stages during the process, including cardiolipin peroxidation, its release from the mitochondria, and its interaction with Apaf-1 to induce the cell's execution. *In vitro* work with phosphomimetic Cyt*c* indeed suggests such a role. Replacement of Tyr48 with phosphomimetic Glu, which mimics the negative charge of the phosphate group, produced kinetics similar to those observed using *in vivo* phosphorylated Cyt*c* with purified COX, suggesting that the replacement is a good model system [82].

Strikingly, Tyr48Glu Cyt*c* showed no detectable downstream caspase activation, suggesting that this site can function as a switch for the regulation of apoptosis. Only two mutations have been reported in human patients. One of them is Tyr48His in a family from Italy [83] in which the patients presented with low platelet counts in their blood (thrombocytopenia). This mutation adds a positive charge to a site that is crucial for energy production and apoptosis. Interestingly, this mutation results in decreased respiration similar to the phosphomimetic substitution, but has the opposite effect on apoptosis which is further activated compared to wild-type. The second mutation reported in humans, Gly41Ser, also causes a relatively mild form of thrombocytopenia [84]. Similar to the Tyr48His mutation, Gly41Ser increases apoptotic activity. The mutation leads to protein folding changes in the Cyt*c* heme environment [85]. It is unclear why no other phenotype is observed in these patients and why no other tissues are affected. One explanation might be that there are several signaling pathways to fine-tune Cyt*c* activity in apoptosis, a concept supported by the presence of multiple tissue-specific phosphorylation sites. Together with the substitutions at Tyr48, the Gly41Ser substitution argues for a localization of an epitope of Cyt*c* on the 40s Ω loop D controlling the mitochondrial pathway of apoptosis, which we suggest is the Apaf-1-interacting face of Cyt*c* (Figure 1A and B).

For Tyr97 no data with phosphomimetic mutants is currently available and it is thus unclear how involved this site is in the regulation of apoptosis. However, binding of Cyt*c* to Apaf-1 involves several amino acids located on the surface of Cyt*c* required for enveloping the molecule as suggested by earlier mutational analysis of Cyt*c*, revealing several key residues required for formation of the apoptosome.

Lys7, which is located near Tyr97, is one of them, without which binding affinity is greatly diminished [50]. Phosphorylation of Tyr97 may lead to salt bridge formation with Lys7, potentially capturing an important residue for the interaction with Apaf-1. It will be interesting to see if the Cyt*c*-Apaf-1 interaction is affected by such a posttranslational modification.

For the step upstream, the release of Cyt*c* from the mitochondria, we have recently shown that treatment with a single bolus of insulin is neuroprotective in a rat model of global brain ischemia/reperfusion injury, shielding CA1 hippocampal neurons from cell death [49]. Insulin treatment results in robust phosphorylation of Cyt*c* Tyr97 in ischemic pig brain *in vitro* as well as in normal and ischemic rat brain *in vivo*. Importantly, it also coincides with inhibition of Cyt*c* release from the mitochondria (see section 6.2 for a possible mechanism). Taken together with the observation that Tyr97 phosphorylation reduces ETC flux, thereby preventing $\Delta\Psi_m$ hyperpolarization and thus ROS production, these findings suggest that Tyr97 phosphorylation reduces oxidative stress and acts as an anti-apoptotic signal. The existence of tyrosine phosphorylations, which can suppress Cyt*c* release from the mitochondria (Tyr97), and limit cardiolipin oxidation and abolish the execution of the caspase cascade (Tyr48), suggests a fourfold control of apoptosis, by suppression of: 1) $\Delta\Psi_m$ hyperpolarization, 2) cardiolipin peroxidation, 3) Cyt*c* release, and 4) the formation of a functional apoptosome (Figure 2). Such multi-level regulation might be expected for a function as crucial as the life-or-death decision for the cell. Once the corresponding kinases and phosphatases involved in Cyt*c* phosphorylation are known they may be specifically targeted to prevent or induce cell death in conditions such as neurodegeneration and cancer, respectively.

Two more phosphorylation sites, Thr28 and Ser47 (Figures 1A and 3B), have recently been reported on human skeletal muscle Cyt*c* by high throughput phospho-proteomic mass-spectroscopy analysis [86]. This indicates that Cyt*c* in this tissue is controlled by a signaling pathway distinct from liver and heart. No information exists about the effects of these phospho-rylations or about the ratio of phosphorylated versus unphosphorylated Cyt*c*.

Other posttranslational modifications have been reported for Cyt*c*. In particular, Cyt*c* was proposed to be an important target of tyrosine nitrations as reaction products of peroxynitrite, which forms in the presence of nitric oxide and superoxide [87]. Although the amount of tyrosine nitrated Cyt*c* is rather low *in vivo* it has been studied quite intensively. In wild-type Cyt*c*, Tyr67 is preferentially nitrated, leading to structural changes and the loss of the heme iron-Met80 bond [88]. As expected, this modification also causes changes in the redox characteristics of Cyt*c*, a strong inhibition of the reaction with purified COX [89], and inhibition of downstream caspase activation [90]. The authors also generated single tyrosine mutants of Cyt*c*, in which the other three tyrosines were replaced with phenylalanines, and reported various effects on function for each individual site after nitration.

They concluded that nitration of Tyr74 resulted in the second largest effects after Tyr67. In addition, Tyr74 nitration abolishes downstream caspase activation but still allows Cyt*c* to bind to Apaf-1 [91].

Interestingly, one study reported that Tyr48 nitration completely blocks downstream caspase activation [87], similar to phosphomimetic Tyr48Glu Cyt*c* [82]. Tyrosine nitration introduces a relatively bulky group with a negative charge similar to tyrosine phosphorylation. Tyrosine nitrations might thus be considered a phosphotyrosine-mimetic substitution, perhaps better than glutamate substitutions for resembling tyrosine phosphorylations.

6. REDOX SIGNALING AND CYTOCHROME *C*

Redox signaling occurs when a change in the level of a reactive oxygen or nitrogen species or a change in the redox state of a molecule causes a response in a biological system [92]. Even the change in the redox state of Cyt*c* as part of its role as an electron carrier in the ETC can constitute a redox signal, as in the example of feedback control described below (see section 6.1). Recent work has shown that Cyt*c* in its role as an executer of apoptosis can respond to redox signaling. Such signals arise from the ETC as a generator of ROS, from p66^{shc}, which oxidizes Cyt*c* and catalyzes the production of hydrogen peroxide, and from the oxidation of cardiolipin. Cyt*c* is bound to cardiolipin at the inner mitochondrial membrane, which causes Cyt*c* to partially unfold, giving rise to peroxidase capability, oxidation of cardiolipin, and its own release into the cytosol, where it binds to Apaf-1 to form the apoptosome. The reader should bear in mind that these processes, since they deal with the life and death of the cell, are necessarily tightly regulated, likely with multiple checkpoints (Figure 2).

6.1. p66^{shc} and Cytochrome *C*

p66^{shc} is an adapter protein that, if rendered inoperative, increases resistance to oxidative stress and increases lifespan [93-95]. p66^{shc} is found throughout the cell, including the mitochondria. Under stress conditions, it oxidizes Cyt*c*, transferring an electron to oxygen thus catalyzing the production of hydrogen peroxide [96], which may act as an apoptotic signal [97]. In fact, release of Cyt*c* correlates with the H_2O_2 production activity of p66^{shc} [98].

Superoxide and subsequently peroxide production by p66^{shc} could contribute to the ability of Cyt$c$, as described below, to oxidize cardiolipin, enabling the release of Cyt$c$ into the cytosol.

A principal role of shc family members is assembly of signaling complexes. Consistent with this role it has recently been shown that p66^{shc} acts to assemble a PKCδ/Cyt$c$/retinol complex in the intermembrane space of the mitochondria, thereby regulating mitochondrial respiration [99, 100]. In that case, the redox state of Cyt$c$ acts as a feedback sensor of the activity level of the ETC, and the signaling complex accordingly adjusts the amount of fuel entering the tricarboxylic acid cycle.

Phosphorylation of p66^{shc} Ser36 appears to be an essential regulator of function and increases with age in several organs including lung, liver, and skin, causing increased ROS production and oxidative damage as was shown in aged mice [101]. However, the possibility that phosphorylation of Cyt$c$ can regulate the interaction between Cyt$c$ and p66^{shc} remains to be explored. Such a regulation would not be surprising given its effect on apoptosome formation and downstream caspase activation (see also section 5.3).

6.2. Cytochrome C, Cardiolipin, and Apoptosis

About 15% of Cyt$c$ is bound to cardiolipin, a mitochondria-specific phospholipid that is primarily found in the inner mitochondrial membrane [102]. During apoptosis, trans-membrane migration of cardiolipin enhances its association with Cyt$c$ in the intermembrane space, resulting in complexes formed of cardiolipin and Cyt$c$ [102]. Before Cyt$c$ can be released from the mitochondria during apoptosis, a redistribution of cardiolipin occurs [103]. Almost 80% of the cardiolipin is located in the inner mitochondrial membrane where it constitutes about 20% of the total membrane lipids. During apoptosis a lipid exchange occurs that results in almost 40% of the cardiolipin of the inner mitochondrial membrane translocating to the outer membrane [104].

The binding of cardiolipin to Cyt$c$ may proceed in various ways (reviewed in [105]); nevertheless, under appropriate conditions, Cyt$c$ is bound by cardiolipin in such a way that it partially unfolds, acquires peroxidase capability, oxidizes and dissociates from cardiolipin, and initiates apoptosis [102]. It is likely that tight binding requires deep penetration of one (or of two) acyl chains into the protein, reaching the heme pocket region. Such binding requires lysines 72, 73, and 79, as shown by Lys72/73/79Asn mutants in horse heart Cyt$c$ [106].

The Spiro group has elucidated a possible sequence of partial unfolding as a result of cardiolipin binding, using horse heart Cyt*c*. At pH 3, thermal unfolding causes loss of the hydrogen bond between His26 and Pro44, which initiates a rapid transformation of the 40s Ω loop to a β-sheet, and extension of the β-sheet into the 60s and 70s helices. These changes cause disruption of the Met80-heme covalent bond, opening of the heme crevice, which allows access of peroxide to the heme and induction of peroxidase activity [107].

Activation of peroxidases that function via a heme group, such as Cyt*c*, usually involves a protein-bound radical. An intermediate of the cardiolipin peroxidation process appears to be a tyrosyl radical, or rather various tyrosyl radicals. Initially, Tyr97 was identified as the site of a tyrosyl radical [102, 108, 109]. The Kagan group later found in studies of tyrosine mutated Cyt*c* that of the four tyrosines that exist in horse heart Cyt*c*, the Tyr67Phe mutation caused the greatest decrease of peroxidase activity of the mutants, and was a likely involved tyrosyl radical [110]. Rajagopal et al., [111] found through electronic paramagnetic resonance (EPR) spectroscopy that Tyr46 and 48 were the putative radical sites, and Tyr/46/48/Phe mutants showed similar EPR signals in all variants, indicating that the radicals are formed on more than one site. Of the two tyrosines, Tyr46 is present in humans but not conserved in mammals and it is therefore unlikely to be a key residue for cardiolipin peroxidation. The conclusion that there are various sites of radical formation seems most reasonable at this time.

Cell signaling, specifically phosphorylation of Cyt*c* tyrosine residues, may also affect cardiolipin peroxidation, as we propose (Figure 2). Pecina et al. [82] used rodent phosphomimetic Tyr48Glu substituted Cyt*c* and reported significantly decreased Cyt*c*-cardiolipin binding and decreased but not abolished peroxidase activity compared to the wild type. It is possible that the bulky phosphate group identified on this position in liver *in vivo* may show an even more pronounced effect on the peroxidase activity of Cyt*c*. Since cardiolipin oxidation precedes Cyt*c* release from the mitochondria, the phosphorylation state of Cyt*c* likely controls this rather early step in the apoptotic cascade.

The Cyt*c*-cardiolipin interaction not only enhances the peroxidase capacity of Cyt*c*, it also leads to the formation of discrete pores in membranes through which Cyt*c* can escape into the cytosol. Groves and colleagues observed Cyt*c* and dextran leakage across cardiolipin-containing membranes into the vesicle interior, which occurred in the absence of other apoptotic machinery [112]. "Bursts" of leakage were interpreted as the opening of stable pores.

The pores may be the result of the ability of Cytc to cause curvature of the cardiolipin-containing membranes. Pletneva and colleagues [113] found, with time-resolved FRET measurements of dansyl variants of horse heart Cytc, that late in the process of cardiolipin binding by Cytc, when the greatest unfolding of the native structure occurs, the C-terminal helix of the protein is unfolded and extended. Interestingly, the C-terminus of Cytc has been identified as containing cell-penetrating peptide (CPP) sequences (Figure 1A, amino acids 77-101), which allow proteins to cross membranes, and which induced apoptosis in an astrocytoma cell line [48]. These CPPs, when in an open conformation, may allow Cytc to translocate into the cytosol independently of the permeability transition pore.

7. CYTOCHROME C IN THE CONTEXT OF NEURODEGENERATION AND CANCER

Cytc, as a protein with functions crucial to life and death, is clearly relevant in the context of therapeutics. This is perhaps most clear in the cases of neurodegenerative diseases and cancer. In neurodegenerative conditions a significant cause of damage is excessive and uncontrolled apoptotic activity.

Mitochondrial dysfunction leading to release of Cytc and induction of apoptosis has been demonstrated in a broad range of neurodegenerative conditions, including acute trauma such as stroke [114-117] and traumatic spinal cord injury [118, 119], and chronic conditions such as multiple sclerosis (MS) [120, 121], Parkinson's Disease [122-124], Huntington Disease [125-127], and amyotrophic lateral sclerosis (ALS) [128-130]. Excessive apoptotic cell death could be prevented if Cytc release into the cytosol or Cytc binding to Apaf-1 could be inhibited.

The mechanisms discussed in the course of this review have led to a number of proposed therapies for neurodegenerative diseases. For example, the Szeto group has investigated the synthetic mitochondrial peptide SS-31, finding that it selectively targets cardiolipin and inhibits Cytc peroxidase activity by protecting the heme, mitigating ischemia-reperfusion injury [131, 132]. The anti-inflammatory and neuroprotective tetracycline-derivative minocycline was investigated by Patriarca et al. who found that it binds to Cytc, decreasing its peroxidase activity and caspase-3 activation [133]. Its anti-apoptotic effect may therefore result from the inhibition of cardiolipin peroxidation by Cytc, or from the inhibition of binding of Cytc to Apaf-1.

Ji and colleagues employed a brain-permeable mitochondria-targeted nitroxide electron scavenger to prevent cardiolipin oxidation in the brain, and were able to inhibit apoptosis that otherwise would occur in rat models of traumatic brain injury *in vitro* and *in vivo* [134].

Since $p66^{shc}$ has been found to be involved in MS, Savino and coworkers [135] investigated the role of $p66^{shc}$ in that disease (see also [136]). They found that deletion of $p66^{shc}$ protects from neurodegenerative stress in experimental autoimmune encephalomyelitis (EAE), a murine model of MS, and inhibits $p66^{shc}$-mediated opening of the mitochondrial permeability transition pore. It therefore could serve as a marker for early detection of MS and other neurodegenerative diseases, and its inhibition could constitute a treatment for such diseases.

We and others have shown that insulin protects hippocampal cells from cell death [137, 138].

As mentioned above, we were able to demonstrate that such treatment leads to Tyr97 phosphorylation, which suppresses its release from the mitochondria [49]. It may be this phosphorylation, predicted to maintain controlled and healthy cell respiration, that is at least in part responsible for the neuroprotective effect of insulin.

In cancer, two typical characteristics related to the life and death functions of Cyt*c* are resistance to apoptosis [139-141] and the preferential switch from aerobic energy metabolism to glycolytic energy metabolism, even in the presence of oxygen, known as the Warburg effect [10, 142].

Glycolytic metabolism is able to produce the ATP that rapidly proliferating cells need, along with precursors of cellular biosynthesis [143], and targeting the glycolytic nature of rapidly proliferating cancer cells has emerged as a promising therapeutic strategy [144-147]. However, cancers constantly evolve against attempts to limit their survival, whether the mechanism of death is apoptosis or other death pathways [148].

With respect to apoptosis, Jones et al. identified a cell penetrating peptide sequence in the C-terminus of Cyt*c*, and added to it an N-terminal sequence that increased the apoptotic potency attributable to the C-terminal section of Cyt*c* alone [48]. The authors foresee the ability to synthesize a class of synthetic proteins that would enhance apoptosis in tumor cells.

Johnson and colleagues have shown that in brain tumors, traditionally refractory to chemotherapy, cytosolic Cyt*c* is sufficient to activate apoptosis in brain tumor cell lines, whereas normal brain cell lines are resistant to apoptosis from cytosolic Cyt*c* [149]. The authors attributed the difference to levels of Apaf-1, which were high in the cancer cells compared to normal tissues.

Thus Cytc may prove to be a therapeutic agent that can selectively kill cancer cells, sparing normal cells in the brain. Another promising strategy, because of development of resistance to chemotherapeutic agents, would be to combine chemotherapy with enhanced apoptosis. For example, since Cytc in its reduced state is less capable of triggering apoptosis, Barros et al. have shown that depleting cells of glutathione or glutathione-S-transferases (by such agents as DNA hairpins or the neurotoxin veratridine) increased the cytotoxic activity of methotrexate in breast cancer cells [150].

Intriguingly, there appears to be a mechanistic connection between the two characteristic features of cancer cells discussed in this section; that is, resistance to apoptosis and a preference in cancer for glycolysis. This connection was suggested by Plas and Thompson [151], and followed up by Bonnet et al. [152], who showed that the small molecule dichloroacetate (DCA), an inhibitor of pyruvate dehydrogenase kinase, decreases cancer growth *in vitro* and *in vivo*, activates aerobic respiration, and promotes apoptosis through release of Cytc. Vaughn and Deshmukh continued this line of research by investigating the similarities between cancer cells and postmitotic neurons, which last for the lifetime of the organism [153]. Both types of cells inhibit the apoptotic pathway, and they both extensively metabolize glucose. The authors suggested that the regulatory feature shared by postmitotic neurons and cancer cells is the redox effect of glycolytic metabolism on Cytc. They further observed that oxidized but not reduced Cytc promotes apoptosis and showed that, both in postmitotic neurons and in cancer cells, glycolytic metabolism, chiefly through the action of the pentose phosphate pathway, reduces Cytc and therefore decreases apoptosis. Similar conclusions where obtained in a study using a yeast model for metabolic switching [154]. Suppression of aerobic respiration inhibited apoptosis, while enhancement of respiration increased it.

CONCLUSION

Cytc plays a key role in pro-life and pro-death processes. Those include electron transfer, radical scavenging, and redox-coupled protein import on the one side, and cardiolipin oxidation, ROS generation through p66^{shc} or as part of the ETC, and apoptosome formation on the other side (Figure 2).

Regulation of these processes is of utmost importance for the fate of the cell. Reversible phosphorylations are arguably the most important regulators and four such modifications have been identified on Cytc.

Identification of the involved kinases, phosphatases, and signaling pathways that modulate them would allow a deeper understanding of the crosstalk between pathways that leads to a final resolution of the cell's destiny. It would thereby also allow targeted control of *Cytc*, which could lead to the development of therapeutic interventions that, for example, increase OxPhos relative to glycolysis in tumors to upset the normal metabolic preference of most cancers, and increase sensitivity to apoptosis. In other conditions, such as neurodegenerative diseases, phosphorylations that inhibit apoptosis could be enhanced and utilized as neuroprotective therapy.

ACKNOWLEDGMENTS

This work was supported by grants from the National Institutes of Health (GM089900 and NS076715) and a contract that was awarded and administered by the US Army Medical Research and Materiel Command (USAMRMC) and the Telemedicine and Advanced Technology Research Center (TATRC), at Fort Detrick, MD under Contract Number: National Oncogenomics and Molecular Imaging Center (NOMIC), W81XWH-08-2-0160, W81XWH-10-2-0068, W81XWH-11-1-0050 (Center Contract PI: Dr. Gerold Bepler), the Center for Molecular Medicine and Genetics, and the Cardiovascular Research Institute, Wayne State University School of Medicine, Detroit. The views, opinions and/or findings contained in this publication are those of the authors and do not necessarily reflect the views of the funding agencies and should not be construed as an official funding agency position, policy or decision unless so designated by other documentation. No official endorsement should be made.

REFERENCES

[1] Jezek, P., Hlavata, L. (2005) Mitochondria in homeostasis of reactive oxygen species in cell, tissues, and organism. *Int. J. Biochem. Cell Biol.* 37: 2478-2503.

[2] Richter, C., Park, J. W., Ames, B. N. (1988) Normal oxidative damage to mitochondrial and nuclear DNA is extensive. *Proc. Natl. Acad. Sci. US* 85: 6465-6467.

[3]   St-Pierre, J., Buckingham, J. A., Roebuck, S. J., Brand, M. D. (2002) Topology of superoxide production from different sites in the mitochondrial electron transport chain. *J. Biol. Chem.* 277: 44784-44790.

[4]   Han, D., Canali, R., Rettori, D., Kaplowitz, N. (2003) Effect of glutathione depletion on sites and topology of superoxide and hydrogen peroxide production in mitochondria. *Mol. Pharmacol.* 64: 1136-1144.

[5]   Rottenberg, H., Covian, R., Trumpower, B. L. (2009) Membrane potential greatly enhances superoxide generation by the cytochrome bc1 complex reconstituted into phospholipid vesicles. *J. Biol. Chem.* 284: 19203-19210.

[6]   Murphy, M. P. (2009) How mitochondria produce reactive oxygen species. *Biochem. J.* 417: 1-13.

[7]   Finkel, T. (2012) Signal transduction by mitochondrial oxidants. *J. Biol. Chem.* 287: 4434-4440.

[8]   Blake, R., Trounce, I. A. (2013) Mitochondrial dysfunction and complications associated with diabetes. *Biochim. Biophys. Acta.*

[9]   Kadenbach, B., Arnold, S., Lee, I., Hüttemann, M. (2004) The possible role of cytochrome *c* oxidase in stress-induced apoptosis and degenerative diseases. *Biochim. Biophys. Acta* 1655: 400-408.

[10] Modica-Napolitano, J. S., Kulawiec, M., Singh, K. K. (2007) Mitochondria and human cancer. *Curr. Mol. Med.* 7: 121-131.

[11] Samavati, L., Lee, I., Mathes, I., Lottspeich, F., Hüttemann, M. (2008) Tumor necrosis factor α inhibits oxidative phosphorylation through tyrosine phosphorylation at subunit I of cytochrome *c* oxidase. *J. Biol. Chem.* 283: 21134-21144.

[12] Duvigneau, J. C., Piskernik, C., Haindl, S., Kloesch, B., Hartl, R. T., Hüttemann, M., Lee, I., Ebel, T., Moldzio, R., Gemeiner, M., Redl, H., Kozlov, A. V. (2008) A novel endotoxin-induced pathway: upregulation of heme oxygenase 1, accumulation of free iron, and free iron-mediated mitochondrial dysfunction. *Lab. Invest.* 88: 70-77.

[13] Sanderson, T. H., Reynolds, C. A., Kumar, R., Przyklenk, K., Hüttemann, M. (2013) Molecular mechanisms of ischemia-reperfusion injury in brain: pivotal role of the mitochondrial membrane potential in reactive oxygen species generation. *Mol. Neurobiol.* 47: 9-23.

[14] Bratic, A., Larsson, N. G. (2013) The role of mitochondria in aging. *J. Clin. Invest.* 123: 951-957.

[15] Hwang, A. B., Jeong, D. E., Lee, S. J. (2012) Mitochondria and organismal longevity. *Curr. Genomics* 13: 519-532.

[16] Calvo, S. E., Mootha, V. K. (2010) The mitochondrial proteome and human disease. *Annu. Rev. Genomics Hum. Genet.* 11: 25-44.

[17] Pagliarini, D. J., Calvo, S. E., Chang, B., Sheth, S. A., Vafai, S. B., Ong, S. E., Walford, G. A., Sugiana, C., Boneh, A., Chen, W. K., Hill, D. E., Vidal, M., Evans, J. G., Thorburn, D. R., Carr, S. A., Mootha, V. K. (2008) A mitochondrial protein compendium elucidates complex I disease biology. *Cell* 134: 112-123.

[18] McMunn, C. A. (1884) On myohaematin, an intrinsic muscle-pigment of vertebrates and invertebrates, on histohaematin, and on the spectrum of the suprarenal bodies. *Proceedings of the Physiological Society* 5: 24-26.

[19] Keilin, D. (1925) On cytochrome, a respiratory pigment, common to animals, yeast, and higher plants. *Proc. R. Soc. London Ser. B* 98: 312–339.

[20] Liu, X., Kim, C. N., Yang, J., Jemmerson, R., Wang, X. (1996) Induction of apoptotic program in cell-free extracts: requirement for dATP and cytochrome c. *Cell* 86: 147-157.

[21] Diekert, K., de Kroon, A. I., Ahting, U., Niggemeyer, B., Neupert, W., de Kruijff, B., Lill, R. (2001) Apocytochrome c requires the TOM complex for translocation across the mitochondrial outer membrane. *Embo J.* 20: 5626-5635.

[22] Dumont, M. E., Cardillo, T. S., Hayes, M. K., Sherman, F. (1991) Role of cytochrome c heme lyase in mitochondrial import and accumulation of cytochrome c in Saccharomyces cerevisiae. *Mol. Cell. Biol.* 11: 5487-5496.

[23] Dickerson, R. E., Kopka, M. L., Borders, C. L., Jr., Varnum, J., Weinzier, J. E. (1967) A centrosymmetric projection at 4A of horse heart oxidized cytochrome c. *J. Mol. Biol.* 29: 77-95.

[24] Bushnell, G. W., Louie, G. V., Brayer, G. D. (1990) High-resolution three-dimensional structure of horse heart cytochrome c. *J. Mol. Biol.* 214: 585-595.

[25] Salemme, F. R. (1977) Structure and function of cytochromes c. *Annu. Rev. Biochem.* 46: 299-329.

[26] Li, K., Li, Y., Shelton, J. M., Richardson, J. A., Spencer, E., Chen, Z. J., Wang, X., Williams, R. S. (2000) Cytochrome c deficiency causes embryonic lethality and attenuates stress-induced apoptosis. *Cell* 101: 389-399.

[27] Morriss, G. M., New, D. A. (1979) Effect of oxygen concentration on morphogenesis of cranial neural folds and neural crest in cultured rat embryos. *J. Embryol. Exp. Morphol.* 54: 17-35.

[28] Sakamoto, K., Kamiya, M., Imai, M., Shinzawa-Itoh, K., Uchida, T., Kawano, K., Yoshikawa, S., Ishimori, K. (2011) NMR basis for interprotein electron transfer gating between cytochrome c and cytochrome c oxidase. *Proc. Natl. Acad. Sci. US* 108: 12271-12276.

[29] Roberts, V. A., Pique, M. E. (1999) Definition of the interaction domain for cytochrome c on cytochrome c oxidase. III. Prediction of the docked complex by a complete, systematic search. *J. Biol. Chem.* 274: 38051-38060.

[30] Chacinska, A., Pfannschmidt, S., Wiedemann, N., Kozjak, V., Sanjuan Szklarz, L. K., Schulze-Specking, A., Truscott, K. N., Guiard, B., Meisinger, C., Pfanner, N. (2004) Essential role of Mia40 in import and assembly of mitochondrial intermembrane space proteins. *Embo J.* 23: 3735-3746.

[31] Stojanovski, D., Bragoszewski, P., Chacinska, A. (2012) The MIA pathway: a tight bond between protein transport and oxidative folding in mitochondria. *Biochimi. Biophys. Acta* 1823: 1142-1150.

[32] Wrobel, L., Trojanowska, A., Sztolsztener, M. E., Chacinska, A. (2013) Mitochondrial protein import: Mia40 facilitates Tim22 translocation into the inner membrane of mitochondria. *Mol. Biol. Cell* 24: 543-554.

[33] Allen, S., Balabanidou, V., Sideris, D. P., Lisowsky, T., Tokatlidis, K. (2005) Erv1 mediates the Mia40-dependent protein import pathway and provides a functional link to the respiratory chain by shuttling electrons to cytochrome c. *J. Mol. Biol.* 353: 937-944.

[34] Aoki, H., Kang, P. M., Hampe, J., Yoshimura, K., Noma, T., Matsuzaki, M., Izumo, S. (2002) Direct activation of mitochondrial apoptosis machinery by c-Jun N-terminal kinase in adult cardiac myocytes. *J. Biol. Chem.* 277: 10244-10250.

[35] Korshunov, S. S., Krasnikov, B. F., Pereverzev, M. O., Skulachev, V. P. (1999) The antioxidant functions of cytochrome c. *FEBS Lett.* 462: 192-198.

[36] Pereverzev, M. O., Vygodina, T. V., Konstantinov, A. A., Skulachev, V. P. (2003) Cytochrome c, an ideal antioxidant. *Biochem. Soc. Trans.* 31: 1312-1315.

[37] Wang, Z. B., Li, M., Zhao, Y., Xu, J. X. (2003) Cytochrome c is a hydrogen peroxide scavenger in mitochondria. *Protein Pept. Lett.* 10: 247-253.

[38] Kim, H. E., Du, F., Fang, M., Wang, X. (2005) Formation of apoptosome is initiated by cytochrome c-induced dATP hydrolysis and

subsequent nucleotide exchange on Apaf-1. *Proc. Natl. Acad. Sci. US* 102: 17545-17550.

[39] Green, D. R. (2000) Apoptotic pathways: paper wraps stone blunts scissors. *Cell* 102: 1-4.

[40] Wang, X. (2001) The expanding role of mitochondria in apoptosis. *Genes Dev.* 15: 2922-2933.

[41] Bender, C. E., Fitzgerald, P., Tait, S. W., Llambi, F., McStay, G. P., Tupper, D. O., Pellettieri, J., Sanchez Alvarado, A., Salvesen, G. S., Green, D. R. (2012) Mitochondrial pathway of apoptosis is ancestral in metazoans. *Proc. Natl. Acad. Sci. US* 109: 4904-4909.

[42] Arama, E., Bader, M., Srivastava, M., Bergmann, A., Steller, H. (2006) The two Drosophila cytochrome C proteins can function in both respiration and caspase activation. *EMBO J.* 25: 232-243.

[43] Zmasek, C. M., Zhang, Q., Ye, Y., Godzik, A. (2007) Surprising complexity of the ancestral apoptosis network. *Genome Biol.* 8: R226.

[44] Madeo, F., Herker, E., Wissing, S., Jungwirth, H., Eisenberg, T., Frohlich, K. U. (2004) Apoptosis in yeast. *Curr. Opin. Microbiol.* 7: 655-660.

[45] Doran, E., Halestrap, A. P. (2000) Cytochrome c release from isolated rat liver mitochondria can occur independently of outer-membrane rupture: possible role of contact sites. *Biochem. J.* 348 Pt 2: 343-350.

[46] Chalmers, S., Nicholls, D. G. (2003) The relationship between free and total calcium concentrations in the matrix of liver and brain mitochondria. *J. Biol. Chem.* 278: 19062-19070.

[47] Jacobs, E. E., Sanadi, D. R. (1960) The reversible removal of cytochrome c from mitochondria. *J. Biol. Chem.* 235: 531-534.

[48] Jones, S., Holm, T., Mager, I., Langel, U., Howl, J. (2010) Characterization of bioactive cell penetrating peptides from human cytochrome c: protein mimicry and the development of a novel apoptogenic agent. *Chem. Biol.* 17: 735-744.

[49] Sanderson, T. H., Mahapatra, G., Pecina, P., Ji, Q., Yu, K., Sinkler, C., Varughese, A., Kumar, R., Bukowski, M. J., Tousignant, R. N., Salomon, A. R., Lee, I., Hüttemann, M. (2013) Cytochrome c is tyrosine 97 phosphorylated by neuroprotective insulin treatment. *PLoS One* 8: e78627.

[50] Yu, T., Wang, X., Purring-Koch, C., Wei, Y., McLendon, G. L. (2001) A mutational epitope for cytochrome C binding to the apoptosis protease activation factor-1. *J. Biol. Chem.* 276: 13034-13038.

[51] Chandra, D., Bratton, S. B., Person, M. D., Tian, Y., Martin, A. G., Ayres, M., Fearnhead, H. O., Gandhi, V., Tang, D. G. (2006) Intracellular nucleotides act as critical prosurvival factors by binding to cytochrome C and inhibiting apoptosome. *Cell* 125: 1333-1346.

[52] Nakabayashi, J., Sasaki, A. (2006) A mathematical model for apoptosome assembly: the optimal cytochrome c/Apaf-1 ratio. *J. Theor. Biol.* 242: 280-287.

[53] Mei, Y., Yong, J., Liu, H., Shi, Y., Meinkoth, J., Dreyfuss, G., Yang, X. (2010) tRNA binds to cytochrome c and inhibits caspase activation. *Mol. Cell* 37: 668-678.

[54] Brown, G. C., Borutaite, V. (2008) Regulation of apoptosis by the redox state of cytochrome c. *Biochim. Biophys. Acta* 1777: 877-881.

[55] Yuan, S., Topf, M., Reubold, T. F., Eschenburg, S., Akey, C. W. (2013) Changes in Apaf-1 conformation that drive apoptosome assembly. *Biochemistry* 52: 2319-2327.

[56] Villani, G., Greco, M., Papa, S., Attardi, G. (1998) Low reserve of cytochrome c oxidase capacity in vivo in the respiratory chain of a variety of human cell types. *J. Biol. Chem.* 273: 31829-31836.

[57] Kunz, W. S., Kudin, A., Vielhaber, S., Elger, C. E., Attardi, G., Villani, G. (2000) Flux control of cytochrome c oxidase in human skeletal muscle. *J. Biol. Chem.* 275: 27741-27745.

[58] Acin-Perez, R., Bayona-Bafaluy, M. P., Bueno, M., Machicado, C., Fernandez-Silva, P., Perez-Martos, A., Montoya, J., Lopez-Perez, M. J., Sancho, J., Enriquez, J. A. (2003) An intragenic suppressor in the cytochrome c oxidase I gene of mouse mitochondrial DNA. *Hum. Mol. Genet.* 12: 329-339.

[59] Villani, G., Attardi, G. (1997) In vivo control of respiration by cytochrome c oxidase in wild-type and mitochondrial DNA mutation-carrying human cells. *Proc. Natl. Acad. Sci. US* 94: 1166-1171.

[60] Piccoli, C., Scrima, R., Boffoli, D., Capitanio, N. (2006) Control by cytochrome c oxidase of the cellular oxidative phosphorylation system depends on the mitochondrial energy state. *Biochem. J.* 396: 573-583.

[61] Dalmonte, M. E., Forte, E., Genova, M. L., Giuffre, A., Sarti, P., Lenaz, G. (2009) Control of respiration by cytochrome c oxidase in intact cells: role of the membrane potential. *J. Biol. Chem.* 284: 32331-32335.

[62] Hüttemann, M., Lee, I., Pecinova, A., Pecina, P., Przyklenk, K., Doan, J. W. (2008) Regulation of oxidative phosphorylation, the mitochondrial membrane potential, and their role in human disease. *J. Bioenerg. Biomembr.* 40: 445-456.

[63] Covian, R., Balaban, R. S. (2012) Cardiac mitochondrial matrix and respiratory complex protein phosphorylation. *Am. J. Physiol. Heart Circ. Physiol.* 303: H940-966.

[64] Goldberg, E., Sberna, D., Wheat, T. E., Urbanski, G. J., Margoliash, E. (1977) Cytochrome c: immunofluorescent localization of the testis-specific form. *Science* 196: 1010-1012.

[65] Liu, Z., Lin, H., Ye, S., Liu, Q. Y., Meng, Z., Zhang, C. M., Xia, Y., Margoliash, E., Rao, Z., Liu, X. J. (2006) Remarkably high activities of testicular cytochrome c in destroying reactive oxygen species and in triggering apoptosis. *Proc. Natl. Acad. Sci. US* 103: 8965-8970.

[66] Vempati, U. D., Diaz, F., Barrientos, A., Narisawa, S., Mian, A. M., Millan, J. L., Boise, L. H., Moraes, C. T. (2007) Role of cytochrome C in apoptosis: increased sensitivity to tumor necrosis factor alpha is associated with respiratory defects but not with lack of cytochrome C release. *Mol. Cell. Biol.* 27: 1771-1783.

[67] Pierron, D., Wildman, D. E., Hüttemann, M., Letellier, T., Grossman, L. I. (2012) Evolution of the couple cytochrome c and cytochrome c oxidase in primates. *Adv. Exp. Med. Biol.* 748: 185-213.

[68] Ferguson-Miller, S., Brautigan, D. L., Margoliash, E. (1976) Correlation of the kinetics of electron transfer activity of various eukaryotic cytochromes c with binding to mitochondrial cytochrome c oxidase. *J. Biol. Chem.* 251: 1104-1115.

[69] Napiwotzki, J., Shinzawa-Itoh, K., Yoshikawa, S., Kadenbach, B. (1997) ATP and ADP bind to cytochrome c oxidase and regulate its activity. *Biol. Chem.* 378: 1013-1021.

[70] Arnold, S., Kadenbach, B. (1999) The intramitochondrial ATP/ADP-ratio controls cytochrome c oxidase activity allosterically. *FEBS Lett.* 443: 105-108.

[71] Craig, D. B., Wallace, C. J. (1995) Studies of 8-azido-ATP adducts reveal two mechanisms by which ATP binding to cytochrome c could inhibit respiration. *Biochemistry* 34: 2686-2693.

[72] Tuominen, E. K., Zhu, K., Wallace, C. J., Clark-Lewis, I., Craig, D. B., Rytomaa, M., Kinnunen, P. K. (2001) ATP induces a conformational change in lipid-bound cytochrome c. *J. Biol. Chem.* 276: 19356-19362.

[73] Liu, S. S. (1999) Cooperation of a "reactive oxygen cycle" with the Q cycle and the proton cycle in the respiratory chain--superoxide generating and cycling mechanisms in mitochondria. *J. Bioenerg. Biomembr.* 31: 367-376.

[74] Lee, I., Salomon, A. R., Ficarro, S., Mathes, I., Lottspeich, F., Grossman, L. I., Hüttemann, M. (2005) cAMP-dependent tyrosine phosphorylation of subunit I inhibits cytochrome c oxidase activity. *J. Biol. Chem.* 280: 6094-6100.

[75] Acin-Perez, R., Gatti, D. L., Bai, Y., Manfredi, G. (2011) Protein phosphorylation and prevention of cytochrome oxidase inhibition by ATP: coupled mechanisms of energy metabolism regulation. *Cell metabolism* 13: 712-719.

[76] Helling, S., Hüttemann, M., Ramzan, R., Kim, S. H., Lee, I., Muller, T., Langenfeld, E., Meyer, H. E., Kadenbach, B., Vogt, S., Marcus, K. (2012) Multiple phosphorylations of cytochrome c oxidase and their functions. *Proteomics* 12: 950-959.

[77] Phillips, D., Aponte, A. M., Covian, R., Balaban, R. S. (2011) Intrinsic protein kinase activity in mitochondrial oxidative phosphorylation complexes. *Biochemistry* 50: 2515-2529.

[78] Hüttemann, M., Helling, S., Sanderson, T. H., Sinkler, C., Samavati, L., Mahapatra, G., Varughese, A., Lu, G., Liu, J., Ramzan, R., Vogt, S., Grossman, L. I., Doan, J. W., Marcus, K., Lee, I. (2012) Regulation of mitochondrial respiration and apoptosis through cell signaling: cytochrome c oxidase and cytochrome c in ischemia/reperfusion injury and inflammation. *Biochim. Biophys. Acta* 1817: 598-609.

[79] Lee, I., Salomon, A. R., Yu, K., Doan, J. W., Grossman, L. I., Hüttemann, M. (2006) New prospects for an old enzyme: mammalian cytochrome c is tyrosine-phosphorylated in vivo. *Biochemistry* 45: 9121-9128.

[80] Lee, I., Salomon, A. R., Yu, K., Samavati, L., Pecina, P., Pecinova, A., Hüttemann, M. (2009) Isolation of regulatory-competent, phosphorylated cytochrome c oxidase. *Methods Enzymol.* 457: 193-210.

[81] Yu, H., Lee, I., Salomon, A. R., Yu, K., Hüttemann, M. (2008) Mammalian liver cytochrome c is tyrosine-48 phosphorylated in vivo, inhibiting mitochondrial respiration. *Biochim. Biophys. Acta* 1777: 1066-1071.

[82] Pecina, P., Borisenko, G. G., Belikova, N. A., Tyurina, Y. Y., Pecinova, A., Lee, I., Samhan-Arias, A. K., Przyklenk, K., Kagan, V. E., Hüttemann, M. (2010) Phosphomimetic substitution of cytochrome c tyrosine 48 decreases respiration and binding to cardiolipin and abolishes ability to trigger downstream caspase activation. *Biochemistry* 49: 6705-6714.

[83] De Rocco, D., Cerqua, C., Goffrini, P., Russo, G., Pastore, A., Meloni, F., Nicchia, E., Moraes, C. T., Pecci, A., Salviati, L., Savoia, A. (2013) Mutations of cytochrome c identified in patients with thrombocytopenia THC4 affect both apoptosis and cellular bioenergetics. *Biochim. Biophys. Acta.*

[84] Morison, I. M., Cramer Borde, E. M., Cheesman, E. J., Cheong, P. L., Holyoake, A. J., Fichelson, S., Weeks, R. J., Lo, A., Davies, S. M., Wilbanks, S. M., Fagerlund, R. D., Ludgate, M. W., da Silva Tatley, F. M., Coker, M. S., Bockett, N. A., Hughes, G., Pippig, D. A., Smith, M. P., Capron, C., Ledgerwood, E. C. (2008) A mutation of human cytochrome c enhances the intrinsic apoptotic pathway but causes only thrombocytopenia. *Nat. Genet.* 40: 387-389.

[85] Liptak, M. D., Fagerlund, R. D., Ledgerwood, E. C., Wilbanks, S. M., Bren, K. L. (2011) The proapoptotic G41S mutation to human cytochrome c alters the heme electronic structure and increases the electron self-exchange rate. *J. Am. Chem. Soc.* 133: 1153-1155.

[86] Zhao, X., Leon, I. R., Bak, S., Mogensen, M., Wrzesinski, K., Hojlund, K., Jensen, O. N. (2011) Phosphoproteome analysis of functional mitochondria isolated from resting human muscle reveals extensive phosphorylation of inner membrane protein complexes and enzymes. *Mol. Cell. Proteomics*: M110.000299.

[87] Garcia-Heredia, J. M., Diaz-Moreno, I., Diaz-Quintana, A., Orzaez, M., Navarro, J. A., Hervas, M., De la Rosa, M. A. (2012) Specific nitration of tyrosines 46 and 48 makes cytochrome c assemble a non-functional apoptosome. *FEBS Lett.* 586: 154-158.

[88] Cassina, A. M., Hodara, R., Souza, J. M., Thomson, L., Castro, L., Ischiropoulos, H., Freeman, B. A., Radi, R. (2000) Cytochrome c nitration by peroxynitrite. *J. Biol. Chem.* 275: 21409-21415.

[89] Jang, B., Han, S. (2006) Biochemical properties of cytochrome c nitrated by peroxynitrite. *Biochimie* 88: 53-58.

[90] Rodriguez-Roldan, V., Garcia-Heredia, J. M., Navarro, J. A., De la Rosa, M. A., Hervas, M. (2008) Effect of nitration on the physico-chemical and kinetic features of wild-type and monotyrosine mutants of human respiratory cytochrome c. *Biochemistry* 47: 12371-12379.

[91] Garcia-Heredia, J. M., Diaz-Moreno, I., Nieto, P. M., Orzaez, M., Kocanis, S., Teixeira, M., Perez-Paya, E., Diaz-Quintana, A., De la Rosa, M. A. (2010) Nitration of tyrosine 74 prevents human cytochrome c to play a key role in apoptosis signaling by blocking caspase-9 activation. *Biochim. Biophys. Acta* 1797: 981-993.

[92] Collins, Y., Chouchani, E. T., James, A. M., Menger, K. E., Cocheme, H. M., Murphy, M. P. (2012) Mitochondrial redox signalling at a glance. *J. Cell Sci.* 125: 801-806.

[93] Migliaccio, E., Giorgio, M., Mele, S., Pelicci, G., Reboldi, P., Pandolfi, P. P., Lanfrancone, L., Pelicci, P. G. (1999) The p66shc adaptor protein controls oxidative stress response and life span in mammals. *Nature* 402: 309-313.

[94] Migliaccio, E., Giorgio, M., Pelicci, P. G. (2006) Apoptosis and aging: role of p66Shc redox protein. *Antioxid. Redox Signal.* 8: 600-608.

[95] Suski, J. M., Karkucinska-Wieckowska, A., Lebiedzinska, M., Giorgi, C., Szczepanowska, J., Szabadkai, G., Duszynski, J., Pronicki, M., Pinton, P., Wieckowski, M. R. (2011) p66Shc Aging Protein in Control of Fibroblasts Cell Fate. *Int. J. Mol. Sci.* 12: 5373-5389.

[96] Giorgio, M., Migliaccio, E., Orsini, F., Paolucci, D., Moroni, M., Contursi, C., Pelliccia, G., Luzi, L., Minucci, S., Marcaccio, M., Pinton, P., Rizzuto, R., Bernardi, P., Paolucci, F., Pelicci, P. G. (2005) Electron transfer between cytochrome c and p66Shc generates reactive oxygen species that trigger mitochondrial apoptosis. *Cell* 122: 221-233.

[97] Gertz, M., Steegborn, C. (2010) The Lifespan-regulator p66Shc in mitochondria: redox enzyme or redox sensor? *Antioxid. Redox Signal.* 13: 1417-1428.

[98] Sun, L., Xiao, L., Nie, J., Liu, F. Y., Ling, G. H., Zhu, X. J., Tang, W. B., Chen, W. C., Xia, Y. C., Zhan, M., Ma, M. M., Peng, Y. M., Liu, H., Liu, Y. H., Kanwar, Y. S. (2010) p66Shc mediates high glucose and angiotensin II induced oxidative stress renal tubular injury via mitochondrial dependent apoptotic pathway. *Am. J. Physiol. Renal Physiol.* 299: F1014-1012.

[99] Acin-Perez, R., Hoyos, B., Gong, J., Vinogradov, V., Fischman, D. A., Leitges, M., Borhan, B., Starkov, A., Manfredi, G., Hammerling, U. (2010) Regulation of intermediary metabolism by the PKCdelta signalosome in mitochondria. *FASEB J.* 24: 5033-5042.

[100] Hoyos, B., Acin-Perez, R., Fischman, D. A., Manfredi, G., Hammerling, U. (2012) Hiding in plain sight: uncovering a new function of vitamin A in redox signaling. *Biochim. Biophys. Acta* 1821: 241-247.

[101] Lebiedzinska, M., Duszynski, J., Rizzuto, R., Pinton, P., Wieckowski, M. R. (2009) Age-related changes in levels of p66Shc and serine 36-phosphorylated p66Shc in organs and mouse tissues. *Arch. Biochem. Biophys.* 486: 73-80.

[102] Kagan, V. E., Tyurin, V. A., Jiang, J., Tyurina, Y. Y., Ritow, V. B., Amoscato, A. A., Osipov, A. N., Belikova, N. A., Kapralov, A. A., Kini, V., Vlasova, I. I., Zhao, Q., Zou, M., Di, P., Svistunenko, D. A., Kurnikov, I. V., Borisenko, G. G. (2005) Cytochrome c acts as a cardiolipin oxygenase required for release of proapoptotic factors. *Nature Chem. Biol.* 1: 223-232.

[103] Garcia Fernandez, M., Troiano, L., Moretti, L., Nasi, M., Pinti, M., Salvioli, S., Dobrucki, J., Cossarizza, A. (2002) Early changes in intramitochondrial cardiolipin distribution during apoptosis. *Cell Growth Differ.* 13: 449-455.

[104] Kagan, V. E., Tyurina, Y. Y., Bayir, H., Chu, C. T., Kapralov, A. A., Vlasova, I. I., Belikova, N. A., Tyurin, V. A., Amoscato, A., Epperly, M., Greenberger, J., Dekosky, S., Shvedova, A. A., Jiang, J. (2006) The "pro-apoptotic genies" get out of mitochondria: oxidative lipidomics and redox activity of cytochrome c/cardiolipin complexes. *Chem. Biol. Interact.* 163: 15-28.

[105] Muenzner, J., Pletneva, E. V. (2013) Structural transformations of cytochrome c upon interaction with cardiolipin. *Chem. Phys. Lipids.*

[106] Sinibaldi, F., Howes, B. D., Droghetti, E., Polticelli, F., Piro, M. C., Di Pierro, D., Fiorucci, L., Coletta, M., Smulevich, G., Santucci, R. (2013) Role of lysines in cytochrome c-cardiolipin interaction. *Biochemistry* 52: 4578-4588.

[107] Balakrishnan, G., Hu, Y., Spiro, T. G. (2012) His26 protonation in cytochrome c triggers microsecond beta-sheet formation and heme exposure: implications for apoptosis. *J. Am. Chem. Soc.* 134: 19061-19069.

[108] Svistunenko, D. A. (2005) Reaction of haem containing proteins and enzymes with hydroperoxides: the radical view. *Biochim. Biophys. Acta* 1707: 127-155.

[109] Tyurina, Y. Y., Kini, V., Tyurin, V. A., Vlasova, I. I., Jiang, J., Kapralov, A. A., Belikova, N. A., Yalowich, J. C., Kurnikov, I. V., Kagan, V. E. (2006) Mechanisms of cardiolipin oxidation by cytochrome c: relevance to pro- and antiapoptotic functions of etoposide. *Mol. Pharmacol.* 70: 706-717.

[110] Kapralov, A. A., Yanamala, N., Tyurina, Y. Y., Castro, L., Samhan-Arias, A., Vladimirov, Y. A., Maeda, A., Weitz, A. A., Peterson, J., Mylnikov, D., Demicheli, V., Tortora, V., Klein-Seetharaman, J., Radi, R., Kagan, V. E. (2011) Topography of tyrosine residues and their involvement in peroxidation of polyunsaturated cardiolipin in

cytochrome c/cardiolipin peroxidase complexes. *Biochim. Biophys. Acta* 1808: 2147-2155.

[111] Rajagopal, B. S., Edzuma, A. N., Hough, M. A., Blundell, K. L., Kagan, V. E., Kapralov, A. A., Fraser, L. A., Butt, J. N., Silkstone, G. G., Wilson, M. T., Svistunenko, D. A., Worrall, J. A. (2013) The hydrogen-peroxide-induced radical behaviour in human cytochrome c-phospholipid complexes: implications for the enhanced pro-apoptotic activity of the G41S mutant. *Biochem. J.* 456: 441-452.

[112] Bergstrom, C. L., Beales, P. A., Lv, Y., Vanderlick, T. K., Groves, J. T. (2013) Cytochrome c causes pore formation in cardiolipin-containing membranes. *Proc. Natl. Acad. Sci. US* 110: 6269-6274.

[113] Muenzner, J., Toffey, J. R., Hong, Y., Pletneva, E. V. (2013) Becoming a peroxidase: cardiolipin-induced unfolding of cytochrome c. *J. Phys. Chem. B* 117: 12878-12886.

[114] Niizuma, K., Endo, H., Chan, P. H. (2009) Oxidative stress and mitochondrial dysfunction as determinants of ischemic neuronal death and survival. *J. Neurochem.* 109 Suppl. 1: 133-138.

[115] Fujimura, M., Morita-Fujimura, Y., Murakami, K., Kawase, M., Chan, P. H. (1998) Cytosolic redistribution of cytochrome c after transient focal cerebral ischemia in rats. *J. Cereb. Blood Flow Metab.* 18: 1239-1247.

[116] Sugawara, T., Fujimura, M., Morita-Fujimura, Y., Kawase, M., Chan, P. H. (1999) Mitochondrial release of cytochrome c corresponds to the selective vulnerability of hippocampal CA1 neurons in rats after transient global cerebral ischemia. *J. Neurosci.* 19: RC39.

[117] Rabuffetti, M., Sciorati, C., Tarozzo, G., Clementi, E., Manfredi, A. A., Beltramo, M. (2000) Inhibition of caspase-1-like activity by Ac-Tyr-Val-Ala-Asp-chloromethyl ketone induces long-lasting neuroprotection in cerebral ischemia through apoptosis reduction and decrease of proinflammatory cytokines. *J. Neurosci.* 20: 4398-4404.

[118] Li, M., Ona, V. O., Chen, M., Kaul, M., Tenneti, L., Zhang, X., Stieg, P. E., Lipton, S. A., Friedlander, R. M. (2000) Functional role and therapeutic implications of neuronal caspase-1 and -3 in a mouse model of traumatic spinal cord injury. *Neuroscience* 99: 333-342.

[119] Chan, P. H. (2004) Mitochondria and neuronal death/survival signaling pathways in cerebral ischemia. *Neurochem. Res.* 29: 1943-1949.

[120] Van Horssen, J., Witte, M. E., Ciccarelli, O. (2012) The role of mito-chondria in axonal degeneration and tissue repair in MS. *Mult. Scler.* 18: 1058-1067.

[121] Mahad, D., Lassmann, H., Turnbull, D. (2008) Review: Mitochondria and disease progression in multiple sclerosis. *Neuropathol. Appl. Neurobiol.* 34: 577-589.

[122] Wu, D. C., Jackson-Lewis, V., Vila, M., Tieu, K., Teismann, P., Vadseth, C., Choi, D. K., Ischiropoulos, H., Przedborski, S. (2002) Blockade of microglial activation is neuroprotective in the 1-methyl-4-phenyl-1,2,3,6-tetrahydropyridine mouse model of Parkinson disease. *J. Neurosci.* 22: 1763-1771.

[123] Berger, A. K., Cortese, G. P., Amodeo, K. D., Weihofen, A., Letai, A., LaVoie, M. J. (2009) Parkin selectively alters the intrinsic threshold for mitochondrial cytochrome c release. *Hum. Mol. Genet.* 18: 4317-4328.

[124] Yan, M. H., Wang, X., Zhu, X. (2013) Mitochondrial defects and oxidative stress in Alzheimer disease and Parkinson disease. *Free Radic. Biol. Med.* 62: 90-101.

[125] Wang, X., Zhu, S., Drozda, M., Zhang, W., Stavrovskaya, I. G., Cattaneo, E., Ferrante, R. J., Kristal, B. S., Friedlander, R. M. (2003) Minocycline inhibits caspase-independent and -dependent mitochondrial cell death pathways in models of Huntington's disease. *Proc. Natl. Acad. Sci. US* 100: 10483-10487.

[126] Wang, X., Zhu, S., Pei, Z., Drozda, M., Stavrovskaya, I. G., Del Signore, S. J., Cormier, K., Shimony, E. M., Wang, H., Ferrante, R. J., Kristal, B. S., Friedlander, R. M. (2008) Inhibitors of cytochrome c release with therapeutic potential for Huntington's disease. *J. Neurosci.* 28: 9473-9485.

[127] Costa, V., Giacomello, M., Hudec, R., Lopreiato, R., Ermak, G., Lim, D., Malorni, W., Davies, K. J., Carafoli, E., Scorrano, L. (2010) Mitochondrial fission and cristae disruption increase the response of cell models of Huntington's disease to apoptotic stimuli. *EMBO Mol. Med.* 2: 490-503.

[128] Bacman, S. R., Bradley, W. G., Moraes, C. T. (2006) Mitochondrial involvement in amyotrophic lateral sclerosis: trigger or target? *Mol. Neurobiol.* 33: 113-131.

[129] Xu, R., Wu, C., Zhang, X., Zhang, Q., Yang, Y., Yi, J., Yang, R., Tao, Y. (2011) Linking hypoxic and oxidative insults to cell death mechanisms in models of ALS. *Brain Res.* 1372: 133-144.

[130] Garcia, M. L., Fernandez, A., Solas, M. T. (2013) Mitochondria, motor neurons and aging. *J. Neurol. Sci.* 330: 18-26.

[131] Birk, A. V., Liu, S., Soong, Y., Mills, W., Singh, P., Warren, J. D., Seshan, S. V., Pardee, J. D., Szeto, H. H. (2013) The mitochondrial-

targeted compound SS-31 re-energizes ischemic mitochondria by interacting with cardiolipin. *J. Am. Soc. Nephrol.* 24: 1250-1261.

[132] Birk, A. V., Chao, W. M., Bracken, C., Warren, J. D., Szeto, H. H. (2013) Targeting Mitochondrial Cardiolipin and the Cytochrome C/ Cardiolipin Complex to Promote Electron Transport and Optimize Mitochondrial Atp Synthesis. *Br. J. Pharmacol.*

[133] Patriarca, A., Polticelli, F., Piro, M. C., Sinibaldi, F., Mei, G., Bari, M., Santucci, R., Fiorucci, L. (2012) Conversion of cytochrome c into a peroxidase: inhibitory mechanisms and implication for neuro-degenerative diseases. *Arch. Biochem. Biophys.* 522: 62-69.

[134] Ji, J., Kline, A. E., Amoscato, A., Samhan-Arias, A. K., Sparvero, L. J., Tyurin, V. A., Tyurina, Y. Y., Fink, B., Manole, M. D., Puccio, A. M., Okonkwo, D. O., Cheng, J. P., Alexander, H., Clark, R. S., Kochanek, P. M., Wipf, P., Kagan, V. E., Bayir, H. (2012) Lipidomics identifies cardiolipin oxidation as a mitochondrial target for redox therapy of brain injury. *Nat. Neurosci.* 15: 1407-1413.

[135] Savino, C., Pelicci, P., Giorgio, M. (2013) The P66Shc/mitochondrial permeability transition pore pathway determines neurodegeneration. *Oxid. Med. Cell Longev.* 2013: 719407.

[136] Su, K., Bourdette, D., Forte, M. (2012) Genetic inactivation of mitochondria-targeted redox enzyme p66ShcA preserves neuronal viability and mitochondrial integrity in response to oxidative challenges. *Front Physiol.* 3: 285.

[137] Endo, H., Saito, A., Chan, P. H. (2006) Mitochondrial translocation of p53 underlies the selective death of hippocampal CA1 neurons after global cerebral ischaemia. *Biochem. Soc. Trans.* 34: 1283-1286.

[138] Sanderson, T. H., Kumar, R., Sullivan, J. M., Krause, G. S. (2008) Insulin blocks cytochrome c release in the reperfused brain through PI3-K signaling and by promoting Bax/Bcl-XL binding. *J. Neurochem.* 106: 1248-1258.

[139] Igney, F. H., Krammer, P. H. (2002) Death and anti-death: tumour resistance to apoptosis. *Nat. Rev. Cancer* 2: 277-288.

[140] Fulda, S. (2010) Evasion of apoptosis as a cellular stress response in cancer. *Int. J. Cell Biol.* 2010: 370835.

[141] Kelly, G. L., Strasser, A. (2011) The essential role of evasion from cell death in cancer. *Adv. Cancer Res.* 111: 39-96.

[142] Koppenol, W. H., Bounds, P. L., Dang, C. V. (2011) Otto Warburg's contributions to current concepts of cancer metabolism. *Nat. Rev. Cancer* 11: 325-337.

[143] Wallace, D. C. (2012) Mitochondria and cancer. *Nat. Rev. Cancer* 12: 685-698.

[144] Schulze, A., Harris, A. L. (2012) How cancer metabolism is tuned for proliferation and vulnerable to disruption. *Nature* 491: 364-373.

[145] Ayyasamy, V., Owens, K. M., Desouki, M. M., Liang, P., Bakin, A., Thangaraj, K., Buchsbaum, D. J., LoBuglio, A. F., Singh, K. K. (2011) Cellular model of Warburg effect identifies tumor promoting function of UCP2 in breast cancer and its suppression by genipin. *PloS One* 6: e24792.

[146] Ko, Y. H., Smith, B. L., Wang, Y., Pomper, M. G., Rini, D. A., Torbenson, M. S., Hullihen, J., Pedersen, P. L. (2004) Advanced cancers: eradication in all cases using 3-bromopyruvate therapy to deplete ATP. *Biochem. Biophys. Res. Commun.* 324: 269-275.

[147] Akers, L. J., Fang, W., Levy, A. G., Franklin, A. R., Huang, P., Zweidler-McKay, P. A. (2011) Targeting glycolysis in leukemia: a novel inhibitor 3-BrOP in combination with rapamycin. *Leuk. Res.* 35: 814-820.

[148] Holohan, C., Van Schaeybroeck, S., Longley, D. B., Johnston, P. G. (2013) Cancer drug resistance: an evolving paradigm. *Nat. Rev. Cancer* 13: 714-726.

[149] Johnson, C. E., Huang, Y. Y., Parrish, A. B., Smith, M. I., Vaughn, A. E., Zhang, Q., Wright, K. M., Van Dyke, T., Wechsler-Reya, R. J., Kornbluth, S., Deshmukh, M. (2007) Differential Apaf-1 levels allow cytochrome c to induce apoptosis in brain tumors but not in normal neural tissues. *Proc. Natl. Acad. Sci. US* 104: 20820-20825.

[150] Barros, S., Mencia, N., Rodriguez, L., Oleaga, C., Santos, C., Noe, V., Ciudad, C. J. (2013) The redox state of cytochrome c modulates resistance to methotrexate in human MCF7 breast cancer cells. *PloS One* 8: e63276.

[151] Plas, D. R., Thompson, C. B. (2002) Cell metabolism in the regulation of programmed cell death. *Trends Endocrinol. Metab.* 13: 75-78.

[152] Bonnet, S., Archer, S. L., Allalunis-Turner, J., Haromy, A., Beaulieu, C., Thompson, R., Lee, C. T., Lopaschuk, G. D., Puttagunta, L., Harry, G., Hashimoto, K., Porter, C. J., Andrade, M. A., Thebaud, B., Michelakis, E. D. (2007) A mitochondria-K+ channel axis is suppressed in cancer and its normalization promotes apoptosis and inhibits cancer growth. *Cancer Cell* 11: 37-51.

[153] Vaughn, A. E., Deshmukh, M. (2008) Glucose metabolism inhibits apoptosis in neurons and cancer cells by redox inactivation of cytochrome c. *Nat. Cell Biol.* 10: 1477-1483.
[154] Ruckenstuhl, C., Buttner, S., Carmona-Gutierrez, D., Eisenberg, T., Kroemer, G., Sigrist, S. J., Frohlich, K. U., Madeo, F. (2009) The Warburg effect suppresses oxidative stress induced apoptosis in a yeast model for cancer. *PloS One* 4: e4592.
[155] Schmidt, T. R., Wildman, D. E., Uddin, M., Opazo, J. C., Goodman, M., Grossman, L. I. (2005) Rapid electrostatic evolution at the binding site for cytochrome c on cytochrome c oxidase in anthropoid primates. *Proc. Natl. Acad. Sci. US* 102: 6379-6384.

In: Cytochromes *b* and *c*
Editor: Rurik Thom

ISBN: 978-1-63117-467-4
© 2014 Nova Science Publishers, Inc.

Chapter 2

CYTOCHROME b_5 AS A PLEIOTROPIC METABOLIC MODULATOR IN MAMMALIAN CELLS

Alejandro K. Samhan-Arias and Carlos Gutierrez-Merino[*]

Dept. Biochemistry and Molecular Biology, School of Sciences,
University of Extremadura, Badajoz, Spain

ABSTRACT

Cytochrome b_5 (Cb_5) acts within the cells as a pleiotropic co-factor of multiple enzymes and redox chains that play critical roles for normal function of healthy mammalian organisms. It is maintained in the reduced form largely by the NADH-dependent cytochrome b_5 reductase activity which catalyzes electron transfer to Cb_5 in mammalian cells. The enzyme system cytochrome b_5 reductase/cytochrome b_5 has been shown to be associated with the endoplasmic reticulum, mitochondria and plasma membrane of mammalian cells, where it is involved in multiple metabolic pathways, such as cholesterol biosynthesis, desaturation and elongation of fatty acids, methemoglobin reduction and steroids and xenobiotics metabolism catalyzed by cytochrome P450s. More recently, this system has been shown to be a component of the 'so-called' redox-chain of the plasma membrane present in mammalian cells, where it clusters within

---

[*] Corresponding author: carlosgm@unex.es.

cholesterol-rich and caveolins-rich lipid rafts-associated sub-microdomains of the plasma membrane. The cytochrome b_5 reductase/cytochrome b_5 is also a relevant system in the redox biology of cell death, as it forms a stable complex with cytochrome c, a pro-apoptotic signalling molecules, and it is involved in the modulation of superoxide generation in mammalian cells, playing a major role in the NADH-dependent superoxide anion production of the neuronal plasma membrane accounting for most of the superoxide anion overshot that is observed in an early stage of the neuronal apoptosis. In addition, an expanding family of proteins containing a Cb_5-like domain is also present in mammalian cells. Both, the novel cellular functions described for Cb_5 and for novel proteins containing a Cb_5-like domain point out that Cb_5 can be seen as an intracellular signaling molecule in redox biology and as a potential cellular biomarker of health and disease.

1. INTRODUCTION

Cytochrome b's are hemeproteins characterized by the presence of a heme group not covalently bound to the protein. The heme group of these proteins is a bis(imidazole) coordinated group displaying different physical properties. Mosbauer studies on the heme coordination led to propose a weak binding of a vicinal histidine to the hemin [Medhi, 1990].

Cytochrome b's are part of redox systems as components of electron chains as individual proteins, like cytochrome b_5 (Cb_5), or enzymatic domains, like molybdenum dependent sulfite oxidase. Mammalian cells express several isoforms of Cb_5, which is one of the most studied proteins of the cytochrome b family. Cb_5 becomes embedded into membranes after being generated in free polyribosomes rather than in membrane-bound ribosomes, as demonstrated by experiments of Cb_5 incorporation in biological and artificial membranes [Rapoport and Wiedmann, 1985]. *In vivo*, two well defined NAD(P)H-dependent reductases, namely, cytochrome b_5 reductase and cytochrome P450 reductase are the major systems catalyzing the reduction of Cb_5. Cb_5, as a hemeprotein coupled to its reductases, accepts and rapidly transfer electrons to other electron partners [Bond et al., 1990]. Many biological roles of Cb_5 were already known nearly 20 years ago, associated to a large number of functions in cells and tissues, such as lipid biosynthesis through desaturases, plasmalogen and cholesterol biosynthesis, fatty acid elongation, biosynthesis of sialic acid and methameoblogin recycling, reviewed in [Vergeres and Waskell, 1995]. However, novel biological functions of Cb_5 are emerging during last years, pointing out that this protein is also involved in intracellular signaling pathways whose deregulation play a key role in the apoptotic cell death. In addition, novel proteins containing a Cb_5 –like domain have been found and reported to be involved in the modulation of cellular redox signaling and steroid hormones signal transduction. Despite that the smooth endoplasmic reticulum has a high content of Cb_5, this protein presents a ubiquitous localization within the cells, as it is also found in the soluble cytosolic fraction and also in the cytoplasmic leaflet of organelles like the plasma membrane, endoplasmic reticulum, outer mitochondrial membrane and the nuclear membrane [Oshino, 1978; Rapoport and Wiedmann, 1985].

In this chapter we shall first describe the structure-function relationships and subcellular localization of the different Cb_5 isoforms expressed in mammalian cells. Particular emphasis will be placed in the homology of their primary sequences and conserved structural motifs and amino acids critical for their function as a redox partner, as well as for the regulation of the reduction potential of its heme b prosthetic group. In the next section of this chapter, we shall systematically present the enzymes that use Cb_5 as a co-factor, highlighting the functional consequences of the complex formation and the known protein residues identified in specific protein/protein interactions. In this section we have also included a sub-section devoted to the proteins containing a Cb_5 –like domain and the proposed biological roles for the most recently discovered members of this family of proteins. Thereafter, in a different section of this chapter we shall analyze the function of Cb_5 as an electron carrier in redox chains known to be present in mammalian cells and their biochemical and biological functions. As briefly indicated above new roles for Cb_5 in intracellular signaling have been proposed during last years in the field of redox biology. On these grounds, we have devoted the next section to the role of Cb_5 in reactive oxygen species (ROS) signaling and apoptosis. Finally, in the conclusion section we have summarized the major conclusions derived from the points addressed in this chapter, which indicate the potential of Cb_5 as a cellular biomarker for metabolic and age-related diseases.

2. STRUCTURE AND SUBCELLULAR LOCALIZATION

2a. Protein Structure of Cb_5

Mammalian Cb_5 is a globular acidic protein formed by 6 α-helices and 5 β-strands [Mathews et al., 1979], see also the Figure 1, with a molecular weigth between 16 and 25 kda depending on the species [Velick and Strittmatter, 1956; Spatz and Strittmatter, 1971].

In rat Cb_5 purified from the soluble fraction of liver homogenates the heme group sits in a cavity formed by 4 α-helices and coordinated by His44 and His68. There are two hydrophobic regions recognized in the structure of the protein named core-1 an core-2. The core-1 is formed by the central part of the protein and determines the protein-heme contact. The core-2 is found within the N- and C- terminal segment and has a certain degree of structural independence with respect to these two regions [Knappenberger et al., 2004]. Using trypsin-solubilized bovine liver microsomal Cb_5 (82 residues in length) it has been shown that the Phe40 is an important residue for stabilization of the protein. Mutation of the phenyl residue to tyrosine increase the stability of the protein in its oxidized state while mutation of this residue by Leu or His decrease its thermal stability with a shift in the redox potential [Yao et al.,1997]. Three highly conserved acidic residues, Glu49, Glu53 and Asp65 of membrane Cb_5 from several species (see the Figure 2), and one of the heme propionate are in the same plane in the solvent being implicated in the charge pairing interaction with other redox partners [Schenkman and Jansson, 2003]. NMR experiments of Cb_5 indicated that a conformational change occurs in the α-helices forming the heme-binding pocket when the oxidized and reduced forms are compared, suggesting a high flexibility of this pocket [Fragai et al., 2006].

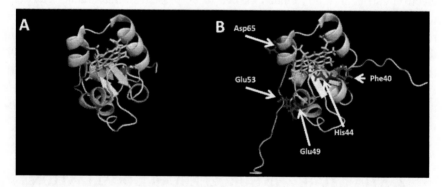

Figure 1. Structure of Cb_5. (A) Soluble fragment of rabbit microsomal Cb_5 (PBD: ID09, [Banci et al., 2000]). (B) Full-length rabbit microsomal Cb_5 (PBD: 2M33, [Ahuja et al., 2013]). Heme group is colored in yellow in panels A and B. Red labeling in panel B, indicates the location of the following side chain residues: Phe40, His44, Glu49, Glu53 and Asp65.

Cb_5 exists in aqueous solution free of detergent as a mixture of monomers and octamers [Konopka and Waskell, 1988]. The monomer form is present at low ionic strength and decreased in a concentration dependent manner with the ionic strength. Binding capacity to vesicles depends on the ionic strength and it has been shown that 30-50 lipid molecules can bind to one molecule of Cb_5 at low ionic strength while up to 250 molecules of Cb_5 have been shown to bind per liposomal vesicle in buffers containing 0.1M salt [Rogers and Strittmatter, 1975; Holloway, 1983]. Studies done with biological and artificial membranes have demonstrated that cholesterol-containing membranes have a lower affinity to Cb_5 [Tajima and Sato, 1979; Enomoto and Sato, 1977]. Stritmatter and co-workers concluded that Cb_5 was stabilized in two different conformations upon binding to membranes, called "loose" and "tight" form [Enoch et al., 1979; Dailey and Strittmatter, 1980].

A water-soluble protein heme domain (wsCyt b_5) from microsomal Cb_5 can be isolated by treatment of the microsomal Cb_5 with trypsin [Strittmatter and Ozols, 1966; Reid and Mauk, 1982]. The properties of this domain and its structure has been studied [Basova et al., 2008]. Proximity to a negatively charged membrane surface destabilizes wsCyt b_5 at neutral pH, and promotes its transition into a more flexible conformational state with molten globule-like properties. It has been observed that wsCyt b_5 can interact with artificial membranes at their surface [Basova et al., 2008]. Its association could be related to the presence of a hydrophobic patch of 320Å^2 adjacent to the anionic residues formed by residues Phe40, Pro45, Leu75 and Phe/Tyr79 (calf), that displays a role in the formation of complexes with redox partners [Mathews et al., 1979]. This hydrophobic patch of the surface of Cb_5 is not part of the hydrophobic core of Cb_5 localized inside the protein and has been associated to redox electron transfer properties to membrane acceptors [Vergeres and Waskell, 1995]. The presence of this hydrophobic patch on the surface of Cb_5 suggests that electrons flow from one side of the protein and could be delivered to membrane associated partners oriented toward this domain.

2b. Cb_5 Homology and Isoforms

Cb_5 keeps a highly conserved region composed by 96 amino acids [Ozols, 1989]. The mammalian form shares an 80% of identity with some conservative substitutions [Schenkman and Jansson, 2003]. Cb_5 from other sources share different percentages of homology with respect to mammals, see the Figures 2 and 3. For example, chicken shares 64%, plants 47%, yeast 26% and bacteria

21% of identical residues. In housefly, there is a form of Cb_5 that shares 44% of the identity with mammal Cb_5 [Guzov et al., 1996]. In rat liver, it has been isolated a type of Cb_5 named outer membrane Cb_5 (OMB5) that has an amino terminal leader sequence that targets the protein to mitochondria. In this type of Cb_5, the heme peptide region has 57% of homology. We will talk about its properties compared to microsomal Cb_5 (MCB5) in a section below in this chapter.

There are two isoforms of Cb_5, named erythrocyte Cb_5 (or soluble isoform) and liver Cb_5 (or membrane anchored), called in that way from the tissues where they were purified and extracted originally. Later it was demonstrated that both proteins are the short and the long isoform from the same protein. The OMB5 isoform contains 146 residues and, therefore, is longer than the MCB5 isoform which has 134 amino acids [Lederer et al., 1983]. The sequence conservation in the central position is very remarkable and includes the heme crevice region [Mathews et al., 1971; Mathews et al., 1972; Mathews et al., 1979]. Both type of proteins contains approximately 100 residues that are exposed to the cytosol, while each protein is anchored to its respective membrane through 20 residues near the protein C-terminus, although the targeting area that attach the protein to the membrane is built by only 10 amino acids [Mitoma and Ito, 1992; De Silvestris et al., 1995; Kuroda et al., 1998]. The first sequence for OMB5 was identified as a human testis isoform, but a nearly identical gene (replacing Lys by Gln95) has been identified in the human, rat and mouse genome [Altschul et al., 1997; Strausberg et al., 2002].

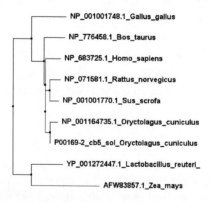

Figure 2. Cladogram-type phylogenetic tree of Cb_5. Shown only the species most used in structural studies of this protein. The phylogenetic tree has been calculated based on neighbour joining using percentage of identity (Waterhouse et al., 2009).

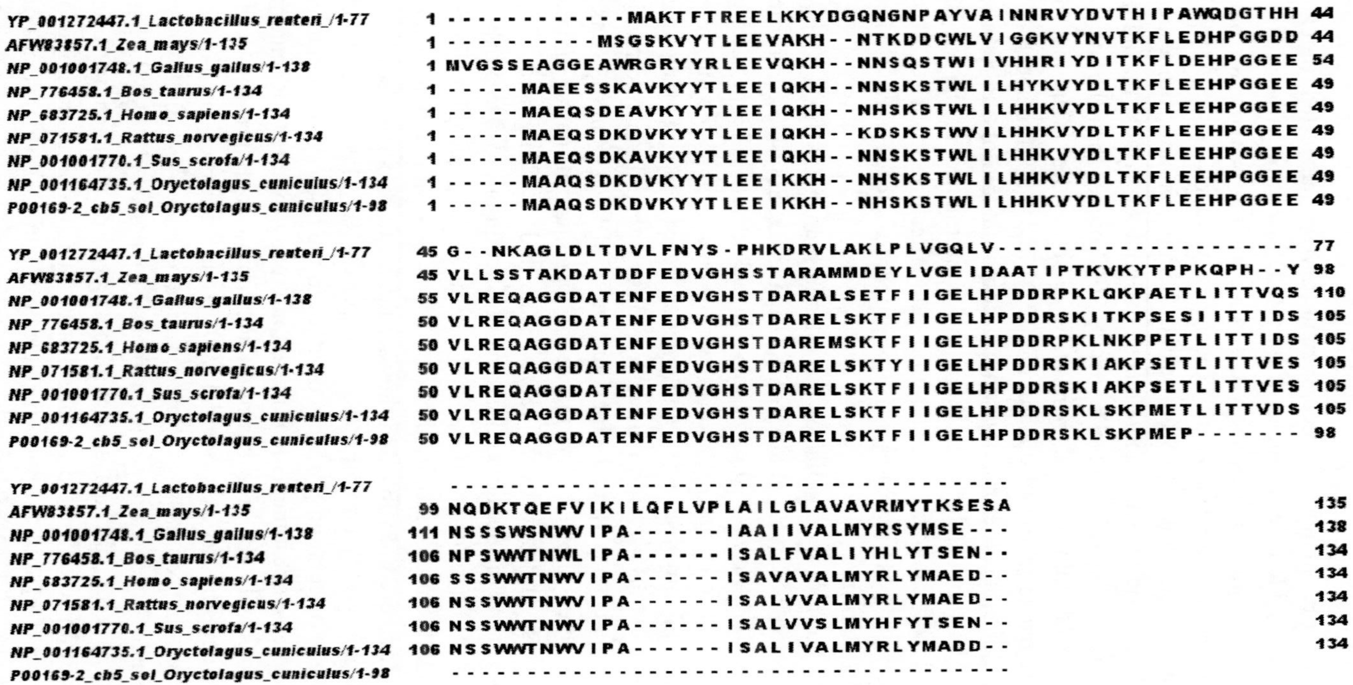

Figure 3 — Amino acid sequence alignment (microsomal Cb_5).

```
YP_001272447.1_Lactobacillus_reuteri_/1-77     1   - - - - - - - - - - - MAKTFTREELKKYDGQNGNPAYVAINNRVYDVTHIPAWQDGTHH  44
AFW93857.1_Zea_mays/1-115                      1   - - - - - - - - - - MSGSKVYTLEEVAKH - - NTKDDCWLVIGGKVYNVTKFLEDHPGGDD  44
NP_001001748.1_Gallus_gallus/1-138             1   MVGSSEAGGEAWRGRYYRLEEVQKH - - NNSQSTWIIVHHRIYDITKFLDEHPGGEE  54
NP_776458.1_Bos_taurus/1-134                   1   - - - - - MAEESSKAVKYYTLEEIQKH - - NNSKSTWLILHYKVYDLTKFLEEHPGGEE  49
NP_683725.1_Homo_sapiens/1-134                 1   - - - - - MAEQSDEAVKYYTLEEIQKH - - NHSKSTWVILHHKVYDLTKFLEEHPGGEE  49
NP_075581.1_Rattus_norvegicus/1-134            1   - - - - MAEQSDKDVKAVKYYTLEEIQKH - - KDSKSTWVILHHKVYDLTKFLEEHPGGEE  49
NP_001040170.1_Sus_scrofa/1-134                1   - - - - - MAEQSDKAVKYYTLEEIQKH - - NNSKSTWLILHHKVYDLTKFLEEHPGGEE  49
NP_001164735.1_Oryctolagus_cuniculus/1-134     1   - - - - - MAAQSDKDVKYYTLEEIKKH - - NHSKSTWLILHHKVYDLTKFLEEHPGGEE  49
P00169-2_cb5_sol_Oryctolagus_cuniculus/1-98    1   - - - - - MAAQSDKDVKYYTLEEIKKH - - NHSKSTWLILHHKVYDLTKFLEEHPGGEE  49

YP_001272447.1_Lactobacillus_reuteri_/1-77    45   G - NKAGLDLTDVLFNYS - PHKDRVLAKLPLVGQLV - - - - - - - - - - - - - -  77
AFW93857.1_Zea_mays/1-115                     45   VLLSSTAKDATDDFEDVGHSSTARAMMDEYLVGEIDAATIPTKVKYTPPKQPH - - Y  98
NP_001001748.1_Gallus_gallus/1-138            55   VLREQAGGDATENFEDVGHSTDARALSETFIIGELHPDDRPKLQKPAETLITTVQS  110
NP_776458.1_Bos_taurus/1-134                  50   VLREQAGGDATENFEDVGHSTDARELSKTFIIGELHPDDRSKITKPSESITTIDS  105
NP_683725.1_Homo_sapiens/1-134                50   VLREQAGGDATENFEDVGHSTDAREMSKTFIIGELHPDDRPKLNKPPETLITTIDS  105
NP_075581.1_Rattus_norvegicus/1-134           50   VLREQAGGDATENFEDVGHSTDARELSKTYIIGELHPDDRSKIAKPSETLITTVES  105
NP_001040170.1_Sus_scrofa/1-134               50   VLREQAGGDATENFEDVGHSTDARELSKTFIIGELHPDDRSKIAKPSETLITTVES  105
NP_001164735.1_Oryctolagus_cuniculus/1-134    50   VLREQAGGDATENFEDVGHSTDARELSKTFIIGELHPDDRSKLSKPMETLITTVDS  105
P00169-2_cb5_sol_Oryctolagus_cuniculus/1-98   50   VLREQAGGDATENFEDVGHSTDARELSKTFIIGELHPDDRSKLSKPMEP - - - - - -  98

YP_001272447.1_Lactobacillus_reuteri_/1-77    99   NQDKTQEFVIKILQFLVPLAILGLAVAVRMYTKSESA  135
AFW93857.1_Zea_mays/1-115                    111   NSSSWSNWVIPA - - - - - IAAIIVALMYRSYMSE - -  138
NP_001001748.1_Gallus_gallus/1-138           106   NPSVWVTNWLIPA - - - - - ISALFVALIYHLYTSEN - -  134
NP_776458.1_Bos_taurus/1-134                 106   SSSVWVTNWVIPA - - - - - ISAVAVALMYRLYMAED - -  134
NP_683725.1_Homo_sapiens/1-134               106   NSSVWVTNWVIPA - - - - - ISALVVALMYRLYMAED - -  134
NP_075581.1_Rattus_norvegicus/1-134          106   NSSVWVTNWVIPA - - - - - ISALVVSLMYHFYTSEN - -  134
NP_001040170.1_Sus_scrofa/1-134              106   NSSVWVTNWVIPA - - - - - ISALVVSLMYHFYTSEN - -  134
NP_001164735.1_Oryctolagus_cuniculus/1-134   106   NSSVWVTNWVIPA - - - - - ISALIVALMYRLYMADD - -  134
```

Figure 3. Amino acids sequence alignment of microsomal Cb_5 from the species most often used in structural and functional studies. Also included for comparison the amino acids sequence of the rabbit soluble Cb_5 isoform (98 amino acids), line P00169-2_cb5-sol_Oryctolagus_cuniculus.

UV–Vis and EPR studies of recombinant OMB5 suggested that its properties were nearly identical to those of the MCB5 isoform [Rivera et al., 1992], and crystallographic studies showed similar folding patterns for both proteins [Durley and Mathews, 1996; Rodriguez-Maranon et al., 1996]. Human and rat OMB5 has also the same hemin binding properties. Nevertheless calorimetric measurements has shown that the critical unfolding temperature for the rat OMB5 isoform is nearly 20°C higher than that of the MCB5 isoform, 85.5 and 67.6°C, respectively, being the midpoints of guanidinium thiocyanate-mediated denaturation 2.04 and 1.52M, respectively [Cowley et al., 2002]. Therefore, the native conformation of the OMB5 isoform seems to be more stable than the native conformation of the MCB5 isoform. Thermal and chemical denaturation properties for human OMB5 (Tm=85.7 and Cm=1.86M) indicates stability properties closer to rat OMB5 than to rat MCB5 isoform.

Interestingly, the redox potential of the rat and human OMB5, -107mV and -40mV, respectively [Rivera et al., 1992; Altuve et al., 2004], differs from that found for MCB5 from rat (~0 to +10mV) [Mauk et al., 1982; Walker et al., 1988; Rodgers and Sligar, 1991; Mauk et al., 1995], bovine liver (~+31mV) [Glenn and Bowden, 1996] and chicken liver (~+40mV) [Bagby et al., 1988]. Human MCB5 isoform have a redox potential approximately 100mV higher than that found for human OMB5 (-40mV). Early electrochemical studies showed that the redox potential of native bovine erythrocyte Cb_5 was varying between values: +0.8 and -26.2mV, and NMR studies using apoCb_5 reconstituted with exogenous hemin allowed to attribute this fact to the two different orientations for the heme in the protein [Walker et al., 1988]. Through the use of modified hemes, it has been shown that both of the orientations are interconvertible and they are the result of heme disorder or rotation of the heme moiety around the α,γ meso axis [La Mar et al., 1981]. The change of heme orientation produces changes in the microenvironment of the heme, placing heme substituents in different microenvironments depending on their interactions with the side chains of the amino acids present in the heme pocket. When the redox potential of Cb_5 is measured by surface modified electrons, the results give more positive values (40-100mV) than when it is measured by potentiometric methods [Rivera et al., 1998]. This difference in redox potentials measured with both type of methods has been related to the neutralization of the surface charge of Cb_5 upon formation of complexes between Cb_5 and the modified electron surface, which leads to exclusion of water from the complex and changes in the dielectric constant of the microenvironment of the heme group and destabilization of the positive charge of the ferricytochrome respect the ferrous form. These experiments suggest that a shift in the redox potential of Cb_5 should be expected upon formation of complexes of Cb_5 with other protein partners within redox chains, provided that the complex formation elicits a re-orientation of the heme group of Cb_5.

1H NMR experiments have shown that the heme group of MCB5 can be in two interconvertible spatial orientations that differ by a 180 degrees rotation around the α,γ-meso axis of the heme, which are named isoforms A and B of Cb_5 [Keller and Wüthrich, 1980; La Mar et al., 1981; Walker et al., 1988]. When bovine MCB5 is reconstituted, it is observed that the equilibrium between these isoforms is largely shifted towards the A isomer, ratio A:B isoforms of 9:1 [La Mar et al., 1981; Walker et al., 1988]. Other mammalian MCB5s keep favoring the A position in different A:B ratios, for example, 1.6:1 for rat and 20:1 for chicken [Lee et al., 1991]. In this work Lee et al. calculated that in the bovine microsomal protein, orientation A is enthalpically favored by 1.4 kcal/mol, whereas in the rat MCB5, orientation B is enthalpically favored by 2.4 kcal/mol. These investigators also pointed out that the steric destabilization of a vinyl substituent at position c in the heme by a hydrophobic cluster of amino acids at positions 23 and 25 is an important factor for heme orientation in Cb_5. For the case of rat OMB5 this A:B ratio is 1:1.2 and for the human form 1:1 [Silchenko et al., 2000].

The large positive shift (+110 mV) observed for rat OMB5 was attributed later to the presence of a multivalent cation site that once is occupied shield the negatively charged protein surface and negatively charged electron surface to facilitate the electron transfer [Glenn and Bowden, 1996]. It has been defined the binding pocket for the multivalent cations being formed by the conserved acidic residues of the rat OMB5 (Glu49, Glu53, Glu61 and Asp60) that correspond to (Glu44, Glu48, Glu56 and Glu65) of human Cb_5. The neutralization of charge as a consequence of the binding of a cation results in water exclusion from the complex inducing a decrease of the dielectric constant in he microenvironment of the heme group that leads to a positive shift of the redox potential [Rivera et al., 1998; Wirtz et al., 2000].

The role of OMB5 has been lately associated to a high reduction of hydroxylamines and imidoximes as a cofactor of molybdenum cofactor sulfurase C-terminal 2 (MOSCO-2), exclusively located at mitochondrial membranes, and cytochrome b_5 reductase [Neve et al., 2012]. Downregulation of MOSCO-2 cause impaired lipid synthesis, and this led these authors to suggest the involvement of these proteins in a new pathway for the synthesis of lipids.

The molecular mechanisms controlling the expression of the *CYB5B* gene encoding for OMB5 or CYB5B protein in the different tissues of mammals, although it has been observed that there is an increase in the levels of this protein in prostate cancer cells treated with luteinizing hormone [Pinski et al., 2011], are a yet unresolved issue despite that cDNA libraries and database analysis has pointed out its expression in many tissues of different mammalian species [Soucy and Luu-The, 2002]. Interestingly, in cancer cells the CYB5B protein has been identified as the 21 KDa protein overexpressed at the cell surface and cytoplasm in Hodgkin lymphoma and aggressive non-Hodgkin lymphomas [Murphy et al., 2010].

3. Cb_5 AS AN ENZYME COFACTOR

Cb_5 plays a pleiotropic role in metabolism acting as cofactor of many enzymes. For the sake of clarity, the role of Cb_5 as enzyme cofactor will be reviewed following the outline indicated next:

(a) Enzymes of lipid metabolism
(b) Methemoglobin reductase activity
(c) Enzymes of xenobiotics detoxification
(d) Proteins containing a Cb_5-like domain

3a. Enzymes of Lipid Metabolism

Cb_5 is used by desaturases to generate an electron-deficiency, to activate oxygen species, and to remove electrons from the saturated hydrocarbon. Cb_5 and its reductase have also been implicated in palmitoyl-CoA elongation in brain microsomes [Takeshita et al., 1985].

Polyunsaturated fatty acids (PUFA) synthesis is catalyzed by the so-called Cb_5 fusion desaturases, since they contain an N-terminal domain orthologous to the microsomal Cb_5 from mammals [Napier et al., 2003]. This is also the case of the moss *Physcomitrella patens* Δ^6-desaturase which is physically associated to its electron donor in the form of an N-terminal extension [Girke et al., 1998], an enzyme that later was found also in in mouse and humans [Cho et al., 1999]. A functional characterization done in *Primula* Cb_5-fusion desaturases revealed that they have strong substrate specificity for α-linolenic acid (ALA; 18:3 n-3). The Δ^6-desaturase enzyme has the ability to work on both C_{18} and C_{24} substrates (but not on any intermediate chain lengths) [de Antueno et al., 2001; D'Andrea et al., 2002], to catalyze the synthesis of docohexanoic acid [Sprecher et al., 1995]. A Δ^5-desaturase has been reported with a proximal relationship to the human Δ^6-desaturase [Leonard et al., 2000]. By heterologous expression in yeast, one of the ORFs was functionally characterized and identified to be the *Thraustochytrium* orthologue recognized as the Δ^5-desaturase, a member of the Cb_5 fusion desaturases being capable of specifically introducing a Δ^4-double bond into the C_{22} PUFA docosapentaenoic acid (DPA; 22:5 n-3) to yield docohexanoic acid. Other member of this family also include the Δ^8-sphingolipid long chain base (LCB) desaturase from higher plants and Fah1p in yeast and *C. elegans*, an enzyme that catalyzes the hydroxylation of the C_2 position of the very long chain (saturated) fatty acid moiety of sphingolipids [Napier et al., 2003].

The human *FA2H* gene encodes a fatty acid 2-hydroxylase that has been reported to contain a N-terminal Cb_5 domain and four potential transmembrane domains [Alderson et al., 2004]. This enzyme has certain homology with flavoctochrome b_2 and its iron-binding histidine motif is also conserved among membrane-bound desaturases/hydroxylases. On the other hand, C-4-hydroxylation requires an electron-transfer system that includes Cb_5 being degenerative spermatocyte 2 protein (Des2) the enzyme responsible for the hydroxylase activity [Enomoto et al., 2006]. The dihydroceramide:sphinganine C-4-hydroxylase requires the formation of a complex between Des2 and MCB5 (but not the soluble form of Cb_5) via their membrane-spanning domains and the electron transfer from NADH to the substrate via the reduction of MCB5 by cytochrome b_5 reductase [Enomoto et al., 2006].

Cb_5 has also been involved in the conversion of lanosterol to cholesterol and more specifically in the microsomal reaction catalyzed by the 4-methyl sterol oxidase where the C-30 methyl group of lanosterol is oxidized to a steroid -4α-oic acid which can subsequently be decarboxylated. The Cb_5-dependent desaturase called lanosterol Δ^5 *desaturase introduces a double bond in lanosterol to produce* 7-dehydrocholesterol [Vergeres and Waskell, 1995]. The biosynthesis of steroid hormones is also modulated by Cb_5, through allosteric modulation of the 3β-hydroxysteroid dehydrogenase/Δ(5)-Δ(4) isomerase (3βHSD) activity resulting in an increase of the affinity of the enzyme toward NAD^+ [Goosen et al., 2013]. A differential modulation by OMB5 and MCB5 has been reported for the 17 α-hydroxylase and 17,20-lyase activities of P450c17 leading to production of 17 α-hydroxypregnenolone (17 α OH-Preg) and dehydroepiandrosterone (DHEA), respectively [Soucy and Luu-The, 2002]. Expression in testis of a cDNA encoding for the outer mitochondrial membrane Cb_5 (*CYB5B* gene encoding for OMB5) and sharing a 58% of homology with type A Cb_5 gene (*CYB5A* gene encoding for MCB5) has been reported to elicit a stronger increase of the 17,20-lyase activities of P450c17 than that induced by type A Cb_5 [Soucy and Luu-The, 2002]. Later, it was studied the role of the two forms of porcine Cb_5, MCB5 and OMB5, in both the andien-β synthase as well as the 17α-hydroxylase and C17,20 lyase reactions by expression of *CYP17A1*, along with cytochrome P450 reductase, cytochrome b_5 reductase and Cb_5 in HEK-293FT cells [Billen and Squires, 2009]. In this study, the authors reported that an increase in the ratio of MCB5 to *CYP17A1* caused a decrease in 17α-hydroxylase, a transient increase in C17,20 lyase and an increase in andien-β synthase activity, while an increase in the ratio of OMB5 to *CYP17A1* decreased 17α-hydroxylase, but did not affect the andien-*β* synthase activity; however, the C17,20 lyase, was significantly increased. Moreover, immunohystochemical studies have suggested a regionalization of the expression of Cb_5 in the adrenal gland, which has been correlated with the regionalization of the synthesis of 19c steroids as dehydroepiandrosterone in this gland [Mellon, 2005].

In addition to cholesterol biosynthesis, Cb_5 has also been implicated in the formation of plasmalogen [Paltuaf et al., 1974]. Conversion of 1-alkyl-2acyl-*sn*-GroPEtn to 1-alk-1'-enyl-2-acyl-sn-GroPEtn is carried out by the presence the cytochrome b_5 reductase / Cb_5 system in addition to a cyanide-sensitive 1-alkyl desaturase [Snyder et al., 1985]. This result was demonstrated by the use of antibodies against Cb_5 that inhibited the synthesis of ethanolamine plasmalogen. As well as plasmalogen, Cb_5 has been involved in sialic acid metabolism, a metabolite required for the synthesis of gangliosides and other glycoproteins. Cb_5 reduced by cytochrome b_5 reductase forms a complex with the cytidine-5'-monophosphate-*N*-acetylneuraminic acid (CMP-Neu5Ac) hydroxylase, and acts as a cofactor for the CMP-Neu5Ac hydroxylase activity in the presence of oxygen [Gollub and Shaw, 2003; Kohla and Schauer, 2005].

3b. Methemoglobin Reductase Activity

A very important function of Cb_5 has been shown in erythrocytes where methemoglobin (MetHb) can act as the final acceptor of the electron carried out by reduced Cb_5 [Kitao et al., 1974; Kuma et al., 1976].

Cyanosis due to pulmonary and cardiac disease is one of the most common blood disorders. In erythrocytes, MetHb is kept by two systems at levels below 1% of the total hemoglobin [Wang et al., 2000; Kinoshita et al.,

2007]. One of them is the NADH: cytochrome b_5 reductase activity that transfers electrons to Cb_5. This pathway is responsible for more than 95% of the erythrocyte reducing capacity. The second system is formed by a NADPH-dependent flavin reductase pathway (FR) considered as a minor contributor to the reduction of MetHb, because its malfunction do not cause a MetHb reduction-deficient phenotype.

Cytochrome b_5 reductase reduces MetHb and the presence of Cb_5 greatly accelerates this reaction. The proposed mechanism of this reaction can be briefly summarized as follows: (1) NADH binds to the reductase and is transformed into NAD^+, reducing FAD to $FADH_2$; (2) then, the Cb_5-Fe^{3+} is reduced to Cb_5-Fe^{2+} coupled to oxidation of $FADH_2$ back to FAD; and (3) MetHb forms a bimolecular complex with reduced Cb_5 and MetHb is reduced to hemoglobin [Steinberg, 2009].

The complex between Cb_5 and MetHb has been generated by NMR and protein docking approaches [Poulos and Mauk, 1983]. For the α-chain of horse hemoglobin / bovine liver Cb_5 complex, the α-chain residues 56 (Lys), 60 (Lys), and 90 (Lys) interact with the Glu44, Glu43 and Glu60 residues on Cb_5, respectively. Lys61 is implicated in a hydrogen bond between a heme propionate from Cb_5 and a heme propionate from the α-chain. The contacts present in the β-chain/ Cb_5 complex involves hydrogen-bonding between the lysil residues 59, 61, 65, and 95 of the β-chain, and Cb_5 residues Glu48, Glu44, Glu43 and Asp60, respectively. As it happens with the α-chain, a hydrogen bond can be formed between the amino group of the Lys66 bridging the heme propionate from Cb_5 and the α-chain heme propionate [Poulos and Mauk, 1983].

The comparison of the complexes formed by Cb_5 with human MetHb reductase and with rat and corn nitrite reductase shows that there is a large main chain shift caused by a single-residue replacement from proline to threonine. A model of the complex between Cb_5 and the human reductase has been built and compared to the heme-containing domain of the nitrate reductase molecule. The interaction between cytochrome b_5 reductase and Cb_5 differs from that described for the nitrate reductase because of differences in the amino acid sequences [Bando et al., 2004]. Modeling analysis of cytochrome b_5 reductase has found 5 mutations key in the formation of a stable complex b_5-cytochrome b_5 reductase : Pro64Leu, Leu72Pro, Val105Met and Pro144Leu [Bando et al., 2004]. The type of electron transfer between Cb_5 and MetHb is the same by formation of an intracomplex electron transfer that it is characterized to be transient, with a low affinity complex formation [Xiong et al., 2009]. In these complexes water plays a double role in the electron-transfer system, decreasing the tunneling barrier and inducing protein interface remodeling that screens the repulsion between the negatively charged propionates of the two hemes [Keinan et al., 2012].

3c. Enzymes of Xenobiotics Detoxification

Cb_5 acts as a cofactor in NADPH dependent cytochrome P450 monoxygenations, reviewed in [Schenkman and Jansson, 2003]. Antibodies against Cb_5 has been reported to produce an 80% blockade of the metabolism of benzo-α-pyrene and ethoxycoumarin, and to strongly inhibit laurate hydroxylation and the microsomal metabolism of testosterone and methoxyflurane. Interestingly, the metabolism of benzphetamine, ethylmorphine, aniline oxidation, and aminopyrine demethylation was not affected, the last three compounds when NADPH was used as a substrate [Schenkman and Jansson, 2003]. Furthermore, an increase of cytochrome P450-mediated metabolism of some xenobiotics in the presence of Cb_5 has been observed, but this was not extensive to all xenobiotics and metabolites that are putative substrates of the large family of cytochrome P450s, as Cb_5 did not stimulate the metabolic rate of all of them. An increase of the cytochrome P450 activities in the presence of Cb_5 has been shown for oxidation of 7-ethoxycoumarin and p-nitrophenatole by CYP2B4 and CYP1A2; benzphetamine demethylation, testosterone hydroxylation, aminopyrine demethylation, p-nitroanisole demethylation by CYP2C11; benzphetamine demethylation, 7-ethoxycoumarin demethylation, acetanilide hydroxylation, testosterone hydroxylation by CYP2B4. For the case of CYP1A2 and the metabolism of prostaglandin E1, E2 and A1, Cb_5 is a mandatory cofactor that enhances the activity [Schenkman and Jansson, 2003]. The steroidogenic cytochrome P450s CYP17A1is also activated by the presence of Cb_5 where it has been observed a buried CYP17A1 active site composed by residues Arg-347, Arg-358, or Arg-449 [Estrada et al., 2013]. Interestingly, apoCb_5 has also been shown to enhance the activities of CYP3A4, CYP2A6, CYP2C19, and CYP17A1 but not that of CYP2E1 or CYP2D6 [Peng and Auchus, 2013]. In addition, it has been noticed that some controversial data reported in the bibliography regarding modulation of cytochrome P450s by Cb_5 can be attributed to the order of addition of substrates and the presence of lipids [Peng and Auchus, 2013]. The potentiation by Cb_5 of the metabolism through cytochrome P450s catalyzed reactions could reflect a more efficient coupling of the system in the presence of Cb_5, which decreases the rate of collateral reactions releasing non-productive superoxide anion and its dismutation metabolite hydrogen peroxide and results in an increasing rate of product formation [Schenkman and Jansson, 2003]. It has been demonstrated that Cb_5 promotes that the electron transfer reaction becomes faster than the competing reaction of superoxide anion diffusion out from the catalytic center, see for example [Gorsky et al., 1984; Schenkman and Jansson, 2003]. Indeed, formation of hydrogen peroxide has been used to monitor uncoupling of the cytochrome P450 system [Gorsky et al., 1984; Jansson and Schenkman, 1987; Locuson et al., 2007].

Recently, it has been identified a system implicated in N- hydroxylation of prodrugs through the molybdenum enzyme mitochondrial Amidoxime Reducing Component (mARC), cytochrome b_5 reductase and Cb_5 [Froriep et al., 2013]. mARC is formed by two isoforms mARC-1 and -2 (also known as MOSCO1 and MOSCO2). These proteins form a novel system that consists in three separate proteins where each mARC reduces N-hydroxylated compounds through the electrons provided by the cytochrome b_5 reductase/Cb_5 redox system. The reconstituted system produces the reduction of N-hydroxy-sulfonamides to sulfonamides like it happens for some prodrugs, e.g. the reduction of N-hydroxy-valdecoxib to valdecoxib, an inhibitor of COX2 activity [Havemeyer et al., 2010].

3d. Proteins Containing a Cb_5-like Domain

A family of proteins of diverse biological functions contains Cb_5-like domains, i.e. with the hemeprotein domain covalently bound to other redox protein domains [Lederer, 1994]. This is the case of multiple enzymes including lactate dehydrogenase [Guiard et al., 1974], sulfite oxidase [Ito, 1971] and nitrate reductase [Le and Lederer, 1983]. The aminoacid homology between Cb_5 and the heme binding region of bakers' yeast cytochrome b_2 [L-(+)-lactate dehydrogenase, EC 1.1.2.3] was shown by [Guiard et al., 1974]. This domain has a strong similarity with the sequence of microsomal Cb_5. Some enzymes involved in lipid metabolism like some "front-end desaturases" or also called Cb_5 fusion desaturases and the fatty acid 2-hydroxylase have also been defined as proteins containing a Cb_5 domains, as indicated above in section 3a of this chapter. Many of these proteins are directed to subcellular membranes through a specific signal-sequence tail that targets and anchors them to mitochondrial or endoplasmic reticulum membranes. The structure of the heme binding domain of the baker's yeast flavocytochrome b_2 or of lactate dehydrogenase, remains similar to the one described for Cb_5, consisting in two cores on each side of a β-sheet (heme crevice). For both proteins heme is bis-His coordinated. The working mechanism of this type of proteins reported for sulfite oxidase can be used to illustrate the cooperation between redox centers in these proteins. Indeed, they can be seen as tight and efficient built-in redox chains. Briefly, after substrate oxidation two electrons are transferred from sulfite to the molybdenum center that are subsequently transferred to the Cb_5 domain in a two-step reaction and finally accepted by cytochrome c (Cyt c) as the final electron acceptor [Rudolph et al., 2003]. The molybdenum cofactor domains of nitrate reductase and sulfite oxidase are homologous [Lederer, 1994]. All members of the cytochrome b_5 family, exhibit a Pro-Gly-Gly motif (residues 41-43 in HSO b_5) at the top of the cleft that promotes the heme exposition to the solvent. The presence of a proline induces a twist in the peptide chain that separates it away from the heme group, producing the exposure of the propionate group due to the presence of two consecutive glycine residues [Rudolph et al., 2003]. This structure has been implicated in protein-protein interactions [Durham et al., 1995] and regulation of the redox potential of Cb_5 [Rivera et al., 1998]. The comparative analysis of a high-resolution structure of human sulfite oxidase cytochrome b_5 domain (HSO b_5) and of Cb_5 has revealed the physical-chemical features that account for the heme redox potential differences found between these proteins.

In addition to the role of Cb_5 as an electron acceptor in the molibdenopterin dependent sulfite oxidase, Cb_5 acts as an acceptor of flavoproteins like cytochrome b_5 reductase, nitrate reductase, cytochrome P450 reductase and flavocytochrome b_2. The final acceptor of the electrons taken up by Cb_5 reduction is Cyt c for the case of flavocytochrome b_2 and sulfite oxidase systems, and in nitrate reductase this final acceptor is Mo-pterin cofactor. In microsomal systems, cytochrome P450 [Henderson et al., 2013] and acyl-CoA desaturases [Oshino and Omura, 1973; Montgomery, 1976] are the electron acceptors from Cb_5.

The NAD(P)H cytochrome b_5 oxidoreductase (NCB5OR) is another example where a flavohemeprotein contains a cytochrome b_5-like domain [Zhu et al., 1999]. NCB5OR has been found in vertebrates and invertebrates and is expressed in a variety of cells and tissues. Because of its weak NAD(P)H oxidase activity, e.g. it has a very low k_{cat} value of ~0.05 s^{-1} and K_M ~12 mm(O_2) for this activity, and based on the experimental evidences showing that cytochrome b-type NAD(P)H oxidase could regulate the gene expression through oxidative modification of hypoxia-inducible factor 1, it has been proposed that NCB5OR can act as an oxygen sensor within the cells [Zhu et al., 2004].

A novel family of proteins containing a cytochrome b_5-like domain is composed by the progesterone receptor membrane component 1 and 2 (PGRMC1 and PGRMC2), neudesin, and neuferricin, all containing a cytochrome b_5-like heme/steroid-binding domain and belong to the membrane-associated progesterone receptor (MAPR) family of proteins [Kimura et al., 2012].The putative membrane receptors for progesterone PGRMC1 and PGRMC2 are transmembrane receptors [Thomas, 2008; Thomas et al., 2009] for progesterone that differs from the nuclear receptors with genomic effects [Peluso, 2007; Kimura et al., 2013]. The activity of PGRMC1 and PGRMC2 is mediated by activation of mitogen-activated protein kinase (MAPK) signaling and intracellular Ca^{2+} increases [Kimura et al., 2012]. It has been shown that PGRMC1 binds and activates cytochrome P450 proteins [Min et al., 2005; Hughes et al., 2007] linking this protein to modulation of drug, hormones and lipid metabolism [Han et al., 2012]. Neudesin (neuron-derived neurotrophic factor; NENF) is a ~18KDa protein that was identified as a neurotrophic factor involved in neuronal differentiation and survival being its neurotrophic activity exerted via the mitogen-activated protein kinase (MAPK) and phosphatidylinositol 3-kinase (PI3K) [Kimura et al., 2013]. Neudesin is highly expressed in the central nervous system and could be involved in the rapid non-genomic actions of progesterone due to similarities to PGRMC [Kimura et al., 2013]. The structure of human neudesin has been obtained by NMR. It is formed by a structure containing 4 α-helices and 6 β-strands (β1-α1-β2-β3-α2-β4-α3-α4-β5-β6), being the heme-binding pocket predicted to be formed between α2 and α3 [Han et al., 2012]. The putative heme-binding domains is located from residues 45–143, in which Tyr-81 and Tyr-87 form the predicted binding site for the heme iron. It has been suggested a role of neudesin as a protein with ability to form a complex with progesterone suppressing the translocation of progesterone to the nuclear receptor in addition to a possible role as a progesterone receptor at the cell surface of the cells [Kimura et al., 2013]. As well as neudesin, another extracellular heme binding protein of ~18KDa with cytochrome b_5-like heme/steroid-binding domain has been recently identified and called neuferricin [Kimura et al., 2010]. Indeed, cytochrome b_5 domain 2 containing protein (CYB5D2 or neuferricin) belongs to the family of membrane-associated progesterone receptors (MAPRs) [Xie et al., 2011]. The expression of the mRNA has been mainly observed in the brain since the embryo stage and increases during development. In primary cultures of mouse neurons, it has been observed that recombinant mouse neuferricin promote neurogenesis providing new insights about the function of heme-binding proteins as extracellular signal transmitters. In addition, neuferricin has been shown to improve HeLa cells survival after etoposide (ETOP)-mediated cytotoxicity [Xie et al., 2011]. Cytochrome b_5 domain-containing protein 1(Cyb5d1) (~18-26KDa) is a protein belonging to the PGRMC1 family with unknown function. There is not information about the function of this protein although there are some studies showing its role a as a survival gene reducing the malignant potency of breast cancer cells [Grade et al., 2006; Grade et al., 2007; Yasrebi et al., 2009].

4. CB_5 AS AN ELECTRON CARRIER IN REDOX CHAINS

Acidic residues of Cb_5 have been proposed as mediators for the complex formation with multiple protein partners in redox reactions catalyzed by Cb_5. The three-dimensional structure of the Cb_5/Cyt c complex has been resolved at atomic level. Glu44, Glu48, Asp60 and the heme propionate group of bovine Cb_5 have been shown to play an important role for the complex stability [Rodgers et al., 1988]. In soluble Cb_5 all residues are mobile except Glu43 that forms an intramolecular salt bridge with Arg47 constraining the mobility of both residues [Mathews and Czerwinski, 1985]. By direct mutagenesis, it was observed that modification of hydrophobic residues didn't have any effect on the binding between Cyt c and Cb_5 although the substitution of residues Phe35, Pro40, Val45, Phe58, and Val61, which provide the thermodynamic driving forces for hydrophobic-mediated interactions in this complex, resulted in changes in the efficiency of the electron transfer reaction [Ren et al., 2004].

The role of acidic residues surrounding the heme group of Cb_5 has been shown also to be critical for its redox coupling to other final electron acceptors. This is the case of proteins like MetHb [Poulos and Mauk, 1983], metmyoglobin [Livingston et al., 1985], cytochrome P450cam (CYP101) [Stayton et al., 1989] and cytochrome b_5 reductase [Meyer et al., 1995]. The residues of Cb_5 involved in complex formation with MetHb have been discussed in the previous section of this chapter. Strittmatter characterized the crosslinking of the complex formed by bovine cytochrome b_5 reductase and bovine Cb_5 and showed also the importance of Glu43, Glu44, Glu48, Glu56, Asp60 and the heme propionate for interfacial interactions [Strittmatter et al., 1990]. The interaction of human Cb_5 with human cytochrome b_5 reductase implicates charge-pair interactions between Lys-41, Lys-125, Lys-162, and Lys-163 of the enzyme, and Glu-47, Glu-48, Glu-52, Glu-60, Asp-64 (group

A), and heme propionate of Cb_5 [Shirabe et al., 1998]. In addition, flash photolysis studies with cytochrome b_5 reductase demonstrated that in the presence of NAD^+ there is an increase in the rate constants of formation and stabilization of the Cb_5/cytochrome b_5 reductase complex resulting in a complex more stable against dissociation at high ionic strength [Meyer et al., 1995]. Experiments done with cytochrome b_5 reductase mutants of Thr66, a critical residue for the one-electron transfer reaction catalyzed by this enzyme, showed that the ternary complex formed with NADH and NAD^+ is a major intermediate in the turnover and that the release of NAD^+ from this complex is the rate limiting step [Kimura et al., 2003].

Cb_5 is also part of the complex involved in aquabalamin reduction. This activity was described early in the presence of NADH or NADPH by Watanabe [Watanabe et al., 1992a; Watanabe et al., 1992b], who showed that partially purified Cb_5/cytochrome b_5 reductase and cytochrome c/ cytochrome P-450 reductase catalyzed aquabalamin reduction. These observations suggested that both enzyme systems could reduce cob(III)alamin as a secondary substrate, being responsible for inner mitochondrial membrane cob(III)alamin reductase activity that participate in the biosynthesis of adenosylcobalamin. Microsomal cytochrome P450 reductase was later shown to efficiently activate methionine synthase but only in the presence of soluble Cb_5 [Chen and Banerjee, 1998], catalyzing the formation of methylcobalamin (MS; 5-methylthetrahydrofolate (Me-H4folate): L-homocysteine S-methyltransferase, EC 2.1.1.13) with simultaneous production of methionine and tetrahydrofolate from homocysteine and 5-methylthetrahydrofolate, respectively [Banerjee and Matthews, 1990]. The authors suggested that either NADPH or NADH can serve as the electron donor for activation of porcine methionine synthase and that one of the two components in the electron transfer pathway is a microsomal component. This suggested that either cytochrome P450 reductase or cytochrome b_5 reductase were the redox partner of porcine methionine synthase [Banerjee and Matthews, 1990]. More recently, a second soluble human dual flavoprotein oxidoreductase NR1 homologous to methionine synthase reductase has been reported [Paine et al., 2000]. This homologous protein was fully activated in the presence of soluble Cb_5 to levels comparable to those seen for methionine synthase reductase [Olteanu and Banerjee, 2003].

Cb_5 as an electron carrier is also involved in fatty acid synthesis through modulation of microsomal cytochrome P450 activities. Reduced Cb_5 can act as an electron donor to reduce the cytochrome P450 ferrous-dioxygen complex, promoting the formation of ferryl-oxo cytochrome P450 [Bonfils et al., 1981;

Pompon and Coon, 1984]. This reductive process was competitive with decomposition of the protein complex through superoxide anion release and dismutation to hydrogen peroxide. The increase in the formation of the ferryl-oxo complex was dependent on Cb_5 and limited to 30%. This effect was observed during steroids oxidation by this system [Perret and Pompon, 1998]. Experiments done with some cytochrome P450s ($P450_{LM2}$ or $P450_{RLM5}$) in the presence of Cb_5, showed that there was a shift of the heme group to high spin in parallel to the increase of the affinity for substrates of the cytochrome P450s, pointing out that binding of Cb_5 altered the conformation of cytochrome P450 [Bonfils et al., 1981, Tamburini et al., 1985; Tamburini and Schenkman, 1987; Perret and Pompon, 1998]. Later, it was reported that Cb_5 inhibits electron transfer from the NADPH: cytochrome P450 reductase to the CYP2B4 isoform [Zhang et al., 2008]. This opposite functional modulation of different cytochrome P450 isoforms by Cb_5 has been proposed to correlate with the presence of two different types of Cb_5 orientations in the multimeric structures of the mixed oxidase system formed between cytochrome P450 reductase and different cytochrome P450 isoforms, reported more recently [Sulc et al., 2012].

Cb_5 can also act as an electron carrier of the 'so-called' redox-chain of the plasma membrane present in plant and mammalian cells, because cytochrome b_5 reductase has been shown to be a component of this redox chain [Villalba et al., 1995; May, 1999; Kim et al., 2002]. Moreover, the cytochrome b_5 reductase pool associated with plasma membranes is clustered within cholesterol-rich and caveolins-rich lipid rafts-associated sub-microdomains of the plasma membrane [Chatenay-Rivauday et al., 2004; Samhan-Arias et al., 2009; Marques-da-Silva et al., 2010]. Thus, the cytochrome b_5 reductase/ Cb_5 complex is a component of the 'so-called' endoplasmic reticulum-plasma membrane junction, which is also known to be associated with lipid rafts of the plasma membrane [Pani et al., 2008; Cahalan, 2009]. Interestingly, the soluble form of Cb_5 has been found to stimulate NADH-dependent cytochrome b_5 reductase activities associated with synaptic plasma membranes [Samhan-Arias et al., 2009], and increase of Cb_5 expression levels are associated with an increase in the production of superoxide anion and clustering of cytochrome b_5 reductase at the plasma membrane at the early steps of the neuronal apoptosis [Samhan-Arias et al., 2012]. Noteworthy, in the type II form of recessive congenital methemoglobinemia due to NADH-dependent Cb_5R deficiency, cyanosis is associated with severe mental retardation and neurologic impairment, and the enzymatic defect is systemic, involving both soluble and membrane-bound isoforms [Leroux et al., 1975;

Vieira et al., 1995]. On the other hand, as noted above in this chapter (section 3a) Cb_5 is a key element in cholesterol synthesis from lanosterol, being the reduced form of the heme protein essential in this metabolic step [Fukushima et al. 1981], and caveolins play a relevant role in cholesterol traffic within the cells [Yamauchi et al., 2007]. Indeed, cytochrome b_5 reductase is inhibited by antibodies directed against the amino terminal domain of caveolins [Samhan-Arias et al., 2009]. Caveolins binding site to cytochrome b_5 reductase is close to the NADH binding site of this flavoprotein and this suggests a possible regulatory role of the enzyme activities of cytochrome b_5 reductase by its interaction with caveolins [Samhan-Arias et al., 2012].

5. CB_5 IN ROS SIGNALING AND APOPTOSIS

Cb_5 as all b type cytochrome can be considered as anionic peroxidases [Kiel, 1995], although cytochrome bs in general show very weak peroxidase activity due to self-bleaching. The reason of this weak peroxidase activity could be generation of an abortive compound II yielding hydroxyl radical that could destroy the heme [DeFilippi et al., 1979; Xu et al., 1993].

Autoxidation of cytochrome b can lead to the generation of superoxide anion and hydrogen peroxide, and later the hydroxyl radical, although only three types of cytochrome b-containing proteins have been proposed as terminal oxidases, namely, erythrocytic green hemeprotein, NADPH oxidase and nitric oxide synthase [Kiel, 1995].

The hypothesis of a role for Cb_5 in apoptosis was postulated by Davydov based on the experimental evidences pointing out that Cyt c and Cb_5 can form a complex [Davydov, 2001]. In this review, it was hypothesized that after induction of the apoptotic stimulus and release of Cyt c from mitochondria, Cyt c would interact with Cb_5 forming a complex that blocks the interaction of Cyt c with other proteins like Apaf or caspase-9. Because of the high affinity for the interaction between both cytochromes, dissociation constant of the Cb_5/Cyt c complex $\sim 10^{-7}$M [McLean and Sligar, 1995; Sun et al., 1999], Cb_5 seems to be one of the major targets for Cyt c after being released from mitochondria.

In addition, the presence of cytosolic Cyt c should also be expected to affect microsomal monoxygenase activities due to competition of cytochrome P450 for association with Cb_5. As indicated above, the interaction of cytochrome P450 with Cb_5 increases the coupling between electron transfer and microsomal monoxygenase activities. Therefore, the presence of Cyt c

would hamper this interaction and therefore produce a ROS burst associated to electron leakiness through the microsomal cytochrome P450 monoxygenase systems. The level of microsomal monoxygenase activity and their role in electron transfer are normally underestimated, although microsomal monoxygenases components (including cytochrome P450s, Cb_5 and their reductases) account for at least half of the electron transfer proteins in liver cells [Archakov, 1975; Venditti et al., 1998]. Moreover, the later discovery of activation of a inner peroxidase activity of Cyt c during apoptosis due complex formation with anionic lipids like cardiolipin, phosphatidylserine and also phosphatidylinositol [Jiang et al., 2004; Kagan et al., 2005; Kapralov et al., 2007], should further potentiate further the pro-oxidant effect of Cyt c on the microsomal oxygenase activity. The redox status and the presence of cellular lipophilic antioxidants like tocopherol are key to stop this reaction [Samhan-Arias et al., 2011]. Additionally, it was early described that at the outer surface of the mitochondria there is an NADH oxidase activity catalyzed by cytochrome b_5 reductase and Cb_5 that could work coupled to the inner mitochondrial membrane cytochrome c oxidase activity using intermembrane Cyt c as an electron shuttle [Nicholls et al., 1969; Bodrova et al., 1998], being this activity increased after addition of exogenous Cyt c to the assay when purified mitochondrias are used. The authors also suggested that Cyt c itself could be responsible for the oxidation of NADH when Cyt c is released from mitochondria rather than solely modulate the NADH:cytochrome c reductase activity. A role of Cyt c in detoxifying endogenous hydrogen peroxide by the presence of NADH has also been proposed recently, producing an increase in the formation of superoxide radical [Velayutham et al., 2011]. In addition, it has also been reported the stimulation by Cyt c of NADH consumption catalyzed by cytochrome b_5 reductase [Bobba et al., 1999], which was proposed to support the hypothesis that a moderate release of Cyt c could contribute to maintaining adequate levels of cellular ATP via direct reduction of Cyt c by cytochrome b_5 reductase through an electron shuttle with cytochrome c oxidase [Skulachev, 1998].

A role of Cb_5 in the attenuation of lipid radical cycles as well as in the scavenging of lipid radical reactions in biological membranes has been proposed [Dmitriev, 2007]. It has been shown that Cb_5 can act as electron donor for reduction of lipid peroxyl radicals (LOO·) via protein-lipid interactions [Dmitriev, 1995; Dmitriev, 1998], resulting in the chemical reaction:

$$Cb_5 \text{ (reduced)} + LOO^{·} \rightarrow Cb_5 \text{ (oxidized)} + LOO^{-}$$

Therefore a key role of cytochrome b_5 reductase in protection against lipid peroxidation in cells has been suggested [Dmitriev, 1998; Dmitriev, 2007]. This protective role can be important in pathophysiological phenomena like aging in liver, where it has been shown a drop of Cb_5 [Plewka et al., 1998]. A *in vivo* form of NCb5OR and Cyb_5r4 (b_5+b_5 reductase) have been shown more recently to protect against endoplasmic reticulum stress-induced lipotoxicity [Zhang et al., 2010]. These findings support the previously suggested role of the cytochrome b_5 reductase/Cb_5 system against lipid peroxidation. On these grounds, it has been suggested that inhibitors of cytochrome b_5 reductase may abolish the cooperation between outer and inner membranes and, therefore, stimulate mitochondrial lipid peroxidation [Dmitriev, 2007]. Therefore, several conditions and treatments that modulate Cb_5 levels could collaterally modulate this function in cells. For example, an increase in Cb_5 levels has been shown during hypothyroidism and after treatment of patients or animals with propylthiouracil, carbon tetrachloride, p-nitroanisole, malotilate and griseofulvin, whereas ethanol consumption in hamsters produce a decrease in Cb_5 levels [Schenkman and Jansson, 2003].

As noted in section 4 of this chapter, part of the neuronal cytochrome b_5 reductase pool is associated with lipid rafts of the plasma membrane, and its deregulation is largely responsible for the early superoxide anion overshot that precedes the activation of caspases in cerebellar granule neurons apoptosis [Valencia and Moran, 2001]. Moreover, the increase of superoxide anion production by cytochrome b_5 reductase in this neuronal model of apoptosis correlated with the increase of the expression level of soluble Cb_5 [Samhan-Arias et al., 2012], which stimulates the cytochrome b_5 reductase associated with synaptic membranes [Samhan-Arias et al., 2009]. Noteworthy, the redox properties of brain Cb_5 have been reported to be different from those of Cb_5 isoforms found in other tissues [Yoshida et al., 1984]. The measurements of redox potential done in this work highlighted the presence of two pools of microsomal brain Cb_5, one with a redox potential near 50 mV and another with a redox potential of ca. -30mV. As brain tissue is a complex tissue, containing many types of neurons, microglia and a large network of capillar-size blood microvessels, the expression of different Cb_5 isoforms in neurons deserved to be demonstrated. The presence of the cDNAs encoding for a soluble and for a membrane-bound isoform of Cb_5 in isolated neuronal and glial cultures was shown in [Yoo, 1999], and this has been recently confirmed by our group using primary cultures of cerebellar granule neurons from rat tissue [Samhan-Arias et al., 2012]. Indeed in this publication, we found that the ratio between the expression of soluble and membrane isoforms of Cb_5 changed during the early stages of the apoptosis of these neurons, i.e. before Cyt c release form mitochondria and loss of mitochondrial membrane potential and well before the activation of caspases. On these grounds, we have proposed a function of soluble Cb_5 associated with deregulation or uncoupling of the plasma membrane-bound cytochrome b_5 reductase, which shows a marked clustering within plasma membrane lipid rafts in primary cultures of mature cerebellar granule neurons [Samhan-Arias et al., 2009; Samhan-Arias et al., 2012].

The molecular mechanisms that control the expression levels of Cb_5 remain to be established. Cb_5 gene has two promoters and 1 silencer segment of the 5'-terminal region of the gene [Li et al., 1995]. The gene is formed by six exons, including a non-functional exon 4 and a span of about 28 kb. Since this is a housekeeping gene in the 5' region a TATA box is absent, but two CAAT boxes and several G:C-rich SpI motifs are present [Cristiano et al., 1993]. The expression of Cb_5 gene has been reported to be under regulation of steroid hormones. Transcription of the gene is regulated by Sp3, GATA-6, and Steroidogenic Factor 1 in human adrenal NCI-H295A cells [Huang et al., 2005]. In cells were silencing of the methylase DNMT3b has been performed using siRNA, it has been observed an increase of apoptosis, decreased growth and migration in parallel to an increase in the expression of Cb_5, caspase-7 and the kinase CDKN3, suggesting that the promoter of Cb_5 gene could be under control of methylation/demethylation [Yaqinuddin et al., 2008]. In addition, the increase of the Cb_5 gene expression is a common feature between this apoptotic process and the apoptosis of cerebellar granule neurons (see above).

CONCLUSION

Cb_5 acts within the cells as a pleiotropic co-factor of multiple enzymes and redox chains that play critical roles for normal function of healthy mammalian organisms, and thus it is a potential biomarker of health and disease. It is maintained in the reduced form largely by the NADH-dependent cytochrome b_5 reductase activity which catalyzes electron transfer to Cb_5 in mammalian cells. In mammalian cells Cb_5 shows a ubiquitous distribution, being present in the cytoplasm and also associated with the components of the endoplasmic reticulum, mitochondria and plasma membrane of mammalian cells. Subcellular compartmentation of Cb_5 also modulates its redox properties, as the redox potential of the heme group of Cb_5 is largely dependent of the spatial conformation of this group within the protein structure and also of the dielectric constant of the microenvironment around the heme group.

The implication of Cb_5 in the modulation of multiple metabolic pathways, such as cholesterol biosynthesis, desaturation and elongation of fatty acids, MetHb reduction and cytochrome P450-dependent reactions of steroids and xenobiotics metabolism, points out a key role of Cb_5 in the maintenance of healthy intracellular metabolic homeostasis in mammals. More recently, Cb_5 has been suggested to be involved in the recycling of lipid peroxyl radicals and also to modulate the methionine synthase reductase activity. In addition, the family of proteins containing a Cb_5-like domain in mammals is expanding, highlighting the relevance of Cb_5 in biological evolution and opening new perspectives on modulation of cellular signaling pathways by b_5-type hemeproteins.

As a co-factor of cytochrome b_5 reductase, Cb_5 has been shown to act as an electron carrier in mitochondria and in the plasma membrane coupled to cytosolic NADH consumption. In addition, as a redox co-factor of cytochrome P450s/cytochrome P450 reductase systems and of cytochrome b_5 reductase Cb_5 is also implicated in the modulation of the production of superoxide anion in mammalian cells. Since deregulation of superoxide anion production can elicit a cellular oxidative stress leading to activation of caspase-9 by Cyt c, the finding that Cb_5 binds Cyt c with high affinity suggested a role for Cb_5 in apoptosis. Indeed, in a well established model for neuronal apoptosis the time course of the increase of superoxide anion and of the increase of the content of soluble Cb_5 are correlated events during the early stage of apoptosis [Samhan-Arias et al., 2012]. Interestingly, several proteins containing a Cb_5-like domain in mammals are NAD(P)H oxidoreductases. Therefore, Cb_5 can also be seen as an intracellular signaling molecule in the field of redox biology, aging and related diseases.

ACKNOWLEDGMENTS

This work has been supported by Grant BFU2011-30178 of the Spanish Plan Nacional de I+D+I and by Grant GR10092 of the Gobierno de Extremadura to the Research Group "Estrés oxidativo y bioenergética en neuronas y cerebro", both with co-financing by the European Funds for Structural Development (FEDER).

REFERENCES

Ahuja, S., Jahr, N., Im, S. -C., Vivekanandan, S., Popovych, N., Le Clair, S. V., Huang, R., Soong, R., Xu, J., Yamamoto, K., Nanga, R. P., Bridges, A., Waskell, L. & Ramamoorthy, A. (2013). A Model of the Membrane-bound Cytochrome b5-Cytochrome P450 Complex from NMR and Mutagenesis Data. *J Biol Chem.*, *288*, 22080-22095.

Alderson, N. L., Rembiesa, B. M., Walla, M. D., Bielawska, A., Bielawski, J. & Hama, H. (2004). The human FA2H gene encodes a fatty acid 2-hydroxylase. *J Biol Chem*, *279*, 48562-48568.

Altschul, S. F., Madden, T. L., Schaffer, A. A., Zhang, J., Zhang, Z., Miller, W. & Lipman, D. J. (1997). Gapped BLAST and PSI-BLAST: a new generation of protein database search programs. *Nucleic Acids Res*, *25*, 3389-3402.

Altuve, A., Wang, L., Benson, D. R. & Rivera, M. (2004). Mammalian mitochondrial and microsomal cytochromes b(5) exhibit divergent structural and biophysical characteristics. *Biochem Biophys Res Commun*, *314*, 602-609.

Archakov, A. I. (1975). *Mikrosomal'noe Okislenie [Microsomal Oxidation]*, Nauka, Moscow.

Bagby, S., Barker, P. D., Di Gleria, K., Hill, H. A. O. & Lowe, V. J. (1988). The direct electrochemistry of cytochrome b5 at peptide-modified electrodes. *Biochem Soc Trans*, *16*, 958-959.

Banci, L., Bertini, I., Rosato, A. & Scacchieri, S. (2000). Solution structure of oxidized microsomal rabbit cytochrome b5. *European Journal of Biochemistry.*, *267*, 755-766.

Bando, S., Takano, T., Yubisui, T., Shirabe, K., Takeshita, M. & Nakagawa, A. (2004). Structure of human erythrocyte NADH-cytochrome b5 reductase. *Acta Crystallogr D Biol Crystallogr*, *60*, 1929-1934.

Banerjee, R. V. & Matthews, R. G. (1990). Cobalamin-dependent methionine synthase. *Faseb J*, *4*, 1450-1459.

Basova, L. V., Tiktopulo, E. I., Kutyshenko, V. P., Mauk, A. G. & Bychkova, V. E. (2008). Phospholipid membranes affect tertiary structure of the soluble cytochrome b5 heme-binding domain. *Biochim Biophys Acta*, *1778*, 1015-1026.

Billen, M. J. & Squires, E. J. (2009). The role of porcine cytochrome b5A and cytochrome b5B in the regulation of cytochrome P45017A1 activities. *J Steroid Biochem Mol Biol*, *113*, 98-104.

Bobba, A., Atlante, A., Giannattasio, S., Sgaramella, G., Calissano, P. & Marra, E. (1999). Early release and subsequent caspase-mediated degradation of cytochrome c in apoptotic cerebellar granule cells. *FEBS Lett*, *457*, 126-130.

Bodrova, M. E., Dedukhova, V. I., Mokhova, E. N. & Skulachev, V. P. (1998). Membrane potential generation coupled to oxidation of external NADH in liver mitochondria. *FEBS Lett*, *435*, 269-274.

Bond, A. M., Hill, H. A., Page, D. J., Psalti, I. S. & Walton, N. J. (1990). Evidence for fast and discriminatory electron transfer of proteins at modified gold electrodes. *Eur J Biochem*, *191*, 737-742.

Bonfils, C., Balny, C. & Maurel, P. (1981). Direct evidence for electron transfer from ferrous cytochrome b5 to the oxyferrous intermediate of liver microsomal cytochrome P-450 LM2. *J Biol Chem*, *256*, 9457-9465.

Cahalan, M. D. (2009). STIMulating store-operated Ca(2+) entry. *Nat Cell Biol*, *11*, 669-677.

Chatenay-Rivauday, C., Cakar, Z. P., Jeno, P., Kuzmenko, E. S. & Fiedler, K. (2004). Caveolae: biochemical analysis. *Mol Biol Rep*, *31*, 67-84.

Chen, Z. & Banerjee, R. (1998). Purification of soluble cytochrome b5 as a component of the reductive activation of porcine methionine synthase. *J Biol Chem*, *273*, 26248-26255.

Cho, H. P., Nakamura, M. T. & Clarke, S. D. (1999). Cloning, expression, and nutritional regulation of the mammalian Delta-6 desaturase. *J Biol Chem*, *274*, 471-477.

Cowley, A. B., Altuve, A., Kuchment, O., Terzyan, S., Zhang, X., Rivera, M. & Benson, D. R. (2002). Toward engineering the stability and hemin-binding properties of microsomal cytochromes b5 into rat outer mitochondrial membrane cytochrome b5: examining the influence of residues 25 and 71. *Biochemistry*, *41*, 11566-11581.

Cristiano, R. J., Giordano, S. J. & Steggles, A. W. (1993). The isolation and characterization of the bovine cytochrome b5 gene, and a transcribed pseudogene. *Genomics*, *17*, 348-354.

D'Andrea, S., Guillou, H., Jan, S., Catheline, D., Thibault, J. N., Bouriel, M., Rioux, V. & Legrand, P. (2002). The same rat Delta6-desaturase not only acts on 18- but also on 24-carbon fatty acids in very-long-chain polyunsaturated fatty acid biosynthesis. *Biochem J*, *364*, 49-55.

Dailey, H. A. & Strittmatter, P. (1980). Characterization of the interaction of amphipathic cytochrome b5 with stearyl coenzyme A desaturase and NADPH:cytochrome P-450 reductase. *J Biol Chem*, *255*, 5184-5189.

Davydov, D. R. (2001). Microsomal monooxygenase in apoptosis: another target for cytochrome c signaling? *Trends Biochem Sci, 26*, 155-160.

de Antueno, R. J., Knickle, L. C., Smith, H., Elliot, M. L., Allen, S. J., Nwaka, S. & Winther, M. D. (2001). Activity of human Delta5 and Delta6 desaturases on multiple n-3 and n-6 polyunsaturated fatty acids. *FEBS Lett, 509*, 77-80.

De Silvestris, M., D'Arrigo, A. & Borgese, N. (1995). The targeting information of the mitochondrial outer membrane isoform of cytochrome b5 is contained within the carboxyl-terminal region. *FEBS Lett, 370*, 69-74.

DeFilippi, L. J., Ballou, D. P. & Hultquist, D. E. (1979). Reaction of bovine erythrocyte green hemoprotein with oxygen and hydrogen peroxide. *J Biol Chem, 254*, 6917-6923.

Dmitriev, L. F. (1995). A novel enzymatic mechanism of protective effect of tocopherol inbiological membranes. *Redox Rep, 1*, 299-301.

Dmitriev, L. F. (1998). Cytochrome b5 and tocopherol provide functions of lipid-radical cycles and energy conversion in membranes. *Biochemistry (Mosc), 63*, 1233-1236.

Dmitriev, L. (2007). Shortage of Lipid-radical Cycles in Membranes as a Possible Prime Cause of Energetic Failure in Aging and Alzheimer Disease. *Neurochem Res, 32*, 1278-1291.

Durham, B., Fairris, J. L., McLean, M., Millett, F., Scott, J. R., Sligar, S. G. & Willie, A. (1995). Electron transfer from cytochrome b5 to cytochrome c. *J Bioenerg Biomembr, 27*, 331-340.

Durley, R. C. & Mathews, F. S. (1996). Refinement and structural analysis of bovine cytochrome b5 at 1.5 A resolution. *Acta Crystallogr D Biol Crystallogr, 52*, 65-76.

Enoch, H. G., Fleming, P. J. & Strittmatter, P. (1979). The binding of cytochrome b5 to phospholipid vesicles and biological membranes. Effect of orientation on intermembrane transfer and digestion by carboxypeptidase Y. *J Biol Chem, 254*, 6483-6488.

Enomoto, A., Omae, F., Miyazaki, M., Kozutsumi, Y., Yubisui, T. & Suzuki, A. (2006). Dihydroceramide:sphinganine C-4-hydroxylation requires Des2 hydroxylase and the membrane form of cytochrome b5. *Biochem J, 397*, 289-295.

Enomoto, K. I. & Sato, R. (1977). Asymmetric binding of cytochrome b5 to the membrane of human erythrocyte ghosts. *Biochim Biophys Acta, 466*, 136-147.

Estrada, D. F., Laurence, J. S. & Scott, E. E. (2013). Substrate-modulated cytochrome P450 17A1 and cytochrome b5 interactions revealed by NMR. *J Biol Chem*, *288*, 17008-17018.

Fragai, M., Luchinat, C. & Parigi, G. (2006). "Four-dimensional" protein structures: examples from metalloproteins. *Acc Chem Res*, *39*, 909-917.

Froriep, D., Clement, B., Bittner, F., Mendel, R. R., Reichmann, D., Schmalix, W. & Havemeyer, A. (2013). Activation of the anti-cancer agent upamostat by the mARC enzyme system. *Xenobiotica*, *43*, 780-784.

Fukushima, H., Grinstead, G. F. & Gaylor, J. L. (1981). Total enzymic synthesis of cholesterol from lanosterol. Cytochrome b5-dependence of 4-methyl sterol oxidase. *J Biol Chem*, *256*, 4822-4826.

Girke, T., Schmidt, H., Zahringer, U., Reski, R. & Heinz, E. (1998). Identification of a novel delta 6-acyl-group desaturase by targeted gene disruption in Physcomitrella patens. *Plant J*, *15*, 39-48.

Glenn, J. D. H. & Bowden, E. F. (1996). Diffusionless Electrochemistry of Cytochrome b_5 Adsorbed on a Multilayer Film Electrode. *Chemistry Letters*, *25*, 399-400.

Gollub, M. & Shaw, L. (2003). Isolation and characterization of cytidine-5'-monophosphate-N-acetylneuraminate hydroxylase from the starfish Asterias rubens. *Comp Biochem Physiol B Biochem Mol Biol*, *134*, 89-101.

Goosen, P., Swart, A. C., Storbeck, K. H. & Swart, P. (2013). Allosteric interaction between 3beta-hydroxysteroid dehydrogenase/Delta(5)-Delta(4) isomerase and cytochrome b5 influences cofactor binding. *Faseb J*, *27*, 322-332.

Gorsky, L. D., Koop, D. R. & Coon, M. J. (1984). On the stoichiometry of the oxidase and monooxygenase reactions catalyzed by liver microsomal cytochrome P-450. Products of oxygen reduction. *J Biol Chem*, *259*, 6812-6817.

Grade, M., Ghadimi, B. M., Varma, S., Simon, R., Wangsa, D., Barenboim-Stapleton, L., Liersch, T., Becker, H., Ried, T. & Difilippantonio, M. J. (2006). Aneuploidy-dependent massive deregulation of the cellular transcriptome and apparent divergence of the Wnt/beta-catenin signaling pathway in human rectal carcinomas. *Cancer Res*, *66*, 267-282.

Grade, M., Hormann, P., Becker, S., Hummon, A. B., Wangsa, D., Varma, S., Simon, R., Liersch, T., Becker, H., Difilippantonio, M. J., Ghadimi, B. M. & Ried, T. (2007). Gene expression profiling reveals a massive, aneuploidy-dependent transcriptional deregulation and distinct differences between lymph node-negative and lymph node-positive colon carcinomas. *Cancer Res*, *67*, 41-56.

Guiard, B., Groudinsky, O. & Lederer, F. (1974). Homology between bakers' yeast cytochrome b2 and liver microsomal cytochrome b5. *Proc Natl Acad Sci U S A*, *71*, 2539-2543.

Guzov, V. M., Houston, H. L., Murataliev, M. B., Walker, F. A. & Feyereisen, R. (1996). Molecular cloning, overexpression in Escherichia coli, structural and functional characterization of house fly cytochrome b5. *J Biol Chem*, *271*, 26637-26645.

Han, K. H., Lee, S. H., Ha, S. A., Kim, H., Lee, C., Kim, D. H., Gong, K., Yoo, J., Kim, S. & Kim, J. (2012). The functional and structural characterization of a novel oncogene GIG47 involved in the breast tumorigenesis. *BMC Cancer*, *12*, 274.

Havemeyer, A., Grunewald, S., Wahl, B., Bittner, F., Mendel, R., Erdelyi, P., Fischer, J. & Clement, B. (2010). Reduction of N-hydroxy-sulfonamides, including N-hydroxy-valdecoxib, by the molybdenum-containing enzyme mARC. *Drug Metab Dispos*, *38*, 1917-1921.

Henderson, C. J., McLaughlin, L. A. & Wolf, C. R. (2013). Evidence that cytochrome b5 and cytochrome b5 reductase can act as sole electron donors to the hepatic cytochrome P450 system. *Mol Pharmacol*, *83*, 1209-1217.

Holloway, P. W. (1983). Fatty acid desaturation. In *The Enzymes: Lipi Enzymology*, (Boyer, P. D., ed) Vol. *XVI*, 63-86, Academic Press, Inc, New York.

Huang, N., Dardis, A. & Miller, W. L. (2005). Regulation of cytochrome b5 gene transcription by Sp3, GATA-6, and steroidogenic factor 1 in human adrenal NCI-H295A cells. *Mol Endocrinol*, *19*, 2020-2034.

Hughes, A. L., Powell, D. W., Bard, M., Eckstein, J., Barbuch, R., Link, A. J. & Espenshade, P. J. (2007). Dap1/PGRMC1 binds and regulates cytochrome P450 enzymes. *Cell Metab*, *5*, 143-149.

Ito, A. (1971). Hepatic sulfite oxidase identified as cytochrome b 5 -like pigment extractable from mitochondria by hypotonic treatment. *J Biochem*, *70*, 1061-1064.

Jansson, I. & Schenkman, J. B. (1987). Influence of cytochrome b5 on the stoichiometry of the different oxidative reactions catalyzed by liver microsomal cytochrome P-450. *Drug Metab Dispos*, *15*, 344-348.

Jiang, J., Kini, V., Belikova, N., Serinkan, B. F., Borisenko, G. G., Tyurina, Y. Y., Tyurin, V. A. & Kagan, V. E. (2004). Cytochrome c release is required for phosphatidylserine peroxidation during Fas-triggered apoptosis in lung epithelial A549 cells. *Lipids*, *39*, 1133-1142.

Kagan, V. E., Tyurin, V. A., Jiang, J., Tyurina, Y. Y., Ritov, V. B., Amoscato, A. A., Osipov, A. N., Belikova, N. A., Kapralov, A. A., Kini, V., Vlasova, II, Zhao, Q., Zou, M., Di, P., Svistunenko, D. A., Kurnikov, I. V. & Borisenko, G. G. (2005). Cytochrome c acts as a cardiolipin oxygenase required for release of proapoptotic factors. *Nat Chem Biol*, *1*, 223-232.

Kapralov, A. A., Kurnikov, I. V., Vlasova, II, Belikova, N. A., Tyurin, V. A., Basova, L. V., Zhao, Q., Tyurina, Y. Y., Jiang, J., Bayir, H., Vladimirov, Y. A. & Kagan, V. E. (2007). The hierarchy of structural transitions induced in cytochrome c by anionic phospholipids determines its peroxidase activation and selective peroxidation during apoptosis in cells. *Biochemistry*, *46*, 14232-14244.

Keinan, S., Nocek, J. M., Hoffman, B. M. & Beratan, D. N. (2012). Interfacial hydration, dynamics and electron transfer: multi-scale ET modeling of the transient [myoglobin, cytochrome b5] complex. *Phys Chem Chem Phys*, *14*, 13881-13889.

Keller, R. M. & Wuthrich, K. (1980). Structural study of the heme crevice in cytochrome b5 based on individual assignments of the 1H-NMR lines of the heme group and selected amino acid residues. *Biochimica et biophysica acta*, *621*, 204-217.

Kiel, J. L. (1995). *Type-B Cytochromes: Sensors and Switches*, CRC Press, Inc, Boca Raton, Florida

Kim, C., Crane, F. L., Faulk, W. P. & Morre, D. J. (2002). Purification and characterization of a doxorubicin-inhibited NADH-quinone (NADH-ferricyanide) reductase from rat liver plasma membranes. *J Biol Chem*, *277*, 16441-16447.

Kimura, I., Nakayama, Y., Konishi, M., Kobayashi, T., Mori, M., Ito, M., Hirasawa, A., Tsujimoto, G., Ohta, M., Itoh, N. & Fujimoto, M. (2010). Neuferricin, a novel extracellular heme-binding protein, promotes neurogenesis. *J Neurochem*, *112*, 1156-1167.

Kimura, I., Nakayama, Y., Zhao, Y., Konishi, M. & Itoh, N. (2013). Neurotrophic effects of neudesin in the central nervous system. *Front Neurosci*, *7*, 111.

Kimura, S., Kawamura, M. & Iyanagi, T. (2003). Role of Thr66 in Porcine NADH-cytochromeb 5 Reductase in Catalysis and Control of the Rate-limiting Step in Electron Transfer. *J Biol Chem.*, *278*, 3580-3589.

Kimura, Y., Nakayama, Y., Konishi, M., Terasawa, K., Ohta, M., Itoh, N. & Fujimoto, M. (2012). Functions of MAPR (Membrane-Associated

Progesterone Receptor) Family Members As Heme/Steroid-Binding Proteins. *Curr Protein Pept Sci, 13,* 687-696.

Kinoshita, A., Nakayama, Y., Kitayama, T. & Tomita, M. (2007). Simulation study of methemoglobin reduction in erythrocytes. Differential contributions of two pathways to tolerance to oxidative stress. *Febs J, 274,* 1449-1458.

Kitao, T., Sugita, Y., Yoneyama, Y. & Hattori, K. (1974). Methemoglobin reductase (cytochrome b5 reductase) deficiency in congenital methemoglobinemia. *Blood, 44,* 879-884.

Knappenberger, J. A., Kraemer-Pecore, C. M. & Lecomte, J. T. (2004). Insertion of the cytochrome b5 heme-binding loop into an SH3 domain. Effects on structure and stability, and clues about the cytochrome's architecture. *Protein Sci, 13,* 2899-2908.

Kohla, G. & Schauer, R. (2005). Sialic acids in gangliosides: origin and function. In *Neuroglycobiology* (Fukuda, M., Rutishauser, U., and Schnaar, R. L., eds) 133-155, Oxford University Press, New York.

Konopka, K. & Waskell, L. (1988). Modification of trypsin-solubilized cytochrome b5, apocytochrome b5, and liposome-bound cytochrome b5 by diethylpyrocarbonate. *Arch Biochem Biophys, 261,* 55-63.

Kuma, F., Prough, R. A. & Masters, B. S. (1976). Studies on methemoglobin reductase. Immunochemical similarity of soluble methemoglobin reductase and cytochrome b5 of human erythrocytes with NADH-cytochrome b5 reductase and cytochrome b5 of rat liver microsomes. *Arch Biochem Biophys, 172,* 600-607.

Kuroda, R., Ikenoue, T., Honsho, M., Tsujimoto, S., Mitoma, J. Y. & Ito, A. (1998). Charged amino acids at the carboxyl-terminal portions determine the intracellular locations of two isoforms of cytochrome b5. *J Biol Chem, 273,* 31097-31102.

La Mar, G. N., Burns, P. D., Jackson, J. T., Smith, K. M., Langry, K. C. & Strittmatter, P. (1981). Proton magnetic resonance determination of the relative heme orientations in disordered native and reconstituted ferricytochrome b5. Assignment of heme resonances by deuterium labeling. *J Biol Chem, 256,* 6075-6079.

Le, K. H. & Lederer, F. (1983). On the presence of a heme-binding domain homologous to cytochrome b(5) in Neurospora crassa assimilatory nitrate reductase. *Embo J, 2,* 1909-1914.

Lederer, F., Ghrir, R., Guiard, B., Cortial, S. & Ito, A. (1983). Two homologous cytochromes b5 in a single cell. *Eur J Biochem, 132,* 95-102.

Lederer, F. (1994). The cytochrome b5-fold: an adaptable module. *Biochimie*, *76*, 674-692.

Lee, K. B., Jun, E., La Mar, G. N., Rezzano, I. N., Pandey, R. K., Smith, K. M., Walker, F. A. & Buttlaire, D. H. (1991). Influence of heme vinyl- and carboxylate-protein contacts on structure and redox properties of bovine cytochrome b5. *J Am Chem Soc*, *113*, 3576-3583.

Leonard, A. E., Kelder, B., Bobik, E. G., Chuang, L. T., Parker-Barnes, J. M., Thurmond, J. M., Kroeger, P. E., Kopchick, J. J., Huang, Y. S. 7 Mukerji, P. (2000). cDNA cloning and characterization of human Delta5-desaturase involved in the biosynthesis of arachidonic acid. *Biochem J*, *347* Pt 3, 719-724.

Leroux, A., Junien, C., Kaplan, J. & Bambenger, J. (1975). Generalised deficiency of cytochrome b_5 reductase in congenital methaemoglobinaemia with mental retardation. *Nature*, *258*, 619-620.

Li, X. R., Giordano, S. J., Yoo, M. & Steggles, A. W. (1995). The isolation and characterization of the human cytochrome b5 gene. *Biochem Biophys Res Commun*, *209*, 894-900.

Livingston, D. J., McLachlan, S. J., La Mar, G. N. & Brown, W. D. (1985). Myoglobin: cytochrome b5 interactions and the kinetic mechanism of metmyoglobin reductase. *J Biol Chem*, *260*, 15699-15707.

Locuson, C. W., Wienkers, L. C., Jones, J. P. & Tracy, T. S. (2007). CYP2C9 protein interactions with cytochrome b(5): effects on the coupling of catalysis. *Drug Metab Dispos*, *35*, 1174-1181.

Marques-da-Silva, D., Samhan-Arias, A. K., Tiago, T. & Gutierrez-Merino, C. (2010). L-type calcium channels and cytochrome b5 reductase are components of protein complexes tightly associated with lipid rafts microdomains of the neuronal plasma membrane. *J Proteomics*, *73*, 1502-1510.

Mathews, F. S. & Czerwinski, E. (1985). Cytochrome b5 and Cytochrome b5 Reductase from a Chemical and X-Ray Diffraction Viewpoint. In: Martonosi, (Ed.), *The Enzymes of Biological Membranes*. Vol., *A*. Springer US, 235-300.

Mathews, F. S., Levine, M. & Argos, P. (1971). The structure of calf liver cytochrome b 5 at 2.8 A resolution. *Nat New Biol*, *233*, 15-16.

Mathews, F. S., Levine, M. & Argos, P. (1972). Three-dimensional Fourier synthesis of calf liver cytochrome b 5 at 2-8 A resolution. *J Mol Biol*, *64*, 449-464.

Mathews, F. S., Czerwinski, E. W. & Argos, P. (1979). The X-ray crystallographic structure of calf liver cytochrome b_5. In *The porphyrins* (Dolphin, D., ed), Academic Press, New York 1979, 107–147.

Mathews, F. S., Czerwinski, F. W. & Argos, P. (1979). *The Porphyrins*, Vol. *VII*, Academic Press, New York.

Mauk, A. G., Mauk, M. R., Moore, G. R. & Northrup, S. H. (1995). Experimental and theoretical analysis of the interaction between cytochrome c and cytochrome b5. *J Bioenerg Biomembr, 27*, 311-330.

Mauk, M. R., Reid, L. S. & Mauk, A. G. (1982). Spectrophotometric analysis of the interaction between cytochrome b5 and cytochrome c. *Biochemistry, 21*, 1843-1846.

May, J. M. (1999). Is ascorbic acid an antioxidant for the plasma membrane? *Faseb J, 13*, 995-1006

McLean, M. A. & Sligar, S. G. (1995). Thermodynamic characterization of the interaction between cytochrome b5 and cytochrome c. *Biochem Biophys Res Commun, 215*, 316-320.

Medhi, O. K. (1990). Models of the cytochromes-b and related heme proteins. *Pror Indian Acad. Sei. (Chem. Sci.), 102*, 353-364.

Mellon, S. H. (2005). Synthesis, Enzyme Localization, and Regulation of Neurosteroids. In *Neurosteroid Effects in the Central Nervous System. The role of the GABA$_A$ receptor* (Smith, S. S., ed), CRC Press, Boca Raton, 1-31.

Meyer, T. E., Shirabe, K., Yubisui, T., Takeshita, M., Bes, M. T., Cusanovich, M. A. & Tollin, G. (1995). Transient kinetics of intracomplex electron transfer in the human cytochrome b5 reductase-cytochrome b5 system: NAD+ modulates protein-protein binding and electron transfer. *Arch Biochem Biophys, 318*, 457-464.

Min, L., Strushkevich, N. V., Harnastai, I. N., Iwamoto, H., Gilep, A. A., Takemori, H., Usanov, S. A., Nonaka, Y., Hori, H., Vinson, G. P. & Okamoto, M. (2005). Molecular identification of adrenal inner zone antigen as a heme-binding protein. *The FEBS journal, 272*, 5832-5843.

Mitoma, J. & Ito, A. (1992). The carboxy-terminal 10 amino acid residues of cytochrome b5 are necessary for its targeting to the endoplasmic reticulum. *Embo J, 11*, 4197-4203.

Montgomery, M. R. (1976). Characterization of fatty acid desaturase activity in rat lung microsomes. *J Lipid Res, 17*, 12-15.

Murphy, D., Parker, J., Zhou, M., Fadlelmola, F. M., Steidl, C., Karsan, A., Gascoyne, R. D., Chen, H. & Banerjee, D. (2010). Constitutively overexpressed 21 kDa protein in Hodgkin lymphoma and aggressive non-

Hodgkin lymphomas identified as cytochrome B5b (CYB5B). *Mol Cancer*, *9*, 14.

Napier, J. A., Michaelson, L. V. & Sayanova, O. (2003). The role of cytochrome b5 fusion desaturases in the synthesis of polyunsaturated fatty acids. *Prostaglandins Leukot Essent Fatty Acids*, *68*, 135-143.

Neve, E. P., Nordling, A., Andersson, T. B., Hellman, U., Diczfalusy, U., Johansson, I. & Ingelman-Sundberg, M. (2012). Amidoxime reductase system containing cytochrome b5 type B (CYB5B) and MOSC2 is of importance for lipid synthesis in adipocyte mitochondria. *J Biol Chem*, *287*, 6307-6317.

Nicholls, P., Mochan, E. & Kimelberg, H. K. (1969). Complex formation by cytochrome c: A clue to the structure and polarity of the inner mitochondrial membrane. *FEBS Lett*, *3*, 242-246.

Olteanu, H. & Banerjee, R. (2003). Redundancy in the pathway for redox regulation of mammalian methionine synthase: reductive activation by the dual flavoprotein, novel reductase 1. *J Biol Chem*, *278*, 38310-38314.

Oshino, N. & Omura, T. (1973). Immunochemical evidence for the participation of cytochrome b5 in microsomal stearyl-CoA desaturation reaction. *Arch Biochem Biophys*, *157*, 395-404.

Oshino, N. (1978). Cytochrome b_5 and its physiological significance. *Pharmacol. Ther.*, *2*, 477-515.

Ozols, J. (1989). Structure of cytochrome b5 and its topology in the microsomal membrane. *Biochim Biophys Acta*, *997*, 121-130.

Paine, M. J., Garner, A. P., Powell, D., Sibbald, J., Sales, M., Pratt, N., Smith, T., Tew, D. G. & Wolf, C. R. (2000). Cloning and characterization of a novel human dual flavin reductase. *J Biol Chem*, *275*, 1471-1478.

Paltuaf, F., Prough, R. A., Masters, B. S. & Johnston, J. M. (1974). Evidence for the participation of cytochrome b5 in plasmalogen biosynthesis. *J Biol Chem*, *249*, 2661-2662.

Pani, B., Ong, H. L., Liu, X., Rauser, K., Ambudkar, I. S. & Singh, B. B. (2008). Lipid rafts determine clustering of STIM1 in endoplasmic reticulum-plasma membrane junctions and regulation of store-operated Ca2+ entry (SOCE). *J Biol Chem*, *283*, 17333-17340.

Peluso, J. J. (2007). Non-genomic actions of progesterone in the normal and neoplastic mammalian ovary. *Semin Reprod Med*, *25*, 198-207.

Peng, H. M. & Auchus, R. J. (2013). The action of cytochrome b(5) on CYP2E1 and CYP2C19 activities requires anionic residues D58 and D65. *Biochemistry*, *52*, 210-220.

Perret, A. & Pompon, D. (1998). Electron shuttle between membrane-bound cytochrome P450 3A4 and b5 rules uncoupling mechanisms. *Biochemistry, 37*, 11412-11424.

Pinski, J., Xiong, S., Wang, Q., Stanczyk, F., Hawes, D. & Liu, S. V. (2011). Effect of luteinizing hormone on the steroidogenic pathway in prostate cancer. *Prostate, 71*, 892-898.

Plewka, A., Kaminski, M. & Plewka, D. (1998). Ontogenesis of hepatocyte respiration processes in relation to rat liver cytochrome P450-dependent monooxygenase system. *Mech Ageing Dev, 105*, 197-207.

Pompon, D. & Coon, M. J. (1984). On the mechanism of action of cytochrome P-450. Oxidation and reduction of the ferrous dioxygen complex of liver microsomal cytochrome P-450 by cytochrome b5. *J Biol Chem, 259*, 15377-15385.

Poulos, T. L. & Mauk, A. G. (1983). Models for the complexes formed between cytochrome b5 and the subunits of methemoglobin. *J Biol Chem, 258*, 7369-7373.

Rapoport, T. A. & Wiedmann, M. (1985). Application of the signal hypothesis to the incorporation of integral membrane proteins, in: P.A. Knauf, J.S. Cook (Eds.), *Current Topics in Membranes and Transport*. Membrane Protein Biosynthesis and Turnover, Academic Press, Inc., Orlando, 1-62.

Reid, L. S. & Mauk, A. G. (1982). Kinetics analysis of cytochrome b5 reduction by (ethylenediaminetetraacetato)ferrate(2-) ion. *J Am Chem Soc, 104*, 841-845.

Ren, Y., Wang, W. H., Wang, Y. H., Case, M., Qian, W., McLendon, G. & Huang, Z. X. (2004). Mapping the electron transfer interface between cytochrome b5 and cytochrome c. *Biochemistry, 43*, 3527-3536.

Rivera, M., Barillas-Mury, C., Christensen, K. A., Little, J. W., Wells, M. A. & Walker, F. A. (1992). Gene synthesis, bacterial expression, and 1H NMR spectroscopic studies of the rat outer mitochondrial membrane cytochrome b5. *Biochemistry, 31*, 12233-12240.

Rivera, M., Seetharaman, R., Girdhar, D., Wirtz, M., Zhang, X., Wang, X. & White, S. (1998). The reduction potential of cytochrome b5 is modulated by its exposed heme edge. *Biochemistry, 37*, 1485-1494.

Rodgers, K. K., Pochapsky, T. C. & Sligar, S. G. (1988). Probing the mechanisms of macromolecular recognition: the cytochrome b5-cytochrome c complex. *Science, 240*, 1657-1659.

Rodgers, K. K. & Sligar, S. G. (1991). Mapping electrostatic interactions in macromolecular associations. *J Mol Biol, 221*, 1453-1460.

Rogers, M. J. & Strittmatter, P. (1975). The interaction of NADH-cytochrome b5 reductase and cytochrome b5 bound to egg lecithin liposomes. *J Biol Chem, 250*, 5713-5718.

Rodriguez-Maranon, M. J., Qiu, F., Stark, R. E., White, S. P., Zhang, X., Foundling, S. I., Rodriguez, V., Schilling, C. L., 3rd, Bunce, R. A. & Rivera, M. (1996). 13C NMR spectroscopic and X-ray crystallographic study of the role played by mitochondrial cytochrome b5 heme propionates in the electrostatic binding to cytochrome c. *Biochemistry, 35*, 16378-16390.

Rudolph, M. J., Johnson, J. L., Rajagopalan, K. V. & Kisker, C. (2003). The 1.2 A structure of the human sulfite oxidase cytochrome b(5) domain. *Acta Crystallogr D Biol Crystallogr, 59*, 1183-1191.

Samhan-Arias, A. K., Garcia-Bereguiain, M. A., Martin-Romero, F. J. & Gutierrez-Merino, C. (2009). Clustering of plasma membrane-bound cytochrome b5 reductase within 'lipid raft' microdomains of the neuronal plasma membrane. *Mol Cell Neurosci, 40*, 14-26.

Samhan-Arias, A. K., Tyurina, Y. Y. & Kagan, V. E. (2011). Lipid antioxidants: free radical scavenging versus regulation of enzymatic lipid peroxidation. *J Clin Biochem Nutr, 48*, 91-95.

Samhan-Arias, A. K., Marques-da-Silva, D., Yanamala, N. & Gutierrez-Merino, C. (2012). Stimulation and clustering of cytochrome b5 reductase in caveolin-rich lipid microdomains is an early event in oxidative stress-mediated apoptosis of cerebellar granule neurons. *J Proteomics, 75*, 2934-2949.

Schenkman, J. B. & Jansson, I. (2003). The many roles of cytochrome b5. *Pharmacol Ther, 97*, 139-152.

Shirabe, K., Nagai, T., Yubisui, T. & Takeshita, M. (1998). Electrostatic interaction between NADH-cytochrome b5 reductase and cytochrome b5 studied by site-directed mutagenesis. *Biochim Biophys Acta, 1384*, 16-22.

Silchenko, S., Sippel, M. L., Kuchment, O., Benson, D. R., Mauk, A. G., Altuve, A. & Rivera, M. (2000). Hemin is kinetically trapped in cytochrome b(5) from rat outer mitochondrial membrane. *Biochem Biophys Res Commun, 273*, 467-472.

Skulachev, V. P. (1998). Cytochrome c in the apoptotic and antioxidant cascades. *FEBS Lett, 423*, 275-280.

Snyder, F., Lee, T. C. & Wykle, R. L. (1985). Ether-linked glycerolipids and their bioactive species: Enzymes and metabolic regulation. In *Enzymes of Biological Membranes* (Martonosi, A. N., ed), Plenum, New York, 1-58.

Soucy, P. & Luu-The, V. (2002). Assessment of the ability of type 2 cytochrome b5 to modulate 17,20-lyase activity of human P450c17. *J Steroid Biochem Mol Biol, 80*, 71-75.

Spatz, L. & Strittmatter, P. (1971). A form of cytochrome b5 that contains an additional hydrophobic sequence of 40 amino acid residues. *Proc Natl Acad Sci U S A, 68*, 1042-1046.

Sprecher, H., Luthria, D. L., Mohammed, B. S. & Baykousheva, S. P. (1995). Reevaluation of the pathways for the biosynthesis of polyunsaturated fatty acids. *J Lipid Res, 36*, 2471-2477.

Stayton, P. S., Poulos, T. L. & Sligar, S. G. (1989). Putidaredoxin competitively inhibits cytochrome b5-cytochrome P-450cam association: a proposed molecular model for a cytochrome P-450cam electron-transfer complex. *Biochemistry, 28*, 8201-8205.

Steinberg, M. H. (2009). Hemoglobins with atered oxygen affinity, unstable Hemoglobins, M-hemoglobins, and Dyshemoglobinemias. In *Wintrobe's Clinical Hematology* (Greer, J. P., Foerster, J., Rodgers, G. M., Paraskevas, F., Glader, B., Arber, D. A., and Maans, R. T. J., eds) Vol. 1, Lippincott Williams & Wilkins, Philadelphia, 589-606.

Strausberg, R. L., Feingold, E. A., Grouse, L. H., Derge, J. G., Klausner, R. D., Collins, F. S., Wagner, L., Shenmen, C. M., Schuler, G. D., Altschul, S. F., Zeeberg, B., Buetow, K. H., Schaefer, C. F., Bhat, N. K., Hopkins, R. F., Jordan, H., Moore, T., Max, S. I., Wang, J., Hsieh, F., Diatchenko, L., Marusina, K., Farmer, A. A., Rubin, G. M., Hong, L., Stapleton, M., Soares, M. B., Bonaldo, M. F., Casavant, T. L., Scheetz, T. E., Brownstein, M. J., Usdin, T. B., Toshiyuki, S., Carninci, P., Prange, C., Raha, S. S., Loquellano, N. A., Peters, G. J., Abramson, R. D., Mullahy, S. J., Bosak, S. A., McEwan, P. J., McKernan, K. J., Malek, J. A., Gunaratne, P. H., Richards, S., Worley, K. C., Hale, S., Garcia, A. M., Gay, L. J., Hulyk, S. W., Villalon, D. K., Muzny, D. M., Sodergren, E. J., Lu, X., Gibbs, R. A., Fahey, J., Helton, E., Ketteman, M., Madan, A., Rodrigues, S., Sanchez, A., Whiting, M., Young, A. C., Shevchenko, Y., Bouffard, G. G., Blakesley, R. W., Touchman, J. W., Green, E. D., Dickson, M. C., Rodriguez, A. C., Grimwood, J., Schmutz, J., Myers, R. M., Butterfield, Y. S., Krzywinski, M. I., Skalska, U., Smailus, D. E., Schnerch, A., Schein, J. E., Jones, S. J. & Marra, M. A. (2002). Generation and initial analysis of more than 15,000 full-length human and mouse cDNA sequences. *Proc Natl Acad Sci U S A, 99*, 16899-16903.

Strittmatter, P. & Ozols, J. (1966). The restricted tryptic cleavage of cytochrome b5. *J Biol Chem, 241*, 4787-4792.

Strittmatter, P., Hackett, C. S., Korza, G. & Ozols, J. (1990). Characterization of the covalent cross-links of the active sites of amidinated cytochrome b5 and NADH:cytochrome b5 reductase. *J Biol Chem*, *265*, 21709-21713.

Sulc, M., Jecmen, T., Snajdrova, R., Novak, P., Martinek, V., Hodek, P., Stiborova, M. & Hudecek, J. (2012). Mapping of interaction between cytochrome P450 2B4 and cytochrome b5: the first evidence of two mutual orientations. *Neuro Endocrinol Lett*, *33* Suppl 3, 41-47.

Sun, Y. L., Wang, Y. H., Yan, M. M., Sun, B. Y., Xie, Y., Huang, Z. X., Jiang, S. K. & Wu, H. M. (1999). Structure, interaction and electron transfer between cytochrome b5, its E44A and/or E56A mutants and cytochrome c. *J Mol Biol*, *285*, 347-359.

Tajima, S. & Sato, R. (1979). Inhibition of the binding of cytochrome b5 to phosphatidylcholine vesicles by cholesterol. *Biochim Biophys Acta*, *550*, 357-361.

Takeshita, M., Tamura, M., Yoshida, S. & Yubisui, T. (1985). Palmitoyl-CoA elongation in brain microsomes: dependence on cytochrome b5 and NADH-cytochrome b5 reductase. *J Neurochem*, *45*, 1390-1395.

Tamburini, P. P., White, R. E. & Schenkman, J. B. (1985). Chemical characterization of protein-protein interactions between cytochrome P-450 and cytochrome b5. *J Biol Chem*, *260*, 4007-4015.

Tamburini, P. P. & Schenkman, J. B. (1987). Purification to homogeneity and enzymological characterization of a functional covalent complex composed of cytochromes P-450 isozyme 2 and b5 from rabbit liver. *Proc Natl Acad Sci U S A*, *84*, 11-15.

Thomas, P. (2008). Characteristics of membrane progestin receptor alpha (mPRalpha) and progesterone membrane receptor component 1 (PGMRC1) and their roles in mediating rapid progestin actions. *Front Neuroendocrinol*, *29*, 292-312.

Thomas, P., Tubbs, C. & Garry, V. F. (2009). Progestin functions in vertebrate gametes mediated by membrane progestin receptors (mPRs): Identification of mPRalpha on human sperm and its association with sperm motility. *Steroids*, *74*, 614-621.

Valencia, A. & Moran, J. (2001). Role of oxidative stress in the apoptotic cell death of cultured cerebellar granule neurons. *Journal of neuroscience research*, *64*, 284-297.

Velayutham, M., Hemann, C. & Zweier, J. L. (2011). Removal of H(2)O(2) and generation of superoxide radical: role of cytochrome c and NADH. *Free Radic Biol Med*, *51*, 160-170.

Velick, S. F. & Strittmatter, P. (1956). The oxidation-reduction stoichiometry and potential of microsomal cytochrome. *J Biol Chem, 221*, 265-275.

Venditti, P., Daniele, C. M., De Leo, T. & Di Meo, S. (1998). Effect of phenobarbital treatment on characteristics determining susceptibility to oxidants of homogenates, mitochondria and microsomes from rat liver. *Cellular Physiology and Biochemistry. 8*, 328-338.

Vergeres, G. & Waskell, L. (1995). Cytochrome b5, its functions, structure and membrane topology. *Biochimie, 77*, 604-620.

Vieira, L. M., Kaplan, J. C., Kahn, A. & Leroux, A. (1995). Four new mutations in the NADH-cytochrome b5 reductase gene from patients with recessive congenital methemoglobinemia type II. *Blood, 85*, 2254-2262.

Villalba, J. M., Navarro, F., Cordoba, F., Serrano, A., Arroyo, A., Crane, F. L. & Navas, P. (1995). Coenzyme Q reductase from liver plasma membrane: purification and role in trans-plasma-membrane electron transport. *Proc Natl Acad Sci U S A, 92*, 4887-4891.

Walker, F. A., Emrick, D., Rivera, J. E., Hanquet, B. J. & Buttlaire, D. H. (1988). Effect of heme orientation on the reduction potential of cytochrome b5. *J Am Chem Soc, 110*, 6234-6240.

Wang, Y., Wu, Y. S., Zheng, P. Z., Yang, W. X., Fang, G. A., Tang, Y. C., Xie, F., Lan, F. H. & Zhu, Z. Y. (2000). A novel mutation in the NADH-cytochrome b5 reductase gene of a Chinese patient with recessive congenital methemoglobinemia. *Blood, 95*, 3250-3255.

Watanabe, F., Nakano, Y., Saido, H., Tamura, Y. & Yamanaka, H. (1992a). Cytochrome b5/cytochrome b5 reductase complex in rat liver microsomes has NADH-linked aquacobalamin reductase activity. *J Nutr, 122*, 940-944.

Watanabe, F., Nakano, Y., Saido, H., Tamura, Y. & Yamanaka, H. (1992b). NADPH-cytochrome c (P-450) reductase has the activity of NADPH-linked aquacobalamin reductase in rat liver microsomes. *Biochim Biophys Acta, 1119*, 175-177.

Waterhouse, A. M., Procter, J. B., Martin, D. M. A, Clamp, M. & Barton, G. J. (2009). "Jalview version 2: A Multiple Sequence Alignment and Analysis Workbench," *Bioinformatics, 25* (9), 1189-1191.

Wirtz, M., Oganesyan, V., Zhang, X., Studer, J. & Rivera, M. (2000). Modulation of redox potential in electron transfer proteins: Effects of complex formation on the active site microenvironment of cytochrome b5. *Faraday Discussions, 116*, 221-234.

Xie, Y., Bruce, A., He, L., Wei, F., Tao, L. & Tang, D. (2011). CYB5D2 enhances HeLa cells survival of etoposide-induced cytotoxicity. *Biochem Cell Biol*, *89*, 341-350.

Xiong, P., Nocek, J. M., Griffin, A. K., Wang, J. & Hoffman, B. M. (2009). Electrostatic redesign of the [myoglobin, cytochrome b5] interface to create a well-defined docked complex with rapid interprotein electron transfer. *J Am Chem Soc*, *131*, 6938-6939.

Xu, F., DeFilippi, L. J., Ballou, D. P. & Hultquist, D. E. (1993). Hydrogen peroxide-dependent formation and bleaching of the higher oxidation states of bovine erythrocyte green hemeprotein. *Arch Biochem Biophys*, *301*, 184-189.

Yao, P., Xie, Y., Wang, Y. H., Sun, Y. L., Huang, Z. X., Xiao, G. T. & Wang, S. D. (1997). Importance of a conserved phenylalanine-35 of cytochrome b5 to the protein's stability and redox potential. *Protein Eng*, *10*, 575-581.

Yamauchi, Y., Reid, P. C., Sperry, J. B., Furukawa, K., Takeya, M., Chang, C. C. & Chang, T. Y. (2007). Plasma membrane rafts complete cholesterol synthesis by participating in retrograde movement of precursor sterols. *J Biol Chem*, *282*, 34994-35004.

Yaqinuddin, A., Qureshi, S. A., Qazi, R. & Abbas, F. (2008). Down-regulation of DNMT3b in PC3 cells effects locus-specific DNA methylation, and represses cellular growth and migration. *Cancer Cell Int*, *8*, 13.

Yasrebi, H., Sperisen, P., Praz, V. & Bucher, P. (2009). Can survival prediction be improved by merging gene expression data sets? *PLoS One*, *4*, e7431.

Yoo, M. (1999). Two homologous cytochrome b5s are expressed in both neurons and glial cells of the rat brain. *Biochem Biophys Res Commun*, *256*, 330-332.

Yoshida, S., Yubisui, T. & Takeshita, M. (1984). Characteristics of b-type cytochromes in brain microsomes: comparison with liver microsomes. *Arch Biochem Biophys*, *232*, 296-304.

Zhang, H., Hamdane, D., Im, S. C. & Waskell, L. (2008). Cytochrome b5 inhibits electron transfer from NADPH-cytochrome P450 reductase to ferric cytochrome P450 2B4. *J Biol Chem*, *283*, 5217-5225.

Zhang, Y., Larade, K., Jiang, Z. G., Ito, S., Wang, W., Zhu, H. & Bunn, H. F. (2010). The flavoheme reductase Ncb5or protects cells against endoplasmic reticulum stress-induced lipotoxicity. *J Lipid Res*, *51*, 53-62

Zhu, H., Qiu, H., Yoon, H. W., Huang, S. & Bunn, H. F. (1999). Identification of a cytochrome b-type NAD(P)H oxidoreductase ubiquitously expressed in human cells. *Proc Natl Acad Sci U S A*, *96*, 14742-14747.

Zhu, H., Larade, K., Jackson, T. A., Xie, J., Ladoux, A., Acker, H., Berchner-Pfannschmidt, U., Fandrey, J., Cross, A. R., Lukat-Rodgers, G. S., Rodgers, K. R. & Bunn, H. F. (2004). NCB5OR is a novel soluble NAD(P)H reductase localized in the endoplasmic reticulum. *J Biol Chem*, *279*, 30316-30325.

In: Cytochromes *b* and *c*
Editor: Rurik Thom

ISBN: 978-1-63117-467-4
© 2014 Nova Science Publishers, Inc.

Chapter 3

CYTOCHROME *C*–LIPID INTERACTION IN THE REGULATION OF CELL FATE: RESPIRATION, APOPTOSIS AND DISEASES

Laura Fiorucci[1],[*] Federica Sinibaldi[2] and Roberto Santucci[1]

[1]Department of Clinical Sciences and Translational Medicine, University of Rome 'Tor Vergata', Italy
[2]Department of Experimental Sciences and Surgery, University of Rome 'Tor Vergata', Italy

ABSTRACT

Cytochrome *c* (cyt *c*) functions as a mobile electron carrier in the respiratory chain anchored to the external side of the inner mitochondrial membrane and shuttling electrons from cyt *c* reductase to cyt *c* oxidase. A further function of cyt *c*, beyond respiration, is realized outside mitochondria in the apoptotic program. Cyt *c* may respond to different environments by changing its fold, thus favouring the exertion of different biological functions in different pathophysiological cell conditions. The binding of lipids (free fatty acids as well as acidic phospholipids) to cyt *c* induces conformational changes and partial

[*] Address for correspondence: *Prof. Laura Fiorucci Department of Clinical Sciences and Translational Medicine, University of Rome 'Tor Vergata', Via Montpellier 1, 00133 Rome, Italy; tel.0039(06)72596478; email fiorucci@uniroma2.it.

unfolding of the protein, strongly influencing cyt c oxidase/peroxidase activity. In the early events of apoptosis, the interaction of cyt c with a mitochondrion-specific phospholipid, cardiolipin (CL), brings about a conformational transition of the protein and acquirement of peroxidase activity. Transitions among different conformations are regulated by endogenous molecules such as ATP. Apoptosis is strictly connected to the pathogenesis of many human diseases, including neoplastic, neurodegenerative and cardiovascular diseases, and derangements of cardiolipin biosynthesis and remodeling are crucial in regulation of apoptosis. So as the role of cyt c in respiration and apoptosis rely on its interaction with CL, in the present book chapter we will review the structural features of this complex. Then we shall describe how perturbations in CL amount, acyl composition and CL-driven allosteric modulation of the cyt c properties, may contribute to cell fate.

INTRODUCTION

Non native states of proteins (i.e. folding variants and molten globule (MG) states) have been proved to exist in living cells and play key roles in many pathophysiological processes. In some cases, such states determine the fate of cells. The role of cofactors enabling misfolded protein variants to attain new functions has been addressed, as in the case of oleic acid-bound α-lactalbumin which shows spectroscopic properties typical of the molten globule and induces apoptosis in cancer cells [1]. As recently reported, this same cofactor (i.e., oleic acid) induces structural changes in cytochrome c (cyt c) favouring the formation of a MG-like state of the protein [2]. Indeed, several non native cyt c conformers with functions different from the native have been detected. In the native state, cyt c acts as an electron transfer protein between cyt c reductase and cyt c oxidase in the mitochondrial respiratory chain. It is a single chain hemoprotein characterized by a relatively high stability due to the covalent attachment of the heme to the polypeptide chain. A further well-known function of cyt c, which is not redox-related, is realized outside mitochondria in the apoptotic program.

Into the cytosol, cyt c interacts with the Apaf-1 protein, forms the apoptosome, and activates the caspase cascade. At the early stages of apoptosis cardiolipin (CL), a mitochondrion-specific phospholipid, binds cyt c in-between the outer and the inner mitochondrial membranes. CL constitutes about the 20% of total lipids of the membrane and is characterized by a unique structure, being composed of four (instead of two) fatty acid tails [3,4], of which linoleic acid (18:2) is the most abundant (about 80%) acyl chain. CL-bound cyt *c* undergoes conformational changes and acquires peroxidase activity [5, 6]. Catalytic cyt *c* peroxidizes CL; the CL peroxidation products in turn are responsible for membrane permeabilization and cyt *c* release. This chapter describes the cyt *c*'s role in cell fate; particular emphasis is deputed to structural and biological aspects concerning cyt *c*'s function in healthy conditions and its conversion into a peroxidase once it interacts with CL in the early events of apoptosis. The structural features responsible for CL peroxidation and perturbation in CL synthesis and/or remodeling (both associated with human disorders) are also reported. The role of cyt *c* in cell death and survival in the complex neurodegeneration scenario inhibition is also discussed; it points out that the peroxidase activity of cyt *c* is a promising target for therapeutic interventions.

CYTOCHROME C: NON-NATIVE CONFORMATIONS AND DISTINCT BIOLOGICAL FUNCTIONS

Cyt *c*, whose structure is shown in Figure 1, is a single chain hemoprotein of 104 amino acids containing three major and two minor α-helices in the structure. The prosthetic group lies within a crevice lined with hydrophobic residues and is covalently attached to the polypeptide by two thioether bridges with residues Cys 14 and Cys 17, while His 18 and Met 80 are the axial ligands of the six-coordinated low spin heme iron [7]. As mitochondrial peripheral membrane protein, it functions in between the inner and the outer membrane, mediating electron transfer (eT) between different proteins of the respiratory chain [8]. Studies on the interaction between cyt *c* and various membrane systems indicate that cyt c mediates eT between cyt *c* reductase and cyt *c* oxidase as unbound or membrane-bound protein showing a limited number of non-native exchangeable compact conformations [9, 10].

It is now well recognized that cyt c *c* plays different roles in different locations of the cell and a functional migration of cyt *c* occurs during the life span of cell (i.e. mitochondria and cytosol). In mitochondria it plays a physiological role not only as electron carrier in the respiratory chain but also as detoxifying function to dispose of ROS [11-13]. Intracellular ROS are generated by the O_2-controlled oxidation of NADH and $FADH_2$; a cascade of multienzyme complexes, located in the mitochondrial membrane and coupled with the ADP phosphorylation to ATP, actively participates to the process.

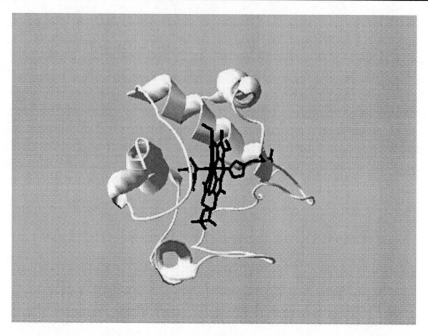

Figure 1. Schematic representation of the ribbon structure of horse cyt c. The heme group (black) and the axial ligands, His18 (right) and Met80 (left), are represented as *sticks*. The protein structure was visualized with the Swiss-Pdb Viewer software [72].

The O_2-to-H_2O reduction consists of a four-step reaction of sequential single electron additive processes; in addition to the superoxide radical anion $(O_2^{-\bullet})$, the one-electron reduction of O_2 generates two other stable intermediates: hydrogen peroxide (H_2O_2), which is produced by dismutation of the superoxide anion, and the highly reactive hydroxyl radical (HO•) [8]. Cyt$c$ operates as a radical scavenger within the inner-membrane space by removing unpaired electrons from superoxide and regenerating O_2 [10, 14]. Cyt c functions also as a hydrogen peroxide scavenger [15, 16]. In contrast to neutralization of superoxide, which requires oxidized cyt c, conversion of hydrogen peroxide will be performed by both reduced and oxidized cyt c. Since cyt c undergoes oxidation/reduction cycles in a respiring cell, both detoxification reactions can take place. Therefore, coupling of ROS neutralization with its redox capabilities makes cyt c an effective antioxidant for the cell.

The finding that cyt c plays a role in cytosol in cell apoptosis has recently renewed the interest in this protein. When released into the cytoplasm cyt c binds to the apoptosis protease activation factor (APAf-1) forming, in the presence of ATP or dATP, the apoptosome; this complex activates pro-caspase 9, which triggers an enzymatic reaction cascade leading to cell apoptosis [17]. In healthy cells a fraction of cyt *c* population (approx. 15%) is tightly bound to the IMM, while the remaining (approx. 85%) is free or loosely bound *via* electrostatic interaction. The loosely bound cyt *c* participates in electron transfer (eT), inhibits ROS formation, and prevents oxidative stress, while the tightly bound cyt *c* is thought to account for peroxidase activity, an event crucial for initiating the apoptotic process. The IMM is composed of several phospholipids; of these, cardiolipin (CL) is that assumed to bind to cyt *c*. The cyt *c*-CL interaction strongly influences the function of the protein (and, thus, the cell fate); at the early stage of apoptosis, the cyt *c*-CL interaction drastically decreases, the (cyt *c*-CL) complex dissociates, and the free soluble protein is released into the cytosol.

In healthy cells the CL-cyt *c* interaction takes place at two distinct protein sites, the A- and C-site, which show different affinity for the phospholipids. At the A-site the interaction is of electrostatic nature and involves some positively charged residues of the protein and the negatively charged phosphate group of CL. Conversely, at the C-site the interaction is of hydrophobic nature; it has been hypothesized that at this site one acyl chain of CL may penetrate into the protein interior [18-20]. The 'extended lipid anchorage' hypothesis, formulated by Kinnunen and collaborators, asserts that at level of the C-site one acyl chain of CL accommodates into the protein whereas a second chain points to the opposite direction from the headgroup [21]; this would ensure a firm anchorage of the protein to the membrane. The protein region initially proposed to host the CL acyl chain is a hydrophobic channel located close to the conservative Asn52 residue. Successively, Kalanxi and Wallace proposed an alternative host site for the acyl chain: a cleft formed by a network of positively charged residues (K72, K73, and K86) located close to the heme-binding region [19]. Recent studies, performed by using site directed mutagenesis, have shown that the invariant Arg91, a residue that anchors the cleft constituted by residues 67-71 and 82-85, affects both the structural and the ligand-exchange properties of the cyt *c*/CL complex [22]. Recently, the hypothesis that two (instead of one) adjacent acyl chains protrude into the protein, has been formulated. This hypothesis is based on the idea that the insertion of a single acyl chain into cyt *c* would cause a partial exposure to the polar solvent of (at least) one adjacent chain in the liposome, thus creating a disfavoured situation from a solvation energy viewpoint. Support to this view comes from the two-transition binding process and from the biphasic character of the binding kinetics [23]. At present, the location of the 'channel' into which CL should protrude is still uncertain and matter of controversy. The existence of a binding site constituted by the K22, K27, H33 and K87 residues, the so-called L-site, was also proposed [24]. This site, located at the opposite side of the macromolecule with respect to the A-site and active at pH < 7.4, seems to play a role in bringing two lipid vesicles together by the same protein molecule, for fusion. Finally, a very recent investigation identifies the cyt c/CL complex as a heterogeneous system constituted by an *ensamble* of non-native CL-bound cyt c conformations in equilibrium, which differ for the degree of unfolding. According with this study, CL should behave as a modulator of the cyt c conformers, acting through interactions of electrostatic nature [25, 26].

Established that the mechanism(s) governing the cyt c-CL interaction still are not fully understood, what is undoubtedly ascertained is that formation of the cyt c/CL complex induces tertiary changes in the protein, the displacement of Met80 from the sixth coordination position of the heme iron and, in some cases, a change of the spin state of the metal [18-22]. Several studies demonstrated that lipids favour formation of non-native conformers of proteins; oleic acid-bound α-lactalbumin shows spectroscopic properties typical of the molten globule and induces apoptosis in cancer cells [1], and a not dissimilar behaviour is shown by oleic acid-bound cyt c [2]. Indeed, in the last two decades several non-native cyt c conformers with functions different from the native have been detected [18-20, 27-29]. Dissociation of Met80 from the sixth coordination position of the heme iron is a common characteristics of these non-native states. Disruption the Fe(III)-Met80 axial bond, an event strictly correlated with the complex formation, influences the spin state of CL-bound cyt c favouring the binding of small molecules, as NO and CO, to the heme-iron [30-32], and triggering peroxidase activity of the protein [33, 34]. NO binding to free ferrous cyt c gives rise to a hexa-coordinated adduct in which NO occupies the distal site of the heme-iron, the proximal site being occupied by the endogeneous His18 residue. The observation that NO binding favours penta-coordination in some proteins due to the proximal His18 dissociation [31], made real the hypothesis that NO may bind to CL-bound cyt c at the proximal site of the metal, with formation of a proximal NO-bound penta-coordinated species [32]. Indeed, it has been recently reported that the horse ferrous cyt c/CL complex binds NO at the proximal side of the heme [31] *via* a complex pathway of successive kinetic steps. These studies are of importance because, in mitochondria, NO acts as a gas modulator and triggers cell apoptosis. The investigations on CO binding to CL-bound horse ferrous cyt c underline the capability of CL to induce changes in the binding properties of the protein. CL-bound horse cyt c interacts with the gaseous compound by a simple second order process [30]. The values of combination and dissociation constants are consistent with the existence of a very open heme crevice in which the Fe(II)-His18 axial bond results to be significantly weaker [32]. This indicates that CL binding induces large conformational changes in cyt c at both the proximal and the distal side of the heme (with loss of the eT properties typical of the protein) and converts it into a peroxidase [5, 6]. The partial unfolding of CL-bound cyt c facilitates small molecules, such as H_2O_2, to get access into the heme site of the protein [34]. The conformational changes and the peroxidase activity of the protein are modulated by ATP which, at a proper concentration, disrupts the cyt c-CL complex and allows protein refolding into its native structure [2, 35-37]. The peroxidase activity acquired by phospholipid membrane-bound cyt c appears critical in the early stages of apoptosis; as recently demonstrated, the cytc/CL complex acts as powerful CL-specific peroxidase and generates CL hydroperoxides, compounds involved in cyt c (and other pro-apoptotic factors) release from mitochondrial membrane [34, 38, 39]. Thus, whereas the native fold and the low-spin hexacoordination of the heme iron are important for cyt c to function as electron carrier, a non-native compact conformation can induce peroxidase activity in the protein, of relevance for the execution of the cell apoptosis program.

One of the early stages of cell apoptosis consists in the cyt c-induced activation of caspase 9, one of the proteases involved in the caspase cascade leading to cell death. Cyt c release into the cytoplasm requires the dissociation of the (cyt c-CL) complex, which is favored by a decrease of the cyt c-CL interaction. Although the mechanisms governing this process are not yet fully understood, CL peroxidation is considered a key factor to obtain complex dissociation. This view is supported by the oxidative degradation of CL observed in the p53-induced apoptosis [40], and by the lower affinity for cyt c shown by CL hydroperoxides when compared to the 'native' CL [41]. Interestingly, CL peroxidation is prevented by BCL-2, an antiapoptotic protein member of the BCL-2 family which is known to inhibit cyt c release from the mitochondrion [34].

CARDIOLIPIN METABOLISM IN HEALTH AND DISEASE

The discovery of a pro-apoptotic protein/lipid complex, namely cyt c/CL, has triggered a renaissance of interest in the functional properties of lipids and their influence on soluble proteins. In particular the exclusive localization of

CL in mitochondria makes comprehension of its role in regulation of mitochondrial function and oxidative stress an exciting field of research. Synthesized in mitochondria on the matrix side of the IMM, CL constitutes about the 20% of total lipids of the membrane and is characterized by a unique structure, being composed of four (instead of two) fatty acid tails [3]. It has been ascertained that CL role is mediated by the unique acyl composition of the side chains and such a feature is not derived from *de novo* synthesis, rather from a remodeling process. As a matter of fact, perturbations in CL synthesis and/or remodeling are associated with a plethora of human disorders.

In most tissues, CL contains only a few acyl residues, mostly 18:1, 18:2, and 18:3 fatty acids. Linoleic acid (18:2) is the most abundant (about 80%) acyl chain in human heart mitochondria, and its presence confers to CL a symmetrical profile (L_4-CL) [4]. At variance, brain contains a substantially more complex fatty acid chain profile with over 100 CL molecular species characterized by an increased presence of signaling fatty acids (i.e. arachidonic acid and docosahexaenoic acids) and a lower symmetrical profile [42], a feature that is likely responsible for the reduced mitochondrial bioenergetic efficiency in brain tissue. In this regard, it is worthwhile to remind that neurons rely on glucose metabolism (phenomenon reported as the 'Warburg effect') rather than on electron-transport chain efficiency, which is not a limiting factor in neuronal cells for energy production. The 'Warburg effect' is typical also for the cancer cells characterized by increased glycolytic fluxes under aerobic conditions and specific alterations associated with mitochondrial functions [43, 44]. Interestingly, abnormalities in the CL content or composition were found in some tumors, i.e., an abundance of immature molecular species and deficiencies of mature molecular species due to major defects in CL synthesis and remodeling [45].

Indeed, the biosynthetic pathway of CL proceeds through several steps of modifications of phosphatidic acid (PA) within the mitochondrion, where CL is exclusively utilized. The conversion of PA to cytidine diphosphate-diacylglycerol (CDP-DAG) is catalyzed by CDP-DAG synthase (CDS), an enzyme operating in multiple phospholipid-synthetic pathways. [46]. In turn, CDP-DAG reacts with glycerol-3-phosphate (G3P) to form phosphatidylglycerolphosphate (PGP) through the action of the PGP synthase (PGPS) [47, 48]. In mammals, PGP is dephosphorylated to phoshatydylglycerol (PG) by a protein tyrosine phosphatase localized in the mitochondrion, the protein tyrosine phosphatase mitochondrial 1 (PTPMT1). Since perturbations in CL levels have been associated with apoptosis and the block of apoptosis is considered to be a hallmark of cancer, the dysregulation of CL homeostasis may affect both the ability of cells to undergo cell death and their tumorigenic potential. Interestingly, inhibition of the PTPMT1 function causes a shift to glycolysis, perhaps for counterbalancing the mitochondrial bioenergetic impairment associated with CL dysregulation. The cardiolipin synthase (CLS) links the phoshatidyl group of CDP-DAG to PG, with elimination of cytidinmonophosphate (CMP) and formation of CL. The eukaryotic cardiolipin synthases show little, if any, acyl chain specificity. Immature CL is characterized by saturated acyl chains of variable length and asymmetry about the central carbon of the bridging glycerol [49, 50]. In mature CL the final acyl chain composition consists of unsaturated fatty acids obtained through deacylation–reacylation/transacylation reactions, a process commonly referred to as CL remodeling. CL deacylation is initiated by a calcium independent phospholipase A2, (iPLA$_2$) [51], that removes one saturated fatty acyl chain forming monolysocardiolipin (MLCL). MLCL is then reacylated by the transacylase tafazzin (Taz), to form mature CL. This step seems to be the major site of regulation in CL remodeling. In heart mitochondria, tafazzin is known to transfer with high selectivity linoleate groups from phosphatidylcholine (PC) to monolysocardiolipin, promoting molecular symmetry among the molecular species of CL acylated at all four positions (with formation of lyso-phosphatidylcholine) [52]. Further enzymes in mammalian cells have the ability to attach an acyl chain to monolysocardiolipin, i.e. monolysocardiolipin acyltransferase-1 (MLCLAT1), that shows specificity for linoleate, and an acyl-CoA:lysocardiolipin acyltransferase-1(ALCAT1) which has a coenzyme A (CoA)-dependent mechanism and shows no specificity for linoleic acid. Strikingly, the latter enzyme catalyzes the incorporation of long polyunsaturated fatty acyl chains and an overexpression of this enzyme makes CL particularly prone to ROS-mediated peroxidation.

In humans, tafazzin deficiency causes Barth syndrome, a X-linked inherited infantile disease, characterized by dilated cardiomyopathy, skeletal muscle weakness, growth retardation and neutropenia [53-55]. Mitochondria from patients with Barth syndrome have an increased MLCL content, a CL content lower than that present in control cells, and display changes in acyl chain composition resulting in the loss of L$_4$-CL. It remains unclear how abnormal CL homeostasis actually plays a role in the pathogenesis of Barth syndrome. By measuring the activity of respiratory enzymes and by electron micrographs, it was demonstrated that the disease has a profound impact on structure and function of mitochondria [55].

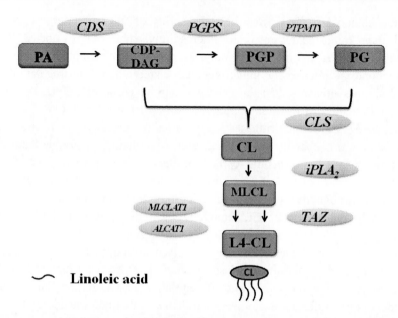

Figure 2. CL biosynthesis and remodeling scheme. ALCAT$_1$, acyl-CoA:lysocardiolipin acyltransferase-1; CDP-DAG, cytidinediphosphate diacylglycerol; CDS, cytidinediphosphatediacylglycerol synthetase ;CL, cardiolipin; L$_4$-CL, tetralinoleoyl CL; CLS, cardiolipin synthase; MLCL, monolysocardiolipin; MLCL AT$_1$, MLCL acyl transferase; PA phosphatidic acid; PG, phosphatidyl glycerol; PGP, phosphatidylglycerolphosphate ; PGPS, PGP synthase; iPLA$_2$, calcium independent phospholipase A2; PTPMT1, protein tyrosine phosphatase, mitochondrial 1; TAZ, tafazzin.

The respiratory chain complexes are organized into multienzyme assemblies, which maximize electron flux. Formation and stability of these functional macromolecular units, called super-complexes, are strictly dependent on CL; their destabilization is expected to lead to electron transport defects [56]. Isolated mitochondria from patient's cells display lower rates of coupled respiration as compared to mitochondria from cells from normal individuals. Upon CL content decrease, the generation of ROS is enhanced. ROS in turn cause peroxidation of the CL unsaturated fatty acids. Perturbations in CL content and acyl composition have been also described in heart failure (HF) [57]. In particular, the mitochondrial CDP-DAG synthase activity increase observed during HF development may be related to the increased secretion of inflammatory mediators, (*i.e.* tumor necrosis factor-α, and interleukin-6) which are known to cause contractile dysfunction [58]. Also the PGPS enzyme activity, which is responsible for condensation of CDP-

DAG with glycerol-3-phosphate to form PG-phosphate (PGP), increases and the protein seems to be post-translational modified during the development of HF [58]. An alternative form of CL remodeling during the development of HF brings about an increase of the CL species containing oleic acid (18:1), arachidonic acid (20:4), and docosahexaenoic acid (22:6) with respect to the normally levels. Compromised CL synthesis and/or oxidation seem to be primary features of aging. In aging cells, CL is pathologically remodeled with polyunsaturated fatty acids instead of linoleic acid present in normal CL [59].

CYTOCHROME C-CARDIOLIPIN INTERACTION IN NEURODEGENERATION AND CANCER

Multiple neurodegenerative diseases are characterized by the loss of specific neuron populations, due to induction of apoptosis. The neurons degeneration, which is responsible for cell death, may be mediated by a number of peroxidase activities, including the peroxidase activity of cyt *c*. In this regard, it is worthy of note the co-localization of cyt *c* and α-synuclein that was observed in the intracellular inclusions of neurons from patients with Parkinson's disease [60]. The formation of millimeter-length fibers, constituted of CL/cyt *c* vesicles displaying amyloid (ß-sheet) characteristics, was detected [61]. The amyloid aggregates interact with the mitochondrial membrane, induce its permeabilisation and, successively, trigger the cytochrome *c* release [62, 63]. CL affinity for amyloid aggregates destabilizes the membrane; this renders CL a specific factor for the targeting of the inner mitochondrial membrane by aggregation-prone proteins and peptides. This finding suggests that the cyt *c*-CL interaction may participate in some of the disorders associated with amyloid formation, such as AA-amyloidosis and Alzheimer's disease. The involvement of tyrosine residues in the mechanism of peroxidase activation of cyt *c* may be explained with the relative stability of the tyrosine radical. Tyrosine residues seem to have a crucial role as target of posttranslational modification of cyt *c*, namely tyrosine phoshorylation [64, 65]. Since the cyt *c* release from the mitochondrion and formation of the apoptosome are the key steps controlling the fate of the cell, the regulation of this mechanism likely involves phosphorylation of cyt *c*. Indeed liver cyt *c* is phosphorylated on Tyr48 *in vivo* [65]. Strikingly, the mutant of cyt *c* containing the negatively charged (and, thus, phosphomimetic) Glu48 residue instead of Tyr48 is incapable of inducing downstream caspase activation [66].

As a matter of fact, the inhibition of the peroxidase activity of cyt c represents a promising target for a therapeutic intervention. Dopamine, L-DOPA, WHI-P131, and minocycline, four compounds having other *in vivo* properties, were found to act as peroxidase inhibitors since they efficiently decrease the progression of neuron degeneration. In particular, it is under debate the hypothesis that minocycline, a derivate of the antibiotc tetracycline, may act as therapeutic agent in processes leading to neurological diseases [67, 68]. Support to this view comes from the observation that minocycline readily crosses the blood–brain barrier at the greatest extent with respect to the other tetracyclines, it is well tolerated, and it acts as an efficient neuroprotector in experimental models of Parkinson's disease, Huntington's disease, multiple sclerosis, amyotrophic lateral sclerosis (ALS), and acute inflammation after brain trauma or cerebral ischemia [67].

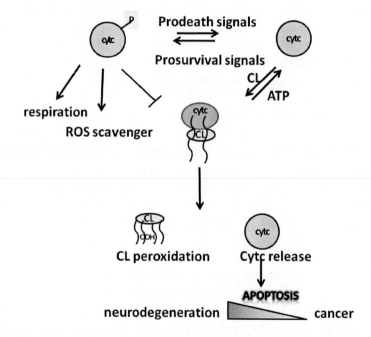

Figure 3. Regulation of cyt c role through phosphorylation and interaction with cardiolipin. Under healthy conditions cyt c is phosphorylated and functions in mitochondrial respiratory chain and as a ROS scavenger. In the presence of apoptotic stimuli, dephoshorylation,of cyt c and interaction with cardiolipin occur (here the cyt c-CL interaction is represented as described in ref. 23). Upon peroxidation of cardiolipin, cyt c release into the cytosol brings about the apoptosome formation, a committing step in the execution of the cell death program. Too much or too little apoptosis are features of neurodegenerative diseases and cancer, respectively.

Further, minocycline weakens the ROS production in cultured neurons and in isolated mitochondria; under pathological conditions it may prevent apoptotic signalling *via* a stabilization of mitochondria-mediated signal cascades [69]. With no doubt, inhibition of the peroxidase activity of cyt *c* remains a promising target for a therapeutic approach finalized to cell protection [36, 67]. Recently, efforts have been directed towards the design and the development of mitochondria-targeted inhibitors of CL peroxidation; more specifically, triphenylphoshonium- and hemigramicidin S-moieties were proposed to act as a vehicle for the mitochondrial delivery of antioxidant molecules [70]. In contrast, an increased apoptotic activity would be beneficial in particular pathological conditions, such as the typical hyperproliferation of cancer cells. A general problem linked to the control of cancer regards the adaptive mechanism that allows cancer cells to evade the apoptotic pathway. Indeed, cyt *c* phosphorylation may interfere with apoptosis; as above reported, phosphomimetic cyt *c* is not able to trigger any measureable caspase activation [66].

Since cancer manages against apoptosis, an increased phosphorylation of cyt *c* (as well as the inability to dephosphorylate it) might represent a mechanism utilized in cancer signaling for the suppression of apoptosis. In order to enhance the programmed death of tumor cells in cancer treatment, new therapeutic strategies based on the peroxidase activity stimulation of the cyt *c*-CL complex, have been developed. To this issue, the effect produced by changes in molecular speciation of CL finalized to enrich the phospholipid with highly oxidizable polyunsaturated fatty acid chains, has been investigated [71].

CONCLUSION

The role of CL-cyt *c* interaction in mitochondria-dependent apoptosis is extremely exciting. This interaction may represent an important target system for the development of new drugs capable to regulate neuron apoptosis in neurodegenerative diseases and induce apoptosis in tumor cells. In this regard, recent findings have suggested that dysregulation of the CL homeostasis may affect the ability of cells to undergo cell death as well as their tumorigenic potential. Indeed, it appears of relevance the view that a proper regulation of enzymes involved in CL metabolism may induce mitochondrial-dependent apoptosis in cancer cells, and/or may sensitize them to chemotherapeutic agents. Due to the fundamental function of cyt *c*-CL complex in cell apoptosis, the designing and testing of new mitochondria-targeted compounds able to regulate CL peroxidation and potentially utilizabled as anti- or pro-apoptotic drugs, seem to be promising future options.

REFERENCES

[1] Mossberg, A.K.; Hun Mok K.; Morozova-Roche, L.A. & Svanborg, C. (2010). Structure and function of human α-lactalbumin made lethal to tumor cells (HAMLET)-type complexes. *FEBS J.*, 277, 4614-4625..

[2] Sinibaldi, F.; Mei, G.; Polticelli, F.; Piro, M.C.; Howes, B.D.; Smulevich G.; Santucci, R.; Ascoli, F. & Fiorucci, L. (2005). ATP specifically drives refolding of non-native conformations of cytochrome *c*. *Protein Sci.*, 14, 1049-1058.

[3] Lewis, R.N. & McElhaney, RN. (2009).The physicochemical properties of cardiolipin bilayers and cardiolipin-containing lipid membranes. *Biochim. Biophys. Acta*, 1788, 2069-2079.

[4] Schlame, M.; Ren, M.; Xu, Y.; Greenberg, M.L. & Haller, I. (2005). Molecular symmetry in mitochondrial cardiolipins. *Chem. Phys. Lipids*, 138, 38-49.

[5] Belikova, N. A.; Vladimirov, Y. A.; Osipov, A. N.; Kapralov, A. A.; Tyurin, V. A.; Potapovich, M. V.; Basova, L. V.; Peterson, J. J.; Kurnikov, I.V. & Kagan, V. E. (2006). Peroxidase activity and structural transitions of cytochrome *c* bound to cardiolipin-containing membranes, *Biochemistry* 45 4998-5009.

[6] Basova, L. V.; Kurnikov, I.V.; Wang, L.; Ritov, V. B.; Belikova, N. A.; Vlasova, I. I.; Pacheco, A. A.; Winnica, D. E.; Peterson, J.; Bayir, H.; Waldeck, D. H. & Kagan, V. E. (2007). Cardiolipin switch in mitochondria: shutting off the reduction of cytochrome *c* and turning on the peroxidase activity, *Biochemistry*, 46, 3423-3434.

[7] Bushnell, G.W.; Louie, G.V. & Brayer G.D. (1990). High-resolution three-dimensional structure of horse heart cytochrome *c*. *J. Mol. Biol.*, 214, 585-595.

[8] Pettigrew, G. W. & Moore, G. R. (1987). Cytochromes *c*. *Biological aspects*. Heidelberg, Springer-Verlag.

[9] Bayir, H.; Fadeel, B.; Palladino, M.J.; Witasp, E.; Kurnikov, I.V.; Tyurina, Y.Y., Tyurin, V.A.; Amoscato, A.A.; Jiang, J.; Kochanek, P.M.; DeKosky, S.T.; Greenberger, J.S. Shvedova, A.A. & Kagan, V.E. (2006). Apoptotic interactions of cytochrome *c*: redox flirting with

anionic phospholipids within and outside of mitochondria. *Biochim. Biophys. Acta,* 1757, 648-659.

[10] Berezhna, S.; Wohlrab, H. & Champion, P.M. (2003). Resonance Raman investigations of cytochrome *c* conformational change upon interaction with the membranes of intact and Ca^{2+}-exposed mitochondria. *Biochemistry,* 42, 6149-6158.

[11] Pereverzev, M.O.; Vygodina T.V.; Konstantinov A.A. & Skulachev V.P. (2003). Cytochrome *c*, an ideal antioxidant. *Biochem. Soc. Trans.,* 31, 1312-1315.

[12] Zhao, Y.; Wang, Z.B. & Xu, J.X. (2003). Effect of cytochrome *c* on the generation and elimination of O_2^- and H_2O_2 in mitochondria. *J. Biol. Chem.,* 278, 2356-2360.

[13] Min, L. & Jian-xing, X. (2007). Detoxifying function of cytochrome *c* against oxygen toxicity. *Mitochondrion,* 7, 13-16.

[14] Caroppi, P.; Sinibaldi, F.; Fiorucci, L. & Santucci, R. (2009). Apoptosis and human diseases: mitochondrion damage and lethal role of cytochrome *c* as proapoptotic protein. *Curr. Med. Chem.,* 16, 4058-4065.

[15] Korshunov, S.S.; Krasnikov, B.F.; Pereverzev, M.O. & Skulachev, V.P. (1999). The antioxidant functions of cytochrome *c*. *FEBS Lett.,* 462, 192-198.

[16] Wang, Z.B.; Li, M.; Zhao, Y.; Xu, J.X. (2003) Cytochrome C is a hydrogen peroxide scavenger in mitochondria. *Protein Pept Lett.,* 10, 247-253.

[17] Antonsson, B. (2004). Mitochondria and the Bcl-2 proteins in apoptosis signaling pathways. *Mol. Cell. Biochem.,* 256–257, 141-155.

[18] Rytömaa, M. & Kinnunen, K.J. (1994). Evidence for two distinct acidic phospholipids-binding sites in cytochrome *c*. *J. Biol. Chem.,* 269, 1770-1774.

[19] Kalanxhi, E. & Wallace, C.J.A. (2007). Cytochrome *c* impaled: investigation of the extended lipid anchorage of a soluble protein to mitochondrial membrane models. *Biochem. J.,* 407, 179-187.

[20] Sinibaldi, F.; Fiorucci, L.; Patriarca, A.; Laceri, R.; Ferri, T.; Coletta, M. & Santucci, R. (2008). Insights into cytochrome *c*-cardiolipin interaction. Role played by ionic strength. Biochemistry, 47, 6928-6935.

[21] Rytömaa, M. & Kinnunen, P. K. J. (1995). Reversibility of the binding of cytochrome *c* liposomes. Implications for lipid-protein interactions. *J. Biol. Chem.,* 270, 3197-3202.

[22] Rajagopal, B.S.; Silkstone, G.G.; Nicholls, P.; Wilson, M.T. & Worrall, J.A. (2012). An investigation into a cardiolipin acyl chain insertion site in cytochrome *c*. *Biochim. Biophys. Acta*, 1817, 780-791.

[23] Sinibaldi, F.; Howes, B.D.; Piro, M.C.; Polticelli, F.; Bombelli, C.; Ferri, T.; Coletta, M.; Smulevich, G. & Santucci, R. (2010). Extended cardiolipin anchorage to cytochrome *c*: a model for protein-mitochondrial membrane binding. *J. Biol. Inorg. Chem.*, 15, 689-700.

[24] Kawai, C; Prado, F.M.; Nunes, G.L.C.; Di Mascio, P.; Carmona-Ribeiro, A.M. & Nantes, I.L. (2005). pH-dependent interaction of cytochrome c with mitochondrial mimetic membranes. The role of an array of positively charged amino acids. *J. Biol. Chem.*, 280, 34709-34717.

[25] Hong, Y.; Muenzner, J.; Grimm, S.K. & Pletneva, E.V. (2012). Origin of the conformational heterogeneity of cardiolipin-bound cytochrome *c*. *J. Am. Chem. Soc.*, 134, 18713-18723.

[26] Hanske, J.; Toffey, J.R.; Morenz, A.M.; Bonilla, A.J.; Schiavoni, K.H. & Pletneva, E.V. (2012). Conformational properties of cardiolipin-bound cytochrome *c*. *Proc. Natl. Acad. Sci.* (USA), 109, 125-130.

[27] Kagan, V.E.; Tyurin, V.A.; Jiang, J.; Tyurina, Y.Y.; Ritov, V.B.; Amoscato, A.A.; Osipov, A.N.; Belikova, N.A.; Kapralov, A.A.; Kini, V.; Vlasova, I.I.; Zhao, Q.; Zou, M.; Di, P.; Svistunenko, D.A.; Kurnikov, I.V. & Borisenko, G.G. (2005). Cytochrome *c* acts as a cardiolipin oxygenase required for release of proapoptotic factors. *Nat. Chem. Biol.*, 1, 223-232.

[28] Schug, Z.T. & Gottlieb, E. (2009). Cardiolipin acts as a mitochondrial signaling platform to launch apoptosis. *Biochim. Biophys. Acta,* 1788, 2022-2031.

[29] Godoy, L.C.; Muñoz-Pinedo, C.; Castro, L.; Cardaci, S.; Schonhoff, C.M.; King, M.; Tórtora, V.; Marín, M., Miao, Q.; Jiang, J.F.; Kapralov, A.; Jemmerson, R.; Silkstone, G.G.; Patel, J.N.; Evans, J.E.; Wilson, M.T.; Green, D.R.; Kagan, V.E.; Radi, R. & Mannick, J.B. (2009). Disruption of the M80-Fe ligation stimulates the translocation of cytochrome *c* to the cytoplasm and nucleus in nonapoptotic cells. *Proc. Natl. Acad. Sci.* (USA), 106, 2653-2658.

[30] Kapetanaki, S.M.; Silkstone, G.; Husu, I.; Liebl, U.; Wilson, M.T. & Vos, M.H. (2009). Interaction of carbon monoxide with the apoptosis-inducing cytochrome *c*-cardiolipin complex. *Biochemistry*, 48, 1613-1619.

[31] Silkstone, G.; Kapetanaki, S.M.; Husu, I.; Vos, M.H. & Wilson, M.T. (2010). Nitric oxide binds to the proximal heme coordination site of the

ferrocytochrome c/cardiolipin complex: formation mechanism and dynamics. *J. Biol. Chem.,* 285, 19785-19792.

[32]   Ascenzi, P.; Ciaccio, C.; Sinibaldi, F.; Santucci, R. & Coletta, M. (2011). Cardiolipin modulates allosterically peronytrite detoxification by horse heart cytochrome c. *Biochim. Biophys. Res. Comm.,* 404, 190-194.

[33]   Kapralov, A.A.; Kurnikov, I.V.; Vlasova, I.I.; Belikova, N.A.; Tyurin, V.A.; Basova, L.V.; Zhao, Q.; Taurina, Y.Y.; Jiang, J.; Bayir, H.; Vladimirov, Y.A. & Kagan, V.E. (2007). The hierarchy of structural transitions induced in cytochrome c by anionic phospholipids determines its peroxidase activation and selective peroxidation during apoptosis in cells. *Biochemistry,* 46, 14232-14244.

[34]   Belikova, N.A.; Tyurina, Y.Y.; Borisenko, G.; Tyurin, V.; Samhan Arias A.K.; Yanamala, N.; Furtmüller, P.G.; Klein-Seetharaman, J.; Obinger, C. & Kagan, V.E. (2009). Heterolytic reduction of fatty acid hydroperoxides by cytochrome c/cardiolipin complexes: antioxidant function in mitochondria. *J. Am. Chem.Soc.,* 131, 11288-11289.

[35]   Patriarca, A.; Eliseo, T.; Sinibaldi, F.; Piro, M.C.; Melis, R.; Paci, M.; Cicero, D.O.; Polticelli, F.; Santucci, R. & Fiorucci, L. (2009). ATP acts as a regulatory effector in modulating structural transitions of cytochrome c: implications for apoptotic activity. *Biochemistry,* 48, 3279-3287.

[36]   Patriarca, A.; Polticelli, F.; Piro, M.C.; Sinibaldi, F.; Mei, G.; Bari, M.; Santucci, R. & Fiorucci, L.(2012) Conversion of cytochrome c into a peroxidase: inhibitory mechanisms and implication for neurodegenerative diseases *Arch. Biochem. Biophys.,* 522,62-69.

[37]   Snider, E.J.; Muenzner, J.; Toffey, J.R.; Hong, Y. & Pletneva, E. (2013). Multifaceted effects of ATP on cardiolipin-bound cytochrome c. *Biochemistry* 12, 993-995.

[38]   Ascenzi, P.; Santucci, R.; Coletta, M. & Polticelli, F. (2010). Cytochromes: reactivity of the 'dark side' of the heme. *Biophys. Chem.,* 152, 21-27.

[39]   Vladimirov, Y.A.; Proskurnina, E.V.; Izmailov, D.Y.; Novikov, A.A.; Brusnichkin, A.V.; Osipov, A.N. & Kagan, V.E. (2006). Cardiolipin activates cytochrome c peroxidase activity since it facilitates H_2O_2 access to heme. *Biochemistry* (Moscow), 71, 998-1005.

[40]   Polyak, K.; Xia, Y.; Zweier J.L.; Kinzler, K.W. & Vogelstein, B. (1997). A model for p53-induced apoptosis. *Nature,* 389, 300-305.

[41] Shidoji, Y.; Hayashi, K.; Komura, S.; Ohishi, N. & Yagi, K. (1999). Loss of molecular interaction between cytochrome c and cardiolipin due to lipid peroxidation. *Biochim. Biophys. Res. Comm.,* 264, 343-347.

[42] Kiebish, M.A.; Han, X.; Cheng, H.; Chuang, J.H. & Seyfried, T.N. (2008). Brain mitochondrial lipid abnormalities in mice susceptible to spontaneous gliomas. *Lipids,* 43, 951-959.

[43] Kiebish, M.A.; Han, X.; Cheng, H.; Chuang, J.H. & Seyfried, T.N. (2008). Cardiolipin and electron transport chain abnormalities in mouse brain tumor mitochondria: lipidomic evidence supporting the Warburg theory of cancer. *J. Lipid Res.,* 49, 2545-2556.

[44] Barbosa, A.; Machado, N.G.; Skildum, A.J.; Scott, P.M. & Oliveira, P.J. (2012). Mitochondrial remodeling in cancer metabolism and survival: potential for new therapies. *Biochim. Biophys. Acta,* 1826, 238–254.

[45] Dumas, J-F.; Peyta, L.; Couet, C. & Servais S. (2013). Implication of liver cardiolipins in mitochondrial energy metabolism disorder in cancer cachexia. *Biochimie,* 95, 27-32.

[46] Mok, A. Y. (1993). Comparative studies of CDP-diacylglycerol synthase in rat liver mitochondria and microsomes. *Biochem. Cell Biol.,* 71, 183–189.

[47] Kawasaki, K.; Kuge, O.; Chang, S.C.; Heacock, P.N.; Rho, M.; Suzuki, K.; Nishijima, M. & Dowan, W. (1999). Isolation of a chinese hamster ovary (CHO) cDNA encoding phosphatidylglycerophosphate (PGP) synthase, expression of which corrects the mitochondrial abnormalities of a PGP synthase-defective mutant of CHO-K1 cells. *J. Biol. Chem.,* 274, 1828-1834.

[48] Serricchio, M. & Bütikofer, P. (2013). Phosphatidylglycerophosphate synthase associates with a mitochondrial inner membrane complex and is essential for growth of Trypanosoma brucei. *Mol. Microbiol.,* 87, 569-579.

[49] Schlame, M. (2008). Cardiolipin synthesis for the assembly of bacterial and mitochondrial membranes. *J. Lipid Res.,* 49, 1607-1620.

[50] Schlame, M. & Ren, M. (2009). The role of cardiolipin in the structural organization of mitochondrial membranes. *Biochim. Biophys. Acta,* 1788, 2080-2083.

[51] Mancuso, D.J.; Sims, H.F.; Yang, K.; Kiebish, M.A.; Su, X.; Jenkins, C.M.; Guan, S.; Moon, S.H.; Pietka, T.; Nassir, F.; Schappe, T.; Moore, K.; Han, X.; Abumrad, N.A. & Gross, R.W. (2010). Genetic ablation of calcium-independent phospholipase A2gamma prevents obesity and insulin resistance during high fat feeding by mitochondrial uncoupling

and increased adipocyte fatty acid oxidation. *J. Biol. Chem.,* 285, 36495-36510.

[52] Ventrella, A.; Catucci, L.; Mascolo, G.; Corcelli, A. & Agostiano, A. (2007). Isolation and characterization of lipids strictly associated to PSII complexes: focus on cardiolipin structural and functional role. *Biochim. Biophys. Acta,* 1768, 1620–1627.

[53] Barth, P.G.; Wanders, R.J. & Vreken, P. (1999). X-linked cardioskeletal myopathy and neutropenia (Barth syndrome)-MIM 302060. *J. Pediatr.,* 135, 273-276.

[54] Vreken, P.; Valianpour, F.; Nijtmans, L.G.; Grivell, L.A.; Plecko, B.; Wanders, R.J. & Barth, P.G. (2000). Defective remodeling of cardiolipin and phosphatidylglycerol in Barth syndrome. *Biochem. Biophys. Res. Comm.,* 279, 378-382.

[55] Gonzalvez, F.; D'Aurelio, M.; Boutant, M.; Moustapha, A.; Puech, J.P.; Landes, T.; Arnauné-Pelloquin, L.; Vial, G.; Taleux, N.; Slomianny, C.; Wanders, R.J.; Houtkooper, R.H.; Bellenguer P.; Møller, I.M.; Gottlieb, E.; Vaz, F.M.; Manfredi, G. & Petit, P.X. (2013). Barth syndrome: Cellular compensation of mitochondrial dysfunction and apoptosis inhibition due to changes in cardiolipin remodeling linked to tafazzin (TAZ) gene mutation. *Biochim Biophys. Acta,* 1832, 1194-1206.

[56] D'Aurelio, M.; Gajewski, C.D.; Lenaz, G. & Manfredi, G. (2006). Respiratory chain super-complexes set the threshold for respiration defects in human mtDNA mutant cybrids. *Hum. Mol. Genet.,* 15, 2157-2169.

[57] Sparagna, G.C.; Chicco, A.J.; Murphy, R.C.; Bristow, M.R.; Johnson, C.A.; Rees, M.L.; Maxey, M.L.; McCune, S.A. & Moore, R.L. (2007). Loss of cardiac tetralinoleoyl cardiolipin in human and experimental heart failure. *J. Lipid Res.,* 48, 1559-1570.

[58] Saini-Chohan, H. K.; Holmes, M.G.; Chicco, A.J.; Taylor, W.A.; Moore, R.L.; McCune, S.A.; Hickson-Bick, D.L.; Hatch, G.M. & Sparagna, G.C. (2009). Cardiolipin biosynthesis and remodeling enzymes are altered during development of heart failure. *J. Lipid Res.,* 50, 1600-1608.

[59] Tamura, Y. & Endo, T. (2013). Unveiling the last missing link of the cardiolipin synthetic pathway in mitochondria. *Aging,* 5, 392-393.

[60] Bayir, H.; Kapralov, A.A.; Jiang, J.; Huang, Z.; Taurina, Y.Y.; Tyurin, V.A.; Zhao, Q.; Belikova, N.A.; Vlasova, I.I.; Maeda, A.; Zhu, J.; Na, H.M.; Mastroberardino, P.G.; Sparvero, L.J.; Amoscato, A.A.; Chu, C.T.; Greenamyre, J.T. & Kagan, V.E. (2009). Peroxidase mechanism of

lipid-dependent cross-linking of synuclein with cytochrome c: protection against apoptosis versus delayed oxidative stress in Parkinson disease. *J. Biol. Chem.* 284, 15951-15969.

[61] Alakoskela, J.M.; Jutila, A.; Simonsen, A.C.; Pirneskoski, J.; Pyhajoki, S.; Turunen, R.; Marttila, S.; Mouritsen, O.G.; Goormaghtigh, E. & Kinnunen, P.K.J. (2006). Characteristics of fibers formed by cytochrome c and induced by anionic phospholipids. *Biochemistry,* 45, 13447-13453.

[62] Tofoleanu, F. & Buchete, N.V. (2012). Alzheimer Aβ peptide interactions with lipid membranes: fibrils, oligomers and polymorphicamyloid channels. *Prion,* 6, 339-345.

[63] Camilleri, A., Zarb, C.; Caruana, M.; Ostermeier, U.; Ghio, S.; Högen, T.; Schmidt, F.; Giese, A. & Vassallo, N. (2013). Mitochondrial membrane permeabilisation by amyloid aggregates and protection by polyphenols. *Biochim. Biophys. Acta,* 1828, 2532-2543.

[64] Lee, I.; Salomon, A.R.; Yu, K.; Doan, J.W.; Grossman, L.I. & Hüttemann, M. (2006). New prospects for an old enzyme: mammalian cytochrome c is tyrosine-phosphorylated in vivo. *Biochemistry,* 45, 9121-9128.

[65] Yu, H.; Lee, I.; Salomon, A.R.; Yu, K. & Hüttemann, M. (2008). Mammalian liver cytochrome c is tyrosine-48 phosphorylated in vivo, inhibiting mitochondrial respiration. *Biochim. Biophys. Acta,* 1777, 1066-1071.

[66] Pecina, P.; Borisenko, G.G.; Belikova, N.A.; Tyurina, Y.Y.; Pecinova, A.; Lee, I.; Samhan-Arias, A.K.; Przyklenk, K.; Kagan, V.E.; Hüttemann, M. (2010). Phosphomimetic substitution of cytochrome c tyrosine 48 decreases respiration and binding to cardiolipin and abolishes ability to trigger downstream caspase activation. *Biochemistry,* 49, 6705-6714.

[67] Everse, J. &, Coates, P.W. (2009). Neurodegeneration and peroxidases. *Neurobiol. Aging,* 30, 1011-1025.

[68] Santucci, R.; Sinibaldi, F.; Patriarca, A.; Santucci, D. & Fiorucci L. (2010). Misfolded proteins and neurodegeneration: role of non-native cytochrome c in cell death. *Exp. Rev. Proteom.,* 7, 507-517.

[69] Garcia-Martinez, E.M.; Sanz-Blasco, S.; Karachitos, A.; Bandez, M.J.; Fernandez-Gomez, F.J.; Perez-Alvarez, S.; de Mera, R.M.; Jordan, M.J.; Aguirre, N.; Galindo, M.F.; Villalobos, C.; Navarro, A.; Kmita, H. & Jordán, J. (2010). Mitochondria and calcium flux as targets of neuroprotection caused by minocycline in cerebellar granule cells. *Biochem. Pharmacol.,* 79, 239-250.

[70] Kagan, V.E.; Wipf, P.; Stoyanovsky, D.; Greenberger, J.S.; Borisenko, G.; Belikova, N.A.; Yanamala, N.; Samhan Arias, A.K.; Tungekar, M.A.; Jiang, J.; Tyurina, Y.Y.; Ji, J.; Klein-Seetharaman, J.; Pitt, B.R.; Shvedova, A.A. & Bayir, H. (2009). Mitochondrial targeting of electron scavenging antioxidants: regulation of selective oxidation *vs* random chain reactions. *Adv. Drug Deliv. Rev.* 61, 1375-1385.

[71] Kagan, V.E.; Bayir, A.; Bayir, H.; Stoyanovsky, D.; Borisenko, G.G.;. Tyurina, Y.Y.; Wipf, P.; Atkinson, J.; Greenberger, J.S.; Chapkin, R.S. & Belikova N.A. (2009) Mitochondria-targeted disruptors and inhibitors of cytochrome *c*/cardiolipin peroxidase complexes. *Mol. Nutr. Food Res.* 53, 104–114.

[72] Guex, N. & Peitsch, M.C. (1997) SWISS-MODEL and the Swiss-PdbViewer: an environment for comparative protein modeling. *Electrophoresis* 18, 2714-2723.

In: Cytochromes b and c
Editor: Rurik Thom

ISBN: 978-1-63117-467-4
© 2014 Nova Science Publishers, Inc.

Chapter 4

THE ROLE OF CYTOCHROME C IN APOPTOSIS: RECENT REVELATIONS

*Thomas Brittain**

School of Biological Sciences, University of Auckland,
Auckland, New Zealand

ABSTRACT

For many decades mitochondrial cytochrome c was assumed to have a single biological role, namely the transfer of electrons from Q-cytochrome c oxido-reductase (cytochrome bc_1) to cytochrome c oxidase in the electron transfer chain responsible for the production of the mitochondrial proton motive gradient. In this chapter we explore the growing range of functions which have been identified for cytochrome c. For example, cytochrome c has been shown to interact with specific lipid molecules which induce peroxidase enzymic activity in the protein. More recently cytochrome c has been shown to have a major role in apoptosis, following its stimulated release from mitochondria into the cytosol, where it provides a 'feed forward' amplification cascade. Evidence is also now emerging that the pro-apoptotic action of cytosolic cytochrome c, at least in some cells, can be further modulated by its reactions with other heme proteins.

* Correspondence: T. Brittain. School of Biological Sciences, University of Auckland, Auckland, New Zealand. T.Brittain@auckland.ac.nz.

INTRODUCTION

Cytochrome c is a small (12.3k Dalton) heme containing protein. The c type heme is attached covalently to the protein *via* two thioether links to protein cysteine residues. The protein is extremely basic, with a pI of 10.2 and is consequently very soluble. The heme group normally undergoes a simple ferrous/ferric transition with a redox potential of 250 mV. For over half a century cytochrome c has been identified as playing an important role in the mitochondrial electron transfer chain, which is employed to convert the redox energy of substrates such as NADH to the synthesis of ATP *via* the generation and dissipation of the mitochondrial proton motive potential. Within this context cytochrome c is found within the mitochondrial inter-membrane space. The role of cytochrome c in the electron transfer chain is to accept electrons from Q-cytochrome c oxido-reductase (cytochrome bc_1) and to pass four of them on to the terminal cytochrome c oxidase which uses them to reduce oxygen to water. In order to carry out this process cytochrome c (the only water soluble member of the mitochondrial electron transfer chain) undergoes a single electron reduction from the ferric to the ferrous state and transfers a single electron to cytochrome c oxidase in a series of four cycles before cytochrome oxidase is sufficiently charged with electrons to carry out the reduction of a single molecule of oxygen to water. For many years it was considered that this electron shuttle function of cytochrome c was its sole biological role. Over the past, more recent years, however it has become apparent that cytochrome c does in fact perform a number of important tasks, which will be the subject of this chapter (Huttermann et al. 2011). In particular cytochrome c has been shown to have a pivotal role in the process of programmed cell death, known as apoptosis, and its role in this pathway will be the prime focus of this discussion of cytochrome c's recently identified biological roles. However, in order to fully appreciate the role played by cytochrome c in apoptotic, programmed cell death, it is crucial to recognize the other biological roles played by cytochrome c. This is critical for, as will be shown, the activity of cytochrome c in the apoptotic pathway is dependent on its structure and redox status and each of these properties can be modified by its actions in biological processes not directly linked to the action of the mitochondrial electron transfer chain as well as by its participation in the electron transfer chain..

1. NON APOPTOTIC LINKED FUNCTIONS

a. Regulation of Electron Flow

It has been shown that not only does cytochrome *c* play a passive role as an electron carrier in the mitochondrial electron transfer chain but it also has regulatory roles in this most important biological process. This is particularly important as the transfer of electrons to cytochrome *c* oxidase, under physiological conditions, appears to be the rate limiting step in the electron transfer chain (Villani and Attardi 1997, Villani et al. 1998, Acin-Perez et al. 2003, Piccoli et al. 2006, Dalmonte et al. 2009). Thus control by regulation of cytochrome c activity controls the rate of the whole electron transfer chain and hence ATP generation. Regulation of cytochrome c activity is achieved by both allosteric mechanisms and by phosphorylation of the cytochrome *c* protein. Allosteric control is achieved by feedback inhibition by ATP binding to cytochrome *c* at Arg91. This binding reduces the charge interactions with cytochrome c oxidase and so leads to a slowing of the electron transfer chain (Craig and Wallace 1995, Tuominen et al. 2001, Patriarca et al. 2009).

This process provides a mechanism for adjusting the rate of electron flow in response to the energy state of the mitochondrion as expressed in terms of the ATP/ADP ratio.

At a different level the action of cytochrome *c* in the electron transfer chain is regulated by phosphorylation processes. Although specific sites have been identified, for the phosphorylation of cytochrome *c* at particular residues, the responsible kinases and phosphatases associated with these processes and their associated signaling pathways are as yet unidentified. Furthermore, the Tyr phosphorylation processes show tissue specificity. Cytochrome *c* obtained from heart tissue has been reported to be phosphorylated on Tyr97 (Lee et al., 2006), whilst in the liver phosphorylation occurs on Tyr48. Phosphorylation of Tyr97 appears to modify the binding of Met80 to the heme iron atom of cytochrome *c* and so suggests a mechanism for the alteration of the heme redox potential (Lee et al., 2006). Both phosphorylation of Tyr97 and Tyr48 significantly reduce the turnover of cytochrome *c* (Yu et al., 2008). In the case of skeletal muscle cytochrome *c* is phosphorylated on Thr28 and Ser47 although no details of the impact of these modifications have been reported (Zhao et al., 2010).

As phosphorylation of cytochrome will not only alter its overall charge but also change site specific charge distribution this process may well also alter its interactions with other proteins and as such affect its actions in the process of apoptosis (see below).

b. Scavenging of Reactive Oxygen Species

By its very nature, the operation of the mitochondrial electron transfer chain leads to the production of unwanted, reactive, side products. The redox cycling of the many electron transfer centres contained within the electron transfer complexes, in the presence of oxygen, leads inevitably to the side reaction production of reactive oxygen species (ROS). In deed between one and two percent of all the oxygen consumed in the mitochondrion is converted to ROS products, mainly by complexes I and III (Papa and Skulachev, 1997, Atlante et al. 2001, Shigenaga et al. 1994). These products are potential very damaging to the cell either through direct reaction with other cellular components or else through the initiation of programmed cell death (see below). The two main products are hydrogen peroxide and super oxide. The capacity of ferric cytochrome c to accept electrons from the super oxide radical has long been recognized (Butler et al. 1982). The reaction between superoxide and ferri-cytochrome c is extremely rapid. Cytochrome c is present within the inter-membrane space at a concentration of approximately 1 mM and reacts with superoxide with a rate constant of approximately $10^7 \, M^{-1} \, s^{-1}$ (Turrens, 2003, Andreyev et al. 2005 Butler et al. 1982). In the inter-membrane space of the mitochondrion this reaction converts superoxide into oxygen and the reduced cytochrome c can then inject the electron into the electron transfer chain (Korshunov et al. 1999, Pereverzev et al. 2003). Hydrogen peroxide can be scavenged by cytochrome c when it is in either the ferric or ferrous state. In the ferric state cytochrome c scavenges hydrogen peroxide via its intrinsic peroxidase activity and although the bimolecular rate of reaction is rather low the high concentration of cytochrome c ,within the inter-membrane space, allows this reaction to be appreciable (Sedlak et al. 2010) It is important to note that this low level peroxidase activity differs from that seen in the reaction with cardiolipin (see below) in which the peroxidase activity of cytochrome c is significantly increased following reaction with lipid. In the case of the ferro-form of the protein cytochrome c has been reported as scavenging hydrogen peroxide (Wang et al. 2003) however, the mechanism of this reaction has not been established.

c. Facilitating Mitochondrial Protein Import

Cytochrome *c* can also input electrons into the electron transport chain which are derived from its role as an oxidizing agent in the process of protein import into the mitochondrion. As the functioning of the mitochondrion relies significantly on imported proteins, the majority of which are nuclear encoded and synthesized in the cytosol, this organelle has a complex set of import mechanisms. Many proteins are imported through specific translocases. This process commonly requires restructuring of the transported proteins by means of disulphide bond formation (Chacinska et al. 2004). This oxidative process involves a small electron transfer chain which terminates in electron acceptance by ferricytochrome *c* (Allen et al. 2005). The reduced cytochrome *c* product then feeds its electron into the mitochondrial electron transfer chain.

Whatever the particular case, be it ROS scavenging or facilitating protein import, each of these roles can be expected to modify the redox status of cytochrome c, independent of the mitochondrial electron transfer chain, and as such influence its apoptotic role (see below).

2. FUNCTIONS RELATED TO APOPTOSIS

In order to fully understand the role of cytochrome *c* in the process of apoptosis it is important to first review the nature of cytochrome *c* as found in the mitochondrial inter-membrane space. Within the inter-membrane space cytochrome *c* is present at a concentration of approximately 1mM. The redox status of cytochrome *c* will, in the main, be determined by the activity of the mitochondrial electron transfer chain *i.e.* the rate of oxygen reduction and the availability of reducing substrates. Recent cell culture studies suggest that under normoxic conditions mitochondrial cytochrome *c* is approximately 60% oxidized (Ripple et al. 2010). Physically, cytochrome *c* is present in the inter-membrane space in one of three separate physical states which are in equilibrium. Cytochrome *c* can be present in a freely mobile form within the inter-membrane space or it can be tightly bound to membrane lipid via specific binding to cardiolipin (see below and Figure 2) or loosely electrostatically bound to other components of the mitochondrial membrane. It should be noted however that even "the freely" mobile form of cytochrome *c* is likely to be spatially confined within the folds of the cristae. It now appears that the cristae rather than being simple folded structures actually consist of partially closed sacks sealed by the protein OPA1 (Scorrano et al., 2002, Frey and Mannella 2000, Frezza et al., 2006).

a. Specific Interaction between Cytochrome C and Cardiolipin

It has long been recognized that cytochrome c interacts specifically with the mitochondrial "signature" lipid cardiolipin (Rietveld et al. 1983, Selishcheva et al., 1978, Selishcheva et al., 1977, Noell 1976) (see Figure 1). Cardiolipin (1,3-bis(sn-3'-phosphatidyl)-sn-glycerol) is a diphosphatidyl-glycerol found only in the mitochondrion in eukaryotes where it constitutes approximately 20% of the mitochondrial phospholipids. In normal cells about 80% of the mitochondrial cardiolipin is associated with the inner mitochondrial membrane. Because of cardiolipin's unique structure it is capable of forming a number of different aggregates.

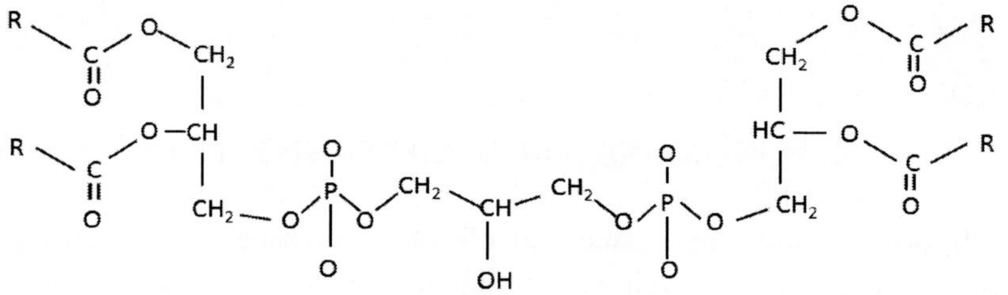

Figure 1. Cardiolipin. In most tissues, cardiolipin contains R groups which are almost exclusively 18 carbon fatty acids, (80% of this is typically linoleic acid (18:2(n-6)). In testis cardiolipin contains mainly palmitic acid, while cardiolipin in the brain contains more fatty acids including arachidonic and docosahexaenoic acids.

The interaction of cytochrome c and cardiolipin involves at least two sites. A low affinity site involves a number of surface Lys residues of cytochrome c (Kagan et al., 2009) and electrostatic forces with the negatively charges cardiolipin. This interaction is sensitive to the presence of ATP, which weakens the interaction (Rytomaa and Paavo, 1995, Sinibaldi et al., 2008) The second high affinity site involves hydrophobic interactions in which a side chain of cardiolipin is inserted into the hydrophobic core of the cytochrome c protein (Rajagopal et al., 2012, Sinibaldi et al., 2010). These two interactions lead sequentially to the destabilization of the cytochrome c protein structure and subsequent weakening or breaking of the heme iron Met80 bond generating a five coordinate structure capable of binding small gaseous ligands such as NO, CO or O_2 (Spooner and Watts, 1991a; Spooner and Watts, 1991b; Kapetanaki et al., 2009; Simon et al., 2013; Silkstone et al., 2012). The breaking of the Met80 heme iron bond also produces a shift in the redox potential of the cytochrome *c* by 350-400 mV (Basova et al., 2007). The shift in redox potential coupled with the increased access to the ferrous heme iron by oxygen leads to the generation of significant peroxidase activity in the cardiolipin/cytochrome c complex (Kapralov et al., 2007; Vladimirov et al., 2006; Belikova et al., 2006; Kagan et al., 2005; Kagan et al., 2004). Consequently in the presence of hydrogen peroxide the bound cardiolipin can become oxygenated to the cardiolipin hydroperoxidase (Nakagawa, 2013). Evidence has been presented which supports the suggestion that the peroxidase activity of the cardiolipin/cytochrome *c* complex follows the same reaction mechanism as the classical peroxidases, namely peroxide oxidation of the cytochrome *c* heme ferric iron to the oxyferryl state, accompanied by the formation of a porphyrin radical to yield "compound 1" followed by electron transfer to produce "compound 2" in which the heme iron remains ferryl but the porphyrin radical is transferred to a local Tyr residue. Radical transfer then proceeds to the formation of the cardiolipin radical which reacts with molecular oxygen to yield the cardiolipin hydroperoxide (Tyurina et al., 2006; Karpalov et al., 2011). The cardiolipin hydroperoxide binds more weakly to cytochrome *c* than the cardiolipin molecule and so dissociates (Shidoji et al., 1999).

b. Release of Cytochrome *C* from the Mitochondrion

Following oxidation cardiolipin moves to the outer membrane of the mitochondrion (Korytowski et al., 2011) such that following activation of the mitochondrion almost 40% cardiolipin previously in the inner membrane translocates to the outer membrane of the mitochondrion Kagan et al., 2006). This significantly alters the properties of the outer membrane and their interactions with cytosolic proteins. In particular, the presence of cardiolipin in the outer membrane leads to binding of tBid (Gonzalvez et al., 2010; Petit et al., 2009; Liu et al., 2005; Liu et al., 2004; Lutter et al., 2000; Korsmeyer et al., 2000) and other Bcl-2 family member (Yin and Zhu, 2012; Jiang et al., 2008; Kuwana et al., 2002). These interactions then lead to Mitochondrial Apoptosis-Induced Channel (or MAC) membrane pore formation (Korytowski et al., 2011; Schug and Gottlieb, 2009) and consequent release of cytochrome *c* into the cytosol (Figure 2). In this way, *via*, the series of steps outlined above, an increase in hydrogen peroxide production within the mitochondrion leads to the permeablization of the outer mitochondrial membrane and release of inter-membrane cytochrome c into the cytosol. The cytochrome c released is not only that previously attached to cardiolipin but also that normally confined in the cristae sacks, as binding of Bak and Bax (see Figure 4) (Ott et al., 2007; Kuwana et al., 2002; Wolter et al., 1997) to the outer mitochondrial membrane also breaks down the oligomerized OPA1 (see 2) above) thus opening the cristae sacks to the general inter-membrane space (Delivani and Martin, 2006). There is evidence that the release of cytochrome c from mitochondria may be different under different stress conditions (Gogvadze et al., 2006; Yamamoto et al., 2012; Garrido et al., 2006; Lim et al., 2002; Dejean et al., 2006; Ott et al., 2002). Furthermore, it also appears that the release of cytochrome c from the mitochondrion is not an "all-or-nothing" event and that different stimuli lead not only to different amounts of cytochrome c release but also to multiphasic release responses (Ott et al., 2002), presumably corresponding to the mobilisation of lipid associated and non-associated cytochrome c pools.

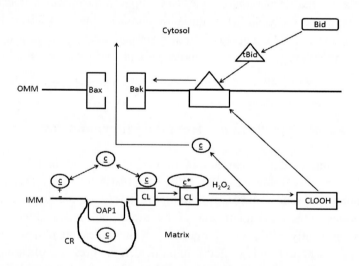

Figure 2. The various forms of cytochrome c and their interactions. Cytochrome c (c) can be constrained in the mitochondrial cristae (CR) by the actions of OAP1. Cytochrome c in the inter-membrane space is in equilibrium with forms electrostatically bound to the inner membrane (IMM) and to forms tightly bound to cardiolipin (CL). Reaction with hydrogen peroxide produces the Hydroperoxy lipid (CLOOH) which can transfer to the outer mitochondrial membrane (OMM) where it promotes aggregation of tBid. tBid then facilitates the formation of pores by oligomerization of Bak leading to release of cytochrome c into the cytosol.

Cytochrome *c* may also be released from mitochondria by an alternative mechanism.

It is now recognised that the mitochondrion plays a significant role is the maintenance of calcium ion homeostasis and as such sees significant calcium transport (Decuypere et al., 2011). In situation in which cytosolic calcium homeostasis is compromised there exists a risk of mitochondrial calcium ion overload, which may result in the induction of cell death. At high calcium concentrations the mitochondrial permeability transition pore (PTP) in the inner mitochondrial membrane opens (Rasola and Bernardi, 2007; Azzolin et al., 2010). The opening of the PTP leads to the release of ions, including calcium, and metabolites including ATP, mitochondrial depolarization, an increase in ROS production, cessation of oxidative phosphorylation followed by ATP hydrolysis, matrix swelling due to osmotic forces, remodelling of the inner mitochondrial membrane, and finally rupture of the outer mitochondrial membrane and thus cytochrome release (Rasola et al., 2010).

c. Apoptosis

During the average day a normal, health, adult human destroys of the order of 10^{10} cells, simply to remove damaged and aged cells. One of the major processes employed in this task is programmed cell death or apoptosis. Apoptosis is a process whereby stimulated cells initiate a complex series of reactions which lead to the activation of a number of self-destructive proteases known of caspases. The activated caspases then dismantle the macro-molecular elements within the cell leading to its ultimate fragmentation and disposal. Apoptosis itself can occur by one of two routes. In the first pathway, known as the extrinsic pathway, extracellular signals are received by the so called death receptors which, *via* a relatively direct route, leads to activation of the caspase enzymes and hence cell destruction. In the alternative pathway, predominately intracellular stressors lead to activation of mitochondrial responses such as increased ROS production. As outlined above, such changes can lead to the release of cytochrome *c* into the cytosol. On entering the cytosol cytochrome *c* encounters the protein Apaf-1. Cytochrome *c* binds to Apaf-1 in the presence of ATP or deoxyATP this initial complex undergoes an oligomerization reaction to yield a heptameric macro-complex known as the apoptosome. The apoptosome then recruits, binds and activates pro-caspase9. Activated caspase9 then activates the, so called, executioner caspase3, which degrades the macromolecular structures of the cell. In this way the release of cytochrome c from the mitochondrion plays a pivotal role in connecting the signal activation of the mitochondrion with the commitment to self-destruction by the cell. The key reaction of binding of cytochrome c and Apaf-1 shows some key characteristics. The binding of cytochrome c is high affinity (K= 10^{-8} M, Purring et al., 1999). Just as importantly the binding process requires cytochrome c to be in the oxidized or ferric state (Borutaite and Brown, 2007; Brittain, 2012). Cytochrome c will normally be released into the cytosol as a mixture of the pro-aptotic ferric and non-apoptotic ferrous states depending on the internal redox status of the mitochondrion (approximately 60% ferric; Ripple et al., 2010)

Once in the cytosol, the pro-apoptotic ferric form of cytochrome c, due to its high redox potential (+250 mV) can be reduced by cytosolic reductant. The committal of a cell to the apoptotic process thus depends on the relative amount of cytochrome c released from a mitochondrion, the balance of ferric and ferrous forms, the redox status of the cytosol and the rate of reaction with Apaf-1.

On its release from the mitochondrion cytochrome c can also activate another crucial processes which relates to apoptosis. Through their interactions with mitochondria, calcium ions (Ca^{2+}) can also promote the apoptotic process in an auto-catalytic fashion. Within cells a major contributor to calcium homeostasis is the release and uptake of calcium by the endoplasmic reticulum. To a large extent this is itself is controlled by the actions of the endoplasmic reticulum IP3 receptor. The type I IP3 receptor releases calcium on stimulation by IP3, but only up to a point. At higher cytosolic calcium concentrations (> approx. 0.2μM) calcium ions auto-inhibit their own further release. (Bezprozvanny et al., 1991). This process tends to maintain cytosolic concentrations to a level whereby they do not significantly perturb mitochondria actions. However cytosolic cytochrome c can bind to the endoplasmic reticulum IP3 receptor and suppress the normal feed-back inhibition of the receptor by high concentrations of calcium (Boehning and Joseph, 2000; Boehning et al., 2003; Boehning et al., 2004). Thus, just a small amount of cytochrome c released by a single mitochondrion can potentially bind to the IP3 receptor leading to a major increase in cytosolic calcium concentration. The raised calcium concentration can then activate other mitochondria to release their cytochrome c and so establish a cytochrome c release "avalanche" within the cell which leads to full commitment to cellular apoptosis. Thus, it is clear that, the process of apoptosis is extremely sensitive to cytochrome c release and so, to avoid "unwanted" cell death, the release of cytochrome c must be a rigorously controlled process.

d. Intervention in the Cytochrome *C* Activated Apoptotic Pathway

Based on the evidence outlined above, it would appear that the escape of cytochrome *c* from the mitochondrion should establish a "point of no return" in the process of committal to a*p*optosis and given the limitations described this does indeed appear to be the case in most cell types. However within the human body there are a few cells type for which the control of apoptosis is even more pressing. In brain neurons and retinal cells, both of which are essentially non replaceable, there can be no room for accidental or unnecessary activation of the apoptotic process. In these cases another level of control is put in place which ensures a higher trigger level is established for the activation of the intrinsic apoptotic pathway. As pointed out above in order to activate the apoptotic process cytochrome *c* does not only have to be released from the mitochondrion but it also must be in the ferric state (Borutaite and Brown, 2007; Brittain, 2012). It is thus possible to intercede in the propagation of the apoptotic process by rapidly reducing the newly liberated cytochrome c to the non-apoptotic ferrous form. A protein capable of rapidly reducing cytochrome *c* (Fago et al., 2006) namely neuroglobin was discovered in 2000 (Burmester et al., 2000). Neuroglobin is a small heme protein with a redox potential of -119mV which is expressed in some brain neurons and retinal cells. It reacts very rapidly with cytochrome *c* in a two-step reaction (us). Initially, neuroglobin binds to cytochrome *c* in a reaction which is driven primarily by electrostatic interactions as neuroglobin is a very acidic protein (pI = 4.9) whilst cytochrome *c* is a very basic protein (pI=10.2). Although very rapid, this binding process is quite weak (K=approx. $100\mu M$, Bonding et al., 2008) as is found in many other redox transfer protein couples (Brittain et al., 2002; Erman et al., 1997, Pelletier and Kraut, 1992; Lange and Hunte, 2002). The neuroglobin-cytochrome c complex is thus short lived, but the structure of the complex is such that internal electron transfer is a very efficient process and so the overall reaction between reduced neuroglobin and ferric cytochrome *c* is a very favourable reaction (Fago et al., 2006). In cells which contain neuroglobin it follows that release of relatively small quantities of cytochrome *c*, rather than leading to apoptosis as it would in other cells, is intercepted by the above reaction and cell death is averted. This is crucial safeguard for those cells which lack the capacity for self-replacement if exposed to low level-"accidental" stimuli (Crompton, 1999). It is important to note however that the presence of neuroglobin merely raises the threshold of cytochrome release which must be achieved before commitment to apoptosis, rather than simply "preventing" apoptosis in these cells. (Fago et al., 2008; Skommer et al., 2010; Brittain et al., 2010; Raychaudhuri et al., 2010). The negative side of this extra protection, from unwanted apoptotic action, lies in the increased potential for cancer formation. The biological conundrum is to protect the cells from unwarranted apoptosis whilst avoiding cancer formation due to the protection of damaged cells. Recent evidence has been presented which indicates that neurons and retinal cells may achieve this by controlling the steady state of reduction of neuroglobin. Preliminary experiments and modeling studies suggest that, due to the existence of a futile cycle, which involves reduction, oxygenation and autoxidation of neuroglobin (Figure 3), under normal physiological conditions the neuroglobin present in neurons will be predominantly in the ineffectual ferric state (Brittain and Skommer, 2012; Skommer et al., 2012).

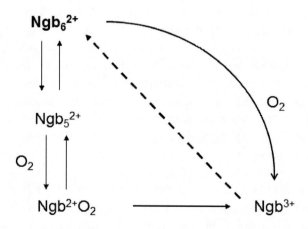

Figure 3. Neuroglobin futile redox cycle. In the presence of oxygen the anti-apoptotic hexa-co-ordinate form of neuroglobin (Ngb_6^{2+}) can either be directly oxidized to the non- active ferric form (Ngb^{3+}) or else be deactivated by oxygen following loss of one of the heme ligands (Ngb_5^{2+}) via the oxygenated form ($Ngb^{2+}O_2$). The non-active oxidized form (Ngb^{3+}) can then be returned to the active form (Ngb_6^{2+}) by reaction with cellular reductants.

During pathological challenge, such as stroke, the cellular oxygen concentration will fall drastically. Under these conditions the futile cycle will ensure rapid conversion of the neuroglobin to the anti-apoptotic ferrous form. The increase in the intracellular level of active ferrous neuroglobin then provides the means to intercept cytochrome c activated apoptosis and protect cell in the penumbra of the stroke site. The coupling of this futile redox cycle to cytochrome *c* activation thus provides a means to avoid cancer formation in under normal physiological conditions whilst providing additional protection under pathological conditions.

CONCLUSION

Although for many years considered simply to be an active member of the mitochondrial electron transfer chain cytochrome *c* is now clearly established as a key player of many crucial biological roles from protein transport to the arbiter of cell life or death (Figure 4).

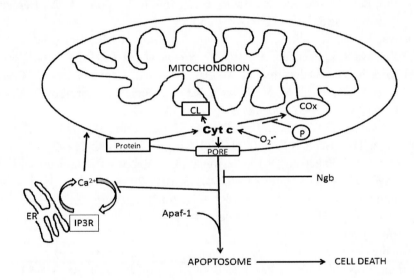

Figure 4. Schematic representation of the known actions of cytochrome *c*. Cytochrome *c* (Cyt *c*) provides electrons to cytochrome *c* oxidase (COx) in the mitochondrial electron transfer chain. This transfer is controlled allosterically by ATP and by phosphorylation of cytochrome *c* (P). Cytochrome *c* can scavenge ROS ($O_2^{\cdot-}$) and peroxidatively cleaves cardiolipin (CL). Redox dependent mitochondrial protein import (Protein) donates electrons to cytochrome *c*. Apoptotic stimuli lead to the release of cytochrome *c* through the mitochondrial outer membrane pore (Pore). In the cytosol cytochrome *c* can inhibit the feedback auto-suppression of calcium release (Ca^{2+}) from the Endoplasmic reticulum (ER) *via* interaction with the IP3 receptor (IP3R). Cytochrome *c* in the cytosol can react with Apaf-1 in the presence of ATP producing the apoptosome, which then activates proteolytic caspase enzymes leading to programmed cell death. Both of these later reactions can be inhibited by reaction of cytochrome *c* with neuroglobin (Ngb).

REFERENCES

Acin-Perez, R., Bayona-Bafaluy, M.P., Bueno, M., Machicado, C., Fernandez-Silva, P., Perez-Martos, A., Montoya, J., Lopez-Perez, M.J., Sancho, J., Enriquez, J.A., 2003, *Hum. Mol. Genet.* 12, 329–339.

Alante, A., Calissano, P., Bobba, A., Giannattasio, S., Marra, E., Passarella, S. 2001, *F.E.B.S. Lett.*, 497, 1-5.

Allen, S., Balabanidou, V., Sideris, D.P., Lisowsky, T., Tokatlidis, K., 2005, *J. Mol. Biol.* 353, 937–944.

Andreyev, A.Y., Kushnareva, Y.E., Starkov, A.A. 2005, *Biochem* (Moscow) 70, 200-214.

Azzolin, L., von Stockum, S., Basso, E., Petronilli, V., Forte, M.A., Bernardi, P. 2010, *F.E.B.S. Lett.* 584, 2504-2509.

Basova, L. V., Kurnikov, I. V., Wang, L, Ritov, V. B., Belikova, N. A., Vlasova, I. I., Pacheco, A. A.. 2007, *Biochemistry*, 46, 3423-3434.

Belikova, N. A., Vladimirov, Y. A., Osipov, A. N., Kapralov, A. A., Tyurin, V. A., Potapovich, M. V., Basova, L. V., Peterson, J, Kurnikov, I. V. and Kagan, V. E.. 2006, *Biochemistry*, 45, 4998-5009.

Bezprozvanny, I., Watras, J., Ehrlich, B.E. 1991, *Nature*, 351, 751-754.

Boehning, D., Joseph, S.K. 2000, J. Biol. Chem. 275, 21492-21499.

Boehning, D., Patterson, R.L., Sedaghat, L., Glebova, N.O., Kurosaki, T., Snyder, S.H. 2003, *Nature Cell. Biol.* 5, 1051-2061.

Boehning, D., Patterson, R.L., Snyder, S.H. 2004, *Cell Cycle* 3, 252-254.

Bonding, S.H., Henty, K., Dingley, A., Brittain, T. 2008, *Int. J. Biol. Macromol.* 43, 295-299.

Borutaite, V., Brown, G.C. 2007, *J. Biol. Chem.* 282, 31124-31130.

Brittain, T., Kidd, R.D., Baker, E.N. 2002, *J. Inorg. Biochem.* 88, 328-334.

Brittain, T. 2012, *Cells*, 1, 1133-1155.

Brittain, T., Skommer, J., Raychaudhuri, S. and Birch, N. 2010, *Int. J. Mol. Sci.,* 11, 2306-2321.

Brittain, T., Skommer, J. *2012, I.U.B.M.B. Life.* 64, 419-422.

Burmester, T., Weich, B., Reinhardt, S., and Hankeln, T. 2000, *Nature* 407, 520–523.

Butler, J., Koppenol, W.H., Margoliash, E. 1982, *J. Biol. Chem.*, 257, 10747-10750.

Chacinska, A., Pfannschmidt, S., Wiedemann, N., Kozjak, V., Sanjuan Szklarz, L.K., Schulze-Specking, A., Truscott, K.N., Guiard, B., Meisinger, C., Pfanner, N., *2004, E.M.B.O. J.* 23, 3735–3746.

Craig, D.B., Wallace, C.J., 1995, *Biochemistry* 34, 2686–2693.

Crompton, M. 1999, *Biochem. J.* 341, 233-249.

Dalmonte, M.E., Forte, E., Genova, M.L., Giuffre, A., Sarti, P., Lenaz, G., 2009, *J. Biol. Chem.* 284, 32331–32335.

Decuypere, J-P., Monaco, G., Bultynck, G., Missiaen, L., De Smedt, H., Parys, J.B. 2011, *Biochim. Biophys. Acta.* 1813, 1003-1013.

Dejean, L.M., Martinez-Caballero, S., Kinnally, K.W. 2006, *Cell Death & Diff.* 13, 1387-1395.

Delvani, P., Martin, S.J., 2006, *Cell Death & Diff.* 13, 12007-2010.

Erman, J.E., Kresheck, G.C., Vitello, L.B., Miller, M.A. 1997, *Biochemistry* 36, 4054-4060.

Fago. A., Mathews, A.J., Moens, L., Dewilde, S., Brittain .T. *2006 F.E.B.S. Letts.* 580, 4884- 4888.

Fago., A., Mathews, A.J., Brittain. T. 2008, *I.U.B.M.B. Life.* 60, 398-401.

Frey, T.G., Mannella, C.A. 2000, *Trends Biochem. Sci.* 25, 319-324.

Frezza, C., Cipolat, S., de Brito, O.M., Micaroni, M.,Beznoussenko, G.V.,Rudka, T., Bartoli, D., Polishuck, R.S., Danial, N.N., De Strooper, B., Scorrano, L., 2006, *Cell*, 126, 177-189.

Garrido, C., Galluzzi, L., Brunet, M., Puig, P. E., Didelot, C., Kroemer, G. 2006, *Cell Death & Diff.* 13, 1423-1433.

Gonzalvez, F., Pariselli, F., Jalmar, O., Dupaigne, P., Sureau, F., Dellinger, M., Hendrickson, E. A., Bernard, S., Petit, P. X. 2010, *PLoS One*, 5, Article No.: e9342.

Gogvadze, V., Orrenius, S., Zhivotovsky, B. 2006, *Biochimica et Biophysica Acta.* 1757, 639-647.

Hüttemann, M., Pecina, P., Rainbolt, M., Sanderson, T.H., Kagan, V.E., Samavati, L., Doan, J.W, Lee, I. 2011, *Mitochondrion* 11, 369-381.

Jiang, J., Huang, Z., Zhao, Q., Feng, W., Belikova, N. A. and Kagan, V. E. 2008, *Biochem. & Biophys. Res. Comm.*, 368, 145-150.

Kagan, V. E., Tyurina, Y. Y., Bayir, H., Chu, C. T., Kapralov, A. A., Vlasova, I. I., Belikova, N. A. 2006, *Chemico-Biol. Interact*, 163, 15-28.

Kagan, V. E., Borisenko, G. G., Tyurina, Y. Y., Tyurin, V. A., Jiang, J., Potapovich, A. I., Kini, V., Amoscato, A. A. and Fujii, Y. 2004, *Free Rad. Biol. & Med.*, 37, 1963-1985.

Kagan, V. E. Tyurin, V. A., Jiang, J, Jianfei,J., Tyurina, Y., Ritov, V., Amoscato, A. A., Osipov, A. 2005, *Nature Chem. Biol.*, 1, 223-232.

Kagan, V.E. Bayir, H.A., Belikova, N. A., Kapralov, O., Tyurina, Y.Y., Tyurin, V. A., Jiang, J, 2009, *Free Rad. Biol. & Med.*, 46, 1439-1453.

Kapetanaki, S.M., Silkstone, G., Husu, I., Liebl, U., Wilson, M. T., Vos, M. H. 2009, *Biochemistry*, 48 1613-1619.

Kapralov, A. A., Yanamala, N., Tyurina, Y.Y., Castro, L., Samhan-Arias, A., Vladimirov, Y.A., Maeda, A. 2011, *Biochimica et Biophysica Acta*, 1808, 2147-2155.

Kapralov, A. A., Kurnikov, I. V., Vlasova, I. I., Belikova, N. A., Tyurin, V. A., Basova, L. V., Zhao, Q. 2007. *Biochemistry*, 46, 14232-14244.

Korshunov, S.S., Krasnikov, B.F., Pereverzev, M.O., Skulachev, V.P. *1999, F.E.B.S. Lett.* 462, 192–198.

Korsmeyer, S. J., Wei, M. C., Saito, M., Weiler, S., Oh, K. J., Schlesinger, P. H. 2000, *Cell Death & Diff.*, 7, 1166-1173.

Korytowski, W, Basova, L.V., Pilat, A., Kernstock, R. M., Girotti, A. W. 2011, *J. Biol. Chem.*, 286 26334-26343.

Kuwana, T., Mackey, M.R., Perkins, G., Ellisman, M.H., Latterich, M., Schneiter, R., Green, D.R., Newmeyer, D. 2002, *Cell*, 111, 331-342.

Lange, C., Hunte,C. *2002 Proc. Natl. Acad. Sci. U.S.A.* 99, 2800-2805

Lee, I., Salomon, A.R., Yu, K., Doan, J.W., Grossman, L.I., Hüttemann, M. 2006, *Biochemistry* 45, 9121–9128.

Lim, M. L. R., Lum, M., Hansen, T. M., Roucou, X., Nagley, P. 2002 *J. Biomed. Sci.* 9, 488-506.

Liu, J., Durrant, D., Yang, H-S., He, Y., Whitby, F. G., Myszka, D. G., Lee, R.M. 2005, *Biochem & Biophys. Res. Comm.*, 330, 865-870.

Liu, J., Weiss, A., Durrant., D., Chi, N., Lee, R. M. 2004, *Apoptosis*, 9, 533-541.

Lutter, M., Fang, M., Luo, X., Nishijima, M., Xie, X. and Wang, X. 2000, *Nature Cell Biol.*, 2, 754-756.

Nakagawa, Y. 2013, *Yakugaku Zasshi,* 133, 561-574.

Noell, G.G. 1976, *J. Memb. Biol*, 27, 335-346.

Ott, M., Robertson, J.D., Gogvadze, V., Zhivotovsky, B., Orrenius, S. 2002, *Proc. Natl. Acad. Sci., U.S.A.* 99, 1259-1263.

Ott, M., Zhivotovsky, B., Orrenius, S. 2007, Cell Death & Diff., 14, 1243-1247.

Papa, S., Skulachev, V.P. 1997, *Mol. Cell. Biochem.* 174, 305-319.

Patriarca, A., Eliseo, T., Sinibaldi, F., Piro, M.C., Melis, R., Paci, M, Cicero, D.O., Polticelli, F., Santucci, R., Fiorucci, L. 2009, *Biochemistry*, 48, 3279-3287.

Pelletier, H., Kraut, J. *Science* 1992, 258, 1748–1755.

Pereverzev, M.O., Vygodina, T.V., Konstantinov, A.A., Skulachev, V.P., 2003, *Biochem. Soc. Trans.* 31, 1312–1315.

Petit, P.X., Dupaigne, P., Pariselli, F., Gonzalvez, F., Etienne, F., Rameau, C., Bernard, S. *2009, F.E.B.S.* J., 276, 6338-6354.

Piccoli, C., Scrima, R., Boffoli, D., Capitanio, N. 2006, *Biochem. J.* 396, 573–583.

Purring, C., Zou, H., Wang, X., McLendon, G. 1999, *J. Amer. Chem. Soc.* 121, 7435-7436.

Rajagopal, B.S., Silkstone, G. G., Nicholls, P., Wilson, M. T., Worrall, J. A. R. 2012, *Biochimica et Biophysica Acta*, 1817, 780-791.

Ripple, M.O., Abajian, M., Springett, R. 2010, *Apoptosis 15*, 563-573.

Rasola, A., Bernardi, P. 2007, *Apoptosis*, 12 815-833.

Rasola, M., Sciacovelli, B., Pantic, P., Bernardi, P. *2010, F.E.B.S. Lett.* 584, 1989-1996.

Raychaudhuri, S., Skommer, J., Henty, K., Birch, N., Brittain, T. 2010, *Apoptosis* 15, 401- 411.

Rietveld, A., Sijens, P., Verkleij, A.J., De Kruijff, B. 1983, *E.M.B.O. Journal*, 2, 907-914.

Rytomaa, M., Paavo K. J. 1995, *J. Biol. Chem.*, 270, 3197-3202.

Schug, Z. T., Gottlieb, E. 2009, *Biochimica et Biophysica Acta*, 1788, 2022-2031.

Scorrano, L. Ashiya, M, Buttle, K., Weiler, S., Oakes, S.A., Mannella, C. A., Korsmeyer, S. J. 2002, *Dev. Cell.* 2, 55-67.

Sedlak, E., Fabian, M., Neal, C., Robinson, N.C., Musatov, A. 2010, *Free Rad. Biol. & Med.* 49, 1574-1581.

Selishcheva, A.A., Obraztsov, V.V., Kozlov, Y.P. 1977, *Biofizika*, 22, 716-719.

Selishcheva, A.A., Obraztsov, V.V., Kozlov, Y.P. 1978, *Biokhimiya*, 43, 2047-2054.

Shidoji, Y., Hayashi, K., Komura, S., Ohishi, N., Yagi, K. 1999, *Biochem. & Biophys. Res. Com*m., 264,343-347.

Shigenaga, M.K., Hagen, T.M., Ames, B.N. 1994, *Proc. Natl. Acad. Sci., U.S.A.,* 91, 10771-10778.

Silkstone, G., Kapetanaki, S. M., Husu, I., Vos, M. H., Wilson, M. T. 2012, *Biochemistry*, 51, 6760-6766.

Simon, M., Metzinger-Le M., Valerie, C., Soizic, D.O., Bondon, A. 2013, *J. Biol. Inorg. Chem*, 18, 27-38.

Sinibaldi, F., Fiorucci, L., Patriarca, A., Lauceri, R., Ferri, T., Coletta, M., and Santucci, R. 2008, *Biochemistry*, 47, 6928-6935.

Sinibaldi, F., Howes, B. D., Piro, M. C., Polticelli, F., Bombelli, C., Ferri, T., Coletta, M., Smulevich, G., Santucci, R. 2010, *J. Biol. Inorg. Chem.*, 15, 689-700.

Skommer, J., Brittain, T. and Raychaudhuri, S. 2010, *Apoptosis15*, 1223-1233.

Skommer, J., Helbo, S., Henty, K., Brittain, T. 2012 *Int. J. Biol. Macromol.* 51, 284-290.

Spooner, P.J.R., Watts, A.1991a, *Biochemistry*, 30, 3871-3879.

Spooner, P.J.R., Watts, A. 1991b, *Biochemistry*, 30, 3880-3885.

Tuominen, E.K., Zhu, K., Wallace, C.J., Clark-Lewis, I., Craig, D.B., Rytomaa, M., Kinnunen, P.K., 2001, *J. Biol. Chem.* 276, 19356–19362.

Turrens, J.F. 2003, *J. Physiol.* 552, 335-344.

Tyurina, Y.Y., Kini, V., Tyurin, V.A., Vlasova, I.I., Jiang, J., Kapralov, A.A., Belikova, N.A., Yalowich, J.C., Kurnikov, I.V., Kagan, V.E., 2006, *Mol. Pharmacol.* 70, 706–717.

Villani, G., Attardi, G., 1997, *Proc. Natl. Acad. Sci. U.S.A.,* 94, 1166–1171.

Villani, G., Greco, M., Papa, S., Attardi, G., 1998, *J. Biol. Chem.*, 273, 31829–31836.

Vladimirov, Y. A., Proskurnina, E. V., Izmailov, D. Y., Novikov, A. A., Brusnichkin, A. V., Osipov, A. N. Kagan, V. E.. 2006, *Biochemistry* (Moscow), 71, 989-997.

Wang, Z.B., Li, M., Zhao, Y., Xu, J.X. 2003, *Prot. Pept. Lett* 10, 247-253.

Wolter, K.G., Hsu, Y.T., Smith, C.L. Nechushtan, A., Xi, X.G., Youle, R.J. 1997, *J. Cell. Biol.* 139, 1281-1292.

Yamamoto, T., Yamada, A., Yoshimura, Y., Terada, H., Shinohara, Y. Yakugaku *Zasshi.* 2012, 132, 1099-1104.

Yin, H. Zhu, M. 2012, *Free Rad. Res.*, 46, 959-974.

Yu, H., Lee, I., Salomon, A.R., Yu, K., Hüttemann, M., 2008, *Biochim. Biophys. Acta* 1777, 1066–1071.

Zhao, X., Leon, I.R., Bak, S., Mogensen, M., Wrzesinski, K., Hojlund, K., Jensen, O.N., 2010. *Mol. Cell. Proteomics*.10 (1) 10.1074/mcp110.000299-1

In: Cytochromes *b* and *c*　　　　　　ISBN: 978-1-63117-467-4
Editor: Rurik Thom　　　　　　© 2014 Nova Science Publishers, Inc.

Chapter 5

REDOX-ACTIVE SILVER(I) COMPLEXES WITH STERICALLY HINDERED 1,2-DIHYDROXYBENZENE DERIVATIVES: REDUCTION OF CYTOCHROME *C* AND ANTIMICROBIAL ACTIVITY

N. V. Loginova[1]*, T. V. Koval'chuk[1,2], N. P. Osipovich[2],
Y. V. Faletrov[2], Yu. S. Halauko[1], G. I. Polozov[1],
A. T. Gres'[1], H. I. Harbatsevich[1], A. V. Hlushko[1],
R. A. Zheldakova[3] and V. M. Shkumatov[1,2]

[1]Faculty of Chemistry, Belarusian State University, Minsk, Belarus
[2]Research Institute for Physico-Chemical Problems of the Belarusian
State University, Minsk, Belarus
[3]Faculty of Biology, Belarusian State University, Minsk, Belarus

ABSTRACT

Novel redox-active metallotherapeutic agents were used to develop effective antimicrobial remedies differing from standard antibiotics in their mechanism of action with participation of free-radical intermediates. For this purpose redox-active compounds carrying sterically hindered

---

* Phone: +375 172 09-51-99, fax: +375 17 2095464, E-mail address: loginonv@gmail.com;
loginonv@bsu.by.

1,2-dihydroxybenzene moieties along with metal ions in a single scaffold have been synthesized and characterized by means of chemical and physicochemical methods as well as screened for their antimicrobial activity against Gram-negative bacteria (*Escherichia coli, Pseudomonas aeruginosa, Serratia marcescens*), Gram-positive bacteria (*Bacillus subtilis, Sarcina lutea, Staphylococcus aureus, Mycobacterium smegmatis*), yeasts (*Cryptococcus laurentii, Lipomyces lipofer, Candida albicans, Candida boidinii, Candida utilis, Saccharomyces cerevisiae*) and fungi (*Aspergillus niger, Alternaria alternata, Mucor spp., Botrytis cinerea, Monilia spp, Fusarium spp., Penicillium lividum, Sclerotinia sclerotiorum*). This screening revealed silver(I) complexes that may be considered as potential chemotherapeutic agents with activity higher than or comparable to that of some standard drugs such as tetracycline, streptomycin, chloramphenicol, isoniazid, amphotericin B, fluconazole, terbinafine. Using the method of cyclic voltammetry, we have shown some phenolic ligands as well as their silver(I) complexes to be also of a pronounced reducing ability. Bacterial cytochrome *c*-like enzymes being among the first targets for redox-active antimicrobials on their way into the cell, spectrophotometric investigation was carried out in order to estimate the rate of bovine heart cytochrome *c* reduction with the compounds synthesized. Oxidation of 1,2-dihydroxybenzene derivatives and their silver(I) complexes *in vitro* under anaerobic conditions can include two successive one-electron steps of oxidation of their ionic forms to yield *o*-benzoquinones on interaction with cytochrome *c* *via* intermediate *o*-benzosemiquinone formation. The results obtained are discussed in view of presumed correlation between the capability of the compounds synthesized for reducing cytochrome *c*, antimicrobial activity, and physico-chemical characteristics (redox properties determined electrochemically, lipophilicity, ionization constants of the ligands and stability constants of the metal complexes).

INTRODUCTION

Biomedical investigations concerning processes with participation of metalloenzymes have a significant place among various aspects of bioinorganic chemistry. They comprise both the development of new bioactive coordination compounds and the study of plausible mechanisms of their interaction with cell components [1, 2]. Besides, the development of new antimicrobial agents with a broad spectrum of action assumes a prime importance in the context of ever growing frequency of infections caused by the strains of bacteria and fungi resistant to widely used pharmaceuticals [3]. In this connection silver-containing pharmaceuticals can be very demanded in medical practice. Complexation with Ag(I) ions as a way to broaden the spectrum of action of known pharmaceuticals, in particular, sulphanilamides, as well as novel bioactive substances is noted to be promising [4–6]. Broad pharmacological screening of Ag(I) complexes with biologically active substances for antimicrobial activity represents a strategy for the development of novel class of antimicrobials that have a different mode of action compared to the commonly used antibiotics. In the last twenty years screening has been carried out intensively to reveal antimicrobial activity of Ag(I) complexes with aminoacids [7–9], tetrazoles [10], imidazoles [11, 12], salicylic [13], 2-mercaptonicotinic [14] and thiomalic [15] acids, and other ligands [16–19].

It is possible that Ag(I) complexes will allow one to overcome the resistance of microorganisms to silver and its compounds which was found thus far in rare cases [20–22], owing to changes in their hydrophilic/lipophilic characteristics, solubility, structure and charge. It was established that for Ag(I) complexes with Ag(I)–O and Ag(I)–N bonds antimicrobial properties are more pronounced, and their activity spectrum is broader than that of Ag(I) complexes with Ag(I)–S and Ag(I)–P bonds [14, 23]. According to [24, 25], explanation for these results is to be looked for in the ability of the complex to take part in exchange reactions with bioligands: the more loosely bound is Ag(I) ion in coordination core of the complex, the more probable is its interaction with soft bases of target biomolecules (proteins, DNA etc.), and primarily with sulphur-containing functional groups of proteins. This concept allows one to predict rather effectively antimicrobial properties of Ag(I) complexes synthesized. However, it doesn't take into account the role of redox activity of silver compounds in realizing their antimicrobial action and doesn't consider a possibility of correlation between these properties.

Electron transfer is known to be one of the key forms of the cell metabolism. According to [26], different antimicrobials act *in vivo* as electron transfer agents in the production of radical species or disruption of normal electron transport. Electron transfer can occur either to the metal center or, if in the biologically accessible range, to redox-active ligands, resulting in reactive species capable of attacking biologically relevant target molecules either by ligand displacement at the metal center or by radicals formed at the ligand entity, respectively [27–29].

Electron transfer provides for the processes of biological oxidation (respiration) localized in mitochondrions [30]. Research on the effect of some transition metal complexes upon fungal and mammalian cell organelles has shown that they have the potential to damage mitochondrial function and uncouple respiration [31–34]. In this connection it may be expected that metal complexes able to participate in redox processes and affect the electron-transport cell systems will be promising in the search for potential chemotherapeutical agents.

In our view, it is redox-active Ag(I) complexes with sterically hindered phenolic (1,2-dihydroxybenzene) derivatives that are a particularly rich source of these broad-spectrum anti-infective agents [35–37]. Phenolic derivatives have been used as antimicrobial agents over a long period of time [38], but nowadays they are of limited utility because of their toxicity and irritating action. Introduction of substituents into benzene ring and metal complexation, which change hydrophilic-lipophilic balance of a compound, allow one not only to achieve an optimal antimicrobial effect, but also to broaden the activity spectrum of these derivatives and decrease their toxity [39–51].

Encouraged by these results, we extended our research to novel modified 1,2-dihydroxybenzene derivatives and their complexes in order to examine how structural modifications of substituents in benzene ring and silver(I) complexation can influence the biological activity and reducing ability of the corresponding complexes. For this purpose we chose hydrazone, thiosemicarbazone derivatives as well as derivatives of thiocarboxylic acids because they have important implications for drug discovery and development owing to their biological effects: antimicrobial, antimalarial, antiviral and others [2, 52–54]. In particular, hydrazones derived from condensation of isonicotinoyl hydrazide (isoniazid) with the appropriate aldehydes and their metal complexes have been found to demonstrate antimicrobial activity higher than that of this effective first-line antitubercular drug [53, 55].

We were thus motivated to undertake a design of the target molecules with promising antimicrobial activity, carrying hydrazone or some other structural fragment (thiosemicarbazone, thiocarboxylic acid) as well as a sterically hindered *o*-diphenol moiety along with active silver(I) ions in a single scaffold, for the purpose of efficient inhibition of a broad spectrum of bacteria and fungi.

In the earlier investigations, using the method of cyclic voltammetry, we have shown some mono- and di-substituted derivatives of sterically hindered phenolic derivatives as well as their transition metal complexes to be also of a pronounced reducing ability correlating with antimicrobial activity and the rate of the reduction of bovine heart cytochrome *c* (Cyt *c*) in a limited series of these compounds [45–50]. These results allowed us to suggest that redox processes could play an important part in biotransformation and pharmacological activity of the said compounds, and one of the possible types of their biological macromolecular targets can be oxidoreductases (for instance, components of electron transport chains such as Cyt *c*-like ones). There is a number of reasons motivating interest in this particular electron-transfer protein.

Owing to subcellular localization, bacterial cytochromes *c* are among the first target enzymes for antimicrobial agents on their way into the cell. Cyt *c* transfers electrons from the complex III (coenzyme Q-cytochrome *c* reductase) to complex IV (cytochrome *c* oxidase) in the mitochondrial respiratory chain [56, 57].

It is noteworthy that mammalian Cyt *c* is able to oxidize different catechols and quinols into respective quinons [58–61]. Account should also be taken of the known relation of the above-mentioned enzyme system to generation and detoxification of reactive oxygen species and to apoptosis [62].

On this basis, the choice of isoniazid, thiosemicarbazide and thiocarboxylic acid moieties for structural modification of sterically hindered 1,2-dihydroxybenzene derivatives is justified, the main mechanism of action for these compounds being realized via the formation of radical intermediate species. In particular, isoniazid derivatives require enzymatic catalysis to promote an electron transfer reaction leading to drug activation [63, 64]. Probably, metal complexes with redox-active ligands of this sort could produce a faster alternative route for intramolecular-assisted ligand oxidation. And this strategy of imitating biocatalysts can be applied in metallotherapeutic drug design [1, 2].

In the present work the reduction of bovine heart Cyt *c* with some of sterically hindered 1,2-dihydroxybenzene derivatives, 2-[4,6-di(*tert*-butyl)-2,3-dihydroxyphenylsulphanyl]acetic acid (HL^I), 2-[4,6-di(*tert*-butyl)-2,3-dihydroxyphenylsulphanyl]propanoic acid (HL^{II}), 2-[4,6-di(*tert*-butyl)-2,3-dihydroxyphenylsulphinyl]acetic acid (HL^{III}), 4,6-di-*tert*-butyl-2,3-dihydroxybenzaldehyde isonicotinoyl hydrazone (HL^{IV}), 4,6-di-*tert*-butyl-2,3-dihydroxybenzaldehyde thiosemicarbazone (HL^V), as well as with their redox-active Ag(I) complexes were investigated spectrophotometrically. Redox properties of the above-mentioned ligands and their complexes were determined electrochemically.

We also report here the characterization and antimicrobial activity of Ag(I) complexes with aforesaid ligands. The results obtained are discussed in view of presumed correlation between the capability of the compounds under study for reducing Cyt *c*, their antimicrobial activity, redox properties determined electrochemically, and lipophilicity.

1. COMPLEXATION OF SILVER(I) IONS WITH STERICALLY HINDERED 1,2-DIDROXYBENZENE DERIVATIVES. PHYSICOCHEMICAL CHARACTERIZATION OF REDOX ACTIVE SILVER(I) COMPLEXES

Synthesis and characterization of the compounds HL^I–HL^V used in this work were described elsewhere [49]. An original procedure was developed of synthesizing Ag(I) complexes with the phenolic ligands [35, 36], making it possible to control ligand environment of Ag(I) ions and thus to produce complexes with specified characteristics, as shown in Figure 1.

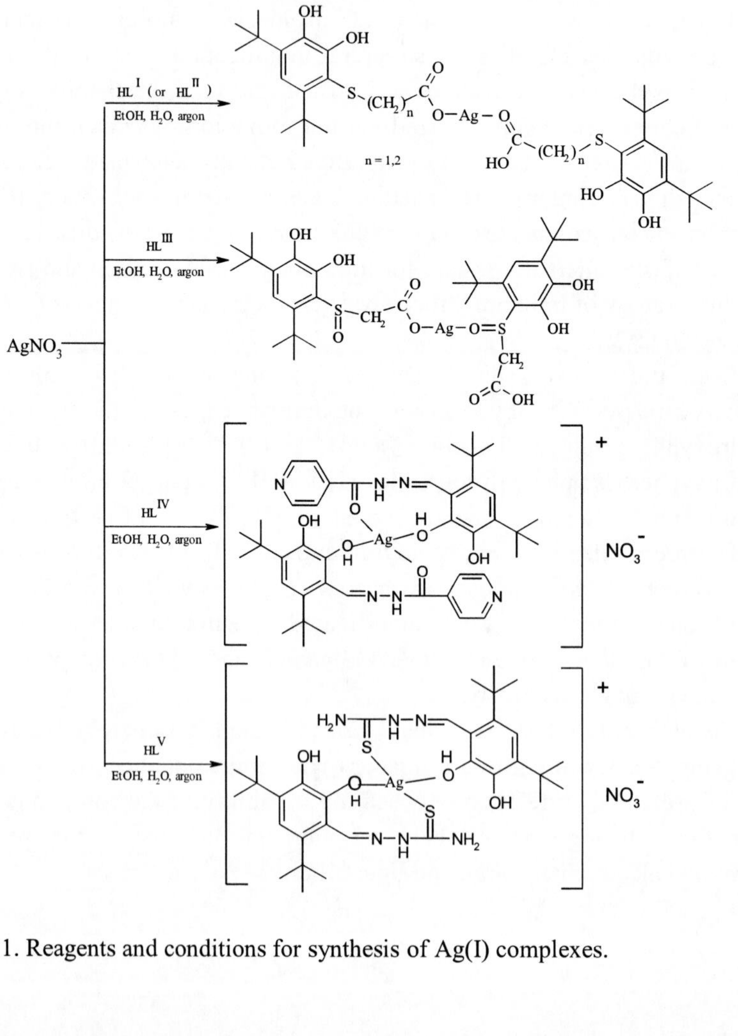

Figure 1. Reagents and conditions for synthesis of Ag(I) complexes.

For the ligands HL^I–HL^V formation of Ag(I) complexes with molar ratio Ag(I):Ligand=1:2 which precipitate in solid state in water-ethanol (1:1) medium was established, the complex $[AgH(L^I)_2]$ having a slightly higher overall stability constant ($\log\beta=9,0\pm0,2$) than the complexes $[AgH(L^{II})_2]$, $[AgH(L^{III})_2]$, $[Ag(HL^{IV})_2]NO_3$ and $[Ag(HL^V)_2]NO_3$ ($\log\beta<7,0$) [36].

To separate stable Ag(I) complexes with these ligands in solid state, following conditions should necessarily be met: i) a very low solubility of the complexes in the reaction medium; ii) stability of the phenolic ligands to oxidation in the presence of Ag(I) ions. The Ag(I) complexes synthesized are stable in air; they are non-hygroscopic and can be stored over a long period of time without decomposition. According to X-ray diffraction analysis, the precipitates are amorphous or very poorly crystallized. The results of their elemental analysis are presented in Table 1.

**Table 1. Analytical data for Ag(I) complexes
with 1,2-dihydroxybenzene derivatives**

Compound	Yield (%)	Colour	Molecular Formula	Elemental Analysis*, % (Found/Calc.)			
				C	H	S	Ag
$[AgH(L^I)_2]$	90	Cream	$C_{32}H_{47}S_2O_8Ag$	52.37/ 52.53	6.40/ 6.43	8.67/ 8.76	14.63/ 14.77
$[AgH(L^{II})_2]$	60	Yellow	$C_{32}H_{47}S_2O_{10}Ag$	50.25/ 50.35	6.07/ 6.16	8.27/ 8.39	14.03/ 14.10
$[AgH(L^{III})_2]$	80	Light beige	$C_{34}H_{51}S_2O_8Ag$	51.15/ 51.27	6.37/ 6.46	7.97/ 8.06	13.46/ 13.55
$[Ag(HL^{IV})_2]NO_3$	90	Cream	$C_{42}H_{54}N_7O_9Ag$	55.52/ 55.46	5.88/ 5.94	10.71/ 10.78	11.80/ 11.34
$[Ag(HL^V)_2]NO_3$	85	Flesh-coloured	$C_{32}H_{50}N_7S_2O_7Ag$	47.11/ 47.02	6.01/ 6.12	11.91/ 11.99	13.12/ 13.21

*Elemental analyses were carried out with an instrument Vario EL (CHNS mode). Silver and sulphur were determined using an atomic emission spectrometer with an inductively coupled plasma excitation source (Spectroflame Modula).

In connection with the fact that the phenolic ligands in transition metal complexes can be in different redox states depending on conditions, formal consideration of their electronic structure is conventionally carried out in the frame of the triad of redox ligand forms [65–67]. The ligands can be coordinated as diamagnetic single- or double-charged anions, neutral o-benzoquinones or paramagnetic o-benzosemiquinone anion-radicals, simultaneous presence of different redox forms in a complex being possible, as shown below (Figure 2):

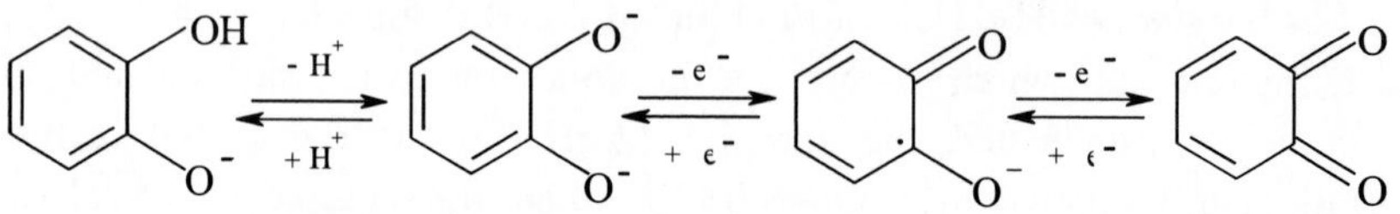

Figure 2. Redox forms of phenolic ligands.

There are several reasons for carrying out an electrochemical investigation of redox properties of the compounds HL^I–HL^V as well as their Ag(I) complexes. First, contrary to the traditional problem of coordination chemistry related primarily to description of electronic structure of the central metal ion, an additional problem arises of determining redox state of the organic ligands in the Ag(I) complexes synthesized. Second, on the basis of our previous data it is safe to assume that redox properties of the phenolic derivatives under study and their metal complexes can significantly affect their bioactivity.

Figure 3 gives voltammograms of the compounds HL^I–HL^V and three Ag(I) complexes as well as 3,5-di-*tert*-butylcatechol HL^{VI} (Sigma) used by us to elucidate the nature of redox transformations taking place. They allow conclusions about electrochemical behaviour of these compounds and make it possible to compare their stability to oxidation and reducing properties. The complexes $[AgH(L^I)_2]$, $[Ag(HL^{IV})_2]NO_3$ and $[Ag(HL^V)_2]NO_3$ were selected for electrochemical investigation as being more stable in experimental conditions (particularly in acetonitrile).

Upon anodic scan HL^I–HL^{VI} undergo electrochemical oxidation. Comparing electrochemical data, one can note an anodic peak at 0.79÷1.33 V, characteristic of all these phenolic derivatives, with a corresponding cathodic peak of reduction of oxidation products on the reverse scan in the range of 0.45÷0.64 V.

Controlled electrolysis of solutions of these compounds showed that upon the anodic oxidation process in the range of 0.79÷1.33 V the quantity of electricity flown corresponds to two electrons per molecule. Note that in the absorption spectra of solutions of the products of electrochemical oxidation of HL^I–HL^{VI} there are absorption bands at 400–480 nm, which may be assigned to absorption of respective *o*-benzoquinones [68].

Thus, at the potentials of the first peak these phenolic derivatives undergo two successive single-electron oxidation processes to form *o*-benzoquinones, with a cathodic peak in the range of 0.45÷0.64 V on reverse scan corresponding to reduction of the latter.

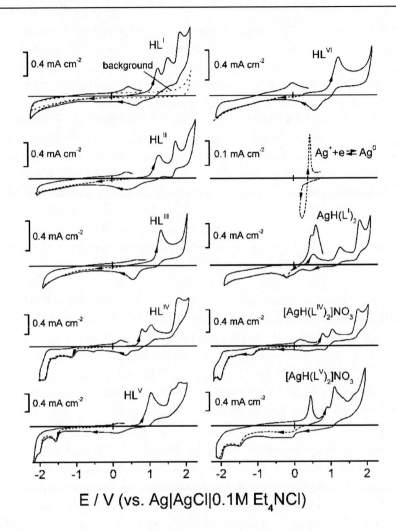

Figure 3. Voltammograms (50 mV/s) of the compounds HL^I–HL^{VI} (1.36 mmol·l^{-1}), Ag(I) complexes and $AgNO_3$ (0.68 mmol·l^{-1}) in 0.1 mol·l^{-1} $(C_2H_5)_4NClO_4$ acetonitrile solution under dry nitrogen on glassy-carbon working electrode (dotted line – background cyclic voltammogram of glassy-carbon electrode). Solid line – polarization in the anodic direction from the open circuit potential; dashed line – polarization in the cathodic direction from the open circuit potential. The Ag|AgCl|0.1 mol·l^{-1} $(C_2H_5)_4NCl$ reference electrode was calibrated with the ferrocenium | ferrocene redox couple located at $E_{1/2}$=+0.54 V.

This redox process for HL^I–HL^{VI} proceeding by phenolic hydroxyls, the potentials of respective peaks are in a narrow range of values (Figure 3), and it is only for HL^{III} that this potential (1.33 V) is somewhat higher, which may be related to acceptor effect of sulphoxide group [66]. For HL^{II} and HL^{VI} the peaks mentioned above, at $1.20 \div 1.33$ V and $0.45 \div 0.64$ V, are the only ones, while for HL^{I} there are several more peaks (Figure 3). Taking into account the absence of sulphur atom in the molecule of HL^{VI}, it may be suggested that in the case of the derivative of thioglycolic acid HL^{I} at 1.54 V and 1.88 V successive oxidation processes take place by the sulphur atom and/or carboxyl group. By contrast, HL^{III} has a sulphoxide side chain, and no redox process with participation of the sulphur atom of this group occurs. This result in just one redox process with participation of hydroxyl groups being observed for HL^{III} in the potential range examined (Figure 3). For HL^{IV} and HL^{V} the anodic wave at 1.80–1.83 V may be related to the redox process involving –CH=N–NH– group. Furthermore, for the compound HL^{V} an anodic process is observed at 1.63 V. Taking into account that the compound HL^{V} comprises >C=S moiety, it may be suggested that the sulphur atom takes part in this process.

Upon cathodic polarization (down to –2.0 V) no reduction of HL^{I}–HL^{III} and HL^{VI} is observed in voltammograms (Figure 3). The compounds HL^{IV} and HL^{V} contain –CH=N–NH– moiety and hence they are reduced upon cathodic polarization. Two main cathodic waves are observed in the voltammograms: (i) at –1.17 and –1.90 V for HL^{IV}; (ii) at –1.58 and –2.02 V for HL^{V}. It is known that in protic media upon electrochemical reduction of hydrazones first N–N bond is cleaved, and then the C=N bond saturation occurs, with two corresponding two-electron waves [69–71]. In aprotic media for hydrazones there are also two cathodic waves being observed in potential ranges $-1.0 \div -1.8$ V and $-2.0 \div -2.3$ V, and one-electron transfer corresponding to the first one [72]. In certain conditions bond saturation in the structural fragment –CH=N–NH– can also take place to give hydrazine derivatives [69]. Controlled electrolysis of solutions of HL^{IV} and HL^{V} at the potentials of the first cathodic wave demonstrated that the quantity of electricity passed corresponds to one electron per molecule. Electrochemical reduction of HL^{IV} and HL^{V} results in formation of products with strong reducing properties.

Upon anodic polarization three anodic peaks at 0.54, 1.27 and 1.82 V are found in voltammogram of $[AgH(L^{I})_2]$, and on reverse scan there are peaks of reduction of oxidation products at 0.03 and 0.44 V (Figure 3). Potentials of anodic peaks at 1.27 and 1.82 V are close to those of anodic peaks of HL^{I}, but the peak of oxidation of the latter at 1.54 V related to oxidation process with participation of sulphur atom is absent in the voltammogram of the complex, while a peak at 0.54 V occurs. According to the results of spectroscopic investigation presented in this paper, only the carboxyl groups of two molecules of the ligand participate in forming coordination core of $[AgH(L^I)_2]$ (Figure 3). It seems likely that the observed shift of the above-mentioned peaks with relation to their position in the voltammogram of the ligand can be due to electron being partially transferred from the ligand orbitals to those of silver(I) [66]. Upon anodic polarization in the voltammograms of $[Ag(HL^{IV})_2]NO_3$ and $[Ag(HL^V)_2]NO_3$ complexes there are two anodic waves (Figure 3): (i) at $0.78 \div 1.05$ V (with two peaks) and at 1.83 V for $[Ag(HL^{IV})_2]NO_3$; (ii) at 1.1 V (with a shoulder at 0.92 V) and at 1.63 V for $[Ag(HL^V)_2]NO_3$, the appearance of the shoulder at 0.92 V possibly indicating a shift along the potential scale of the redox processes involving phenolic hydroxyls. Potential values of the peaks are in a narrow range for each couple of the ligand and its Ag(I) complex, thus suggesting ligand-centered redox processes.

Upon cathodic polarization a peak of reduction at −0.18 V and a small peak at −0.32 V are observed in the voltammogram of $[AgH(L^I)_2]$. On reverse scan several peaks of oxidation of products of cathodic reduction appear in the range $0.40 \div 0.70$ V (Figure 3). One of them, at 0.48 V, corresponds to oxidation of silver metal produced upon $[AgH(L^I)_2]$ reduction, which is evident on comparison of this peak and that of oxidation of silver deposited on the electrode from a silver nitrate solution (Figure 3). However, it is not improbable that in the process of $[AgH(L^I)_2]$ reduction and concomitant chemical reactions other products are also formed (both inorganic, particularly silver sulphide, and organic ones), responsible for the complicated pattern in the reverse scan in the potential range $0.46 \div 0.73$ V. Upon cathodic polarization on the voltammograms of $[Ag(HL^{IV})_2]NO_3$ and $[Ag(HL^V)_2]NO_3$ complexes two cathodic waves are observed which are due to ligand-centered redox processes (Figure 3): (i) at −1.17 and −2.02 V for $[Ag(HL^{IV})_2]NO_3$; (ii) at −1.54 and −2.06 V for $[Ag(HL^V)_2]NO_3$.

Besides, silver is reduced from $[Ag(HL^V)_2]NO_3$ complex (cathodic wave at −0.14 V) (Figure 3), which is supported by the presence of Ag(0) oxidation peak at 0.39 V on reverse scan (Figure 3). No silver reduction is observed in voltammogram of $[Ag(HL^{IV})_2]NO_3$ complex. After polarization down to −2 V a small peak at 0.28 V appears on the reverse anodic scan, which may be assigned to Ag(0) oxidation. Probably, the appearance of Ag(0) on the electrode surface becomes possible already after the complex degradation resulting from cathodic ligand reduction. The absence of silver reduction from $[Ag(HL^{IV})_2]NO_3$ complex may be related to charge transfer from the ligand orbitals to those of the metal. On the basis of the electrochemical findings the compounds investigated can be graded in their reducing ability as follows:

i) $HL^{IV} \geq HL^{V} > HL^{I} > HL^{II} > HL^{III}$;

ii) $[AgH(L^{I})_2] > [Ag(HL^{IV})_2]NO_3 \geq [Ag(HL^{V})_2]NO_3$.

Table 2. Thermal analysis data for decomposition of the Ag(I) complexes

Complex	Ranges of decomposition (°C)	Process	Assignment	Mass loss, %	
				Found	Calculated
$[AgH(L^{I})_2]$	150–380	Endothermic Endothermic	Decomposition of two ligand molecules	84.4	85.2
$[AgH(L^{II})_2]$	160–310	Endothermic	Decomposition of two ligand molecules	85.4	86.5
$[AgH(L^{III})_2]$	160–370	Endothermic	Decomposition of two ligand molecules	87.3	85.9
$[Ag(HL^{IV})_2]NO_3$	180–200 210–390	Endothermic Endothermic, exothermic	Decomposition of two ligand molecules	87.2	88.1
$[Ag(HL^{V})_2]NO_3$	170–200 205–380	Endothermic Endothermic, exothermic	Decomposition of two ligand molecules	85.7	86.8

*Thermal analysis was performed using a Simultaneous Thermal Analyzer STA 449 C with identification of the final products by X-ray powder diffraction. In the present investigation the heating rates were suitably controlled at 5 °C min^{-1} under argon atmosphere, and the mass loss was measured from ambient temperature up to 700 °C.

The Ag(I) complexes are thermally stable up to 160 °C. Note the absence of endothermic effects, characteristic of complex desolvation, in the temperature range from 60 to 150 C [73]. This is consistent with the data of elemental analysis testifying that the coordination sphere of the Ag(I) complexes contains no solvent molecules (Table 2). The complete decomposition of the complexes takes place beyond 400°C to give elemental silver [35, 74].

The Ag(I) complexes are practically insoluble in water, but they are readily soluble in many organic solvents. These complexes are characterized by high values of the *n*-octanol/water partition coefficient (Table 3) which was determined as reported in [75]. The lipophilicity parameters of these complexes suggest their potential ability for transmembrane transfer and are also important for assessment of their bioavailability.

Table 3. Octanol/water partition coefficients (logP_{ow}*) of the ligands and their Ag(I) complexes

Compound	logP_{ow}	Compound	logP_{ow}
HL^I	3.73±0.38	[AgH(L^I)$_2$]	4.10±0.35
HL^{II}	4.00±0.36	[AgH(L^{II})$_2$]	4.20±0.34
HL^{III}	2.34±1.08	[AgH(L^{III})$_2$]	4.07±0.36
HL^{IV}	4.09±0.36	[Ag(HL^{IV})$_2$]NO$_3$	4.50±0.22
HL^V	3.60±0.34	[Ag(HL^V)$_2$]NO$_3$	4.70±0.20

*P_{ow}=C$_{octanol-1}$/C$_{water}$ (C, mol·l^{-1}).

The values of the molar conductivity in acetonitrile for the complexes [AgH(L^I)$_2$], [AgH(L^{II})$_2$] and [AgH(L^{III})$_2$] (Λ_{mol}=50.8÷70.6 Ω^{-1}cm^{2}mol^{-1}) demonstrate that two ligands are coordinated to the Ag(I) ion as monoanionic and molecular species, since the above-mentioned data indicate the complexes being essentially non-electrolytes [76]. The values of the molar conductivity in acetonitrile for these complexes Λ_{mol}=130–200 Ω^{-1}cm^{2}mol^{-1} suggest that the compounds of the [Ag(HL^{IV})$_2$]NO$_3$ and [Ag(HL^V)$_2$]NO$_3$ dissociate in acetonitrile and behave as 1:1 electrolytes [76]. Thus, these data indicate that the ligands HL^{IV} and HL^V may be coordinated to the Ag(I) ion as molecular species.

Light sensitivity of the Ag(I) complexes synthesized limits the choice of methods to investigate their structure. They are amorphous powders, and it is virtually impossible to produce them as single crystals suitable for complete structural analysis. Besides, dissolution of these complexes in various solvents is accompanied by a redox process.

Information on stereochemistry of coordination core of complexes of transition metals can be obtained by analyzing the form and intensity of *d-d* bands in their UV-Vis absorption spectra [77], but this method is not used for Ag(I) complexes, as *d-d* transitions for Ag(I) are forbidden. In this connection the characteristic of coordination cores of the Ag(I) complexes synthesized is given on the basis of the results of their investigation by spectroscopic methods (IR, ESR, luminescence) and DFT calculations; the results obtained are presented in Tables 4, 5 and Figure 4.

When considering the structures of the phenolic ligands, one can easily understand the difficulties in predicting molecular geometries of complexes. Unfortunately, in our case it proved impossible to prepare a sample for X-ray diffraction analysis. So, our strategy included the indirect structure elucidation, which is based on combination of spectral data and quantum chemical calculations. It was proved earlier that such an approach is sufficiently effective for transition metal complexes, in particular for Ag(I) complexes [51, 78, 79].

All the complexes synthesized can potentially exist as different isomers, where Ag(I) ion is bonded by the phenolic ligand in different ways. Using DFT calculations together with the spectral data, we have determined geometric parameters of these complexes. First of all, the Mulliken orbital population analysis of free ligands HL^I–HL^V allowed us to outline their most probable binding sites. Regarding the mechanism of donor-acceptor bond formation, the main input from ligand`s HOMO and Ag`s LUMO can be expected. Actually, for HL^{III} HOMO is localized mainly on the sulphoxide group, whereas for HL^I and HL^{II} the main input is brought by phenolic oxygen atoms, while the carboxyl groups have strong input in LUMO. And for HL^{IV} HOMO is localized mainly on the hydrazone group and HOMO-1 on phenolic oxygen atoms, whereas for HL^V the main contribution in both HOMO and HOMO-1 is made by the thiosemicarbazone fragment. So, noticeable differences in the core organization of the complexes are to be expected.

Analysis of IR spectra of HL^I–HL^{III} and their Ag(I) complexes made it possible to identify donor sites of binding of the ligands with Ag(I). The general characteristic of IR spectra of these complexes is the fixed position of the bands assigned to vibrations of the structural fragments not linked to Ag(I) (benzene ring, *tert*-butyl groups) and corresponding to those found in the spectra of free ligands [83, 84].

Ag(I) complexation with HL^I and HL^{II} is responsible for significant changes in the bands of stretching and deformation vibrations of ligand hydroxyls. An intensive band of stretching vibrations at 3430 cm^{-1} (HL^I) and bands at 3538, 3340 cm^{-1} (HL^{II}) are significantly shifted in the spectra of the complexes.

A weak broad band (3300–3000 cm^{-1}) present in the spectra of $[AgH(L^I)_2]$, $[AgH(L^{II})_2]$ and $[AgH(L^{III})_2]$ suggests that carboxyl group is involved into formation of chelate rings through intramolecular hydrogen bonds.

Table 4. Prominent IR absorption bands (ν cm⁻¹) of the ligands HL^I–HL^{III} and their Ag(I) complexes

Compound	Source	ν(OH)	ν(COO⁻)	ν(C=O)	δ(OH)carb	ν(C-O)	ν(S=O)	ν(C-S)	ν(Ag-O)
HL^I	Exp.[a]	3430m 3270w	–	1773s	910w	1277m 1243m 1176m	–	668m	–
	Calc.[b]	3420	–	1744	882	1248		670	–
[AgH(L^I)₂]	Exp.	3430w	1557m.	1773m 1695m	891w	1287m 1266m 1226s 1147m	–	669m	574w
	Calc.	3450	1547	1659	875	1265	–	657	590
HL^{II}	Exp.	3538m 334m	–	1711m	902m	1360s 1291s 1233s 1205s 1183s	–	764w 697w 679m 648m 617w	
	Calc.	3335	–	1708	912	1299 1148	–	690	–
[AgH(L^{II})₂]	Exp.	3309m	1548s 1391s	1692m	878w	1306s 1279m 1154m 1085m	–	760w 677m 648m 613w	565w 511w
	Calc.	3368	1529 1411	1676	912	1311 1150	–	749	561 513
HL^{III}	Exp.	3460m 3345w 3160w	–	1712s	905m 890m	1375s 1315s 1261m 1240s	1000s	677m	–

Table 4. (Continued)

Compound	Source	ν(OH)	ν(COO⁻)	ν(C=O)	δ(OH)$_{carb}$	ν(C–O)	ν(S=O)	ν(C–S)	ν(Ag–O)
	Calc.	3332	–	1720	906	1319 1226	1023	695	–
[AgH(L^{III})$_2$]	Exp.	3460m 3345w 3160w	1570w 1549m 1508m	1713m 1690m	906w 890w	1315m 1293m 1262m 1241s 1218w	1003w	680m	540m
	Calc.	3338 3174	1590 1543	1719	910 884	1258 1213	1034	688	556

[a] Infrared spectra of solids were recorded with a Nicolet 380 spectrometer in the wavelength range 4000–400 cm⁻¹ at room temperature, using «Smart Performer»; spectra in the range 400–50 cm⁻¹ were registered using «Vertex 70» instrument (Bruker Optik GmbH).

[b] All calculations were performed using the GAUSSIAN03 software package [80] and the theoretical approach described thoroughly in the previous paper [48]. MO calculations were carried out using the density functional theory B3PW91 method together with the combined 6-31G(d) + LANL2DZ basis set (for nonmetal and metal atoms, respectively) [81]. No symmetry constraints were implemented during the optimization process. In order to perform the stationary point characterization, harmonic vibrational frequencies were calculated at the same level of theory. The Mulliken orbital population analysis was performed for a better understanding of electronic structure of the complexes. The scaling factor of 0.951 [82] was applied to the calculated frequencies.

Table 5. Prominent IR absorption bands (ʏ cm-1) of the ligands HLIV, HLV and their Ag(I) complexes

Compound	Source	v(OH)	v(NH)	v(C=N)	v(C=O)	v(C-O)	v(C=S)	v(Ag-O), v(Ag-S)
HL^{IV}	Exp.	3620m 3190m	3090w 3037w	1614m 159m0	1660m	1122m		–
	Calc.	3396 3204	3136	1621 1605	1657	1102		–
[Ag(HL^{IV})$_2$]NO$_3$	Exp.	3596m 3398w 3205w	3250m 3047w	1614m 1595m	1669m	110m		533w
	Calc.	3594 3414 3382 3227	3249	1625 1567	1647 1627	1112		567 526
HL^{V}	Exp.	3476m 3400m 3290w	3524w 3364m 3164m	1612m 1592m	–	1169m 1098w	1221m	–
	Calc.	3384 3280	3506 3356 3309	1570	–	1209	1237	–
[Ag(HL^{V})$_2$]NO$_3$	Exp.	3430m 3183m	3290w 3175m	1617m 1589m	–	1116m 1041w	1216m	557m 544w 507m 334m 332m
	Calc.	3432 3230	3477 3360 3288	1580	–	1116	1234	563 515 335

In the frequency range from 1350 to 1200 cm^{-1} in the spectra of HL^{I} and HL^{II} there are bands which in the spectra of their complexes are markedly shifted to the lower-frequency region (Table 4). These data are indicative of a change in the state of hydroxyls of HL^{I} and HL^{II} on complexation, presumably through their involvement into formation of hydrogen bonds. In the spectrum of [AgH(L^{III})$_2$] no significant changes in the positions of bands of vibrations of hydroxyls are observed in comparison with that of HL^{III}, but their intensity is lower.

Bands at 1600–1548 cm^{-1} appearing in IR spectra of Ag(I) complexes are suggestive of carboxylate anion being present in coordination cores [85]. The bands of deformation vibrations (O–H) of carboxyl group at 910–890 cm^{-1}, characteristic of HL^{I}–HL^{III}, are still present in the spectra of their complexes. On the basis of these data it may be concluded that only one of the two coordinated ligand molecules in the complexes is in monoanionic form (Figure 1). When considering the peculiarities of ligand coordination in Ag(I) complexes, the band at 1695–1690 cm^{-1} is worthy to note (Table 4): its occurrence is indicative of chelate structures being formed through hydrogen bonds with participation of hydroxyl fragment of carboxyl group [84]. Besides, the shift of the band of deformation vibrations (O–H) of carboxylic group in the spectra of these complexes (890–878 cm^{-1}) as compared to its position in the ligand spectra (910–902 cm^{-1}) results from this group participating in formation of hydrogen bonds.

The position and intensity of the bands of C–S bond vibrations at 764–668 cm^{-1} in the spectra of the ligands and their Ag(I) complexes virtually do not change on complexation (Table 4), suggesting that the sulphur atoms of ligand molecules take no part in forming coordination sphere of Ag(I) complexes. Lone electron pairs of sulphur seem to be involved into π-conjugation with benzene ring [83, 84]. In the spectra of HL^{III} and [AgH(L^{III})$_2$] the band at 1005–1000 cm^{-1} is related to stretching vibrations of S=O bond, its intensity in the spectrum of the complex being substantially lower than in that of the ligand, which may be due to complexation with sulphoxide group participating therein [83, 84]. As noted above, sulphur atom isn't coordinationally bound to Ag(I), and the coordination core incorporates oxygen atom of sulphoxide group (Figure 1), as the donor ability of this oxygen atom is higher than that of oxygen atom of carboxyl group [86, 87]. The bands in the range of 574÷511 cm^{-1} in the spectra of these complexes are due to Ag–O bonds, substantiating the participation of oxygen atoms in forming coordination cores [AgO$_2$] (Figure 1). In the IR spectra of HL^{IV} and HL^{V} there are some bands in the range of 3600–3200 cm^{-1} indicating the presence of intermolecular hydrogen bonds involving phenolic hydroxyls [83, 84]. In the spectra of the complexes [Ag(HL^{IV})$_2$]NO$_3$ and [Ag(HL^V)$_2$]NO$_3$ these bands are shifted (Table 5). These data are indicative of a change in the state of hydroxyls of HL^{IV} and HL^V on complexation or on their involvement into formation of hydrogen bonds. Besides, the frequencies and the intensity of C–O stretching bands in the spectra of the Ag(I) complexes also are evidence in favour of the ligands being coordinated to Ag(I) ions via the oxygen atom of the phenolic hydroxyl group [83].

The position and intensity of the bands of C=N bond vibrations at 1614–1590 cm^{-1} in spectra of HL^{IV} and HL^V and their Ag(I) complexes virtually do not change on complexation (Table 5). Hence, the azomethine nitrogen atom of the ligands isn't coordinated to the metal ion. Moreover, the v(NH) stretching vibrations for free ligands, occurring at 3200–3050 cm^{-1}, remain unaffected after complexation. These data are evidence for the nitrogen atom being absent in coordination cores of the complexes.

The shift of the band at 1660 cm^{-1} assignable to v(C=O), observed for the ligand L^{IV} in the spectra of the complex [Ag(HL^{IV})$_2$]NO$_3$, suggests that the carbonyl oxygen atom of the amide group takes part in complexation [83]. There is no medium intensity band at 1050 cm^{-1} characteristic of the enolic v(C–O) stretching vibrations, which suggests that there is no enolate form of the ligand (Table 5). In the spectrum of this ligand the strong bands at 1068 and 1005 cm^{-1} due to pyridine ring stretching vibrations remain unchanged on complexation, indicating non-involvement of the pyridine nitrogen atom in complex formation [84].

The absence of any band in the region 2600–2500 cm^{-1} due to v(C–SH) vibrations suggests that the thiosemicarbazone HL^V remains in its thione form. The shift of absorption bands characteristic for the vibrations of C=S group to the lower frequency in the spectrum of the complex [Ag(HL^V)$_2$]NO$_3$ was attributed to the coordination of the thione sulphur atom to the metal ion [83].

The coordination behaviour of these ligands HL^I–HL^V is also proved by the appearance of new bands in the low frequency regions at 533–507 cm^{-1} and at 334–332 cm^{-1} (Tables 4 and 5), which may be assigned respectively to the stretching vibrations of Ag–O and Ag–S bonds [51] and substantiate the participation of oxygen and sulphur atoms in forming coordination cores: [AgO$_4$] (for the complex [Ag(HL^{IV})$_2$]NO$_3$) and [AgO$_2$S$_2$] (for the complex [Ag(HL^V)$_2$]NO$_3$) (Figure 1).

The infrared spectral data for the complexes [Ag(HL^{IV})$_2$]NO$_3$ and [Ag(HL^V)$_2$]NO$_3$ show two strong absorption bands in the regions 1310–1295

cm^{-1} and 870–800 cm^{-1}, which are attributed to vibrations of the non-coordinated nitrate anion (outside the coordination sphere) [83, 88].

It should be emphasized that in the spectra of all the Ag(I) complexes there is no band characteristic of *o*-benzoquinones [89], which suggests that there are no oxidized ligands in their coordination sphere.

Finally, plausible molecular structures of the compounds were suggested based on the array of spectral data and quantum chemical calculations from different initial guesses (Figure 4). One can see noticeable differences in the core organization of $[AgH(L^I)_2]$, $[AgH(L^{II})_2]$, $[AgH(L^{III})_2]$ as well as $[Ag(HL^{IV})_2]^+$ and $[Ag(HL^V)_2]^+$ cations. The structures of all the complexes can favour possible argentophilic interactions.

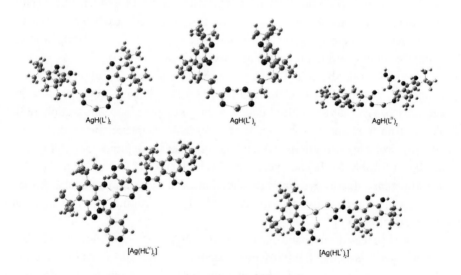

Figure 4. DFT optimized molecular structures of the Ag(I)complexes.

As the compounds HL^I–HL^V are potential Ag(I) reductants, their complexes were investigated by ESR method in order to elucidate the possibility of formation of paramagnetic particles due to redox interaction between Ag(I) ions and the ligands. The solid state ESR spectra of the Ag(I) complexes were recorded both at room temperature and at 77 K, as reported in [51]. At room temperature the spectra look virtually the same as at liquid nitrogen temperature (77 K), and it is just the signal intensity that is significantly lower. Only one signal with $g_{iso}=2.0033\div2.0035$, close to g_e, is registered in the spectra. It is unlikely that this signal is related to phenoxyl radicals, because it is a signal with $g=2.005\div2.006$ that corresponds to them

[90]. Thus, the above-mentioned signal is related to paramagnetic species occurring due to complexation. ESR method is known to be widely applied to detect and identify paramagnetic silver species. It was found that isolated silver atoms Ag(0) are absent in these Ag(I) complexes [91], as no doublet signals (g_{iso}=1.987 [92]) characteristic of atomic silver were registered in their ESR spectra. The presence of paramagnetic Ag^{2+} ions isn't likely either [93], Ag(I) complexation having been carried out with reductants.

For interpretation of ESR spectra of Ag(I) complexes a concept can be used of complexes with partial charge transfer (PCT) as a special class of compounds of transition metal ions with redox-active ligands [94]. According to the results of our previous study on the nature of paramagnetic species in Ag(I) complexes with phenolic ligands [36, 51], there is good reason to believe that the signal in ESR spectrum belongs to the PCT complex between Ag(I) and the phenolic ligand owing to partial electron transfer from the ligand to silver ion.

In addition, the luminescent behaviour of the Ag(I) complexes (as well as of the compounds HL^I–HL^V) was studied at room temperature in the solid state. The complexes show a very broad luminescence band at 320–400 nm (λ_{exc}=280 nm), but the ligands exhibit no emission bands at these wavelengths. The luminescent behaviour of the complexes is mainly similar to that previously reported for other Ag(I) complexes with sterically hindered o-diphenol derivatives [36, 51].

These luminescence characteristics resulting from complexation may be related to the charge transfer with ligand and silver orbitals participating, particularly for structural motifs (coordination cores) with argentophilic interactions, their presence in previously investigated Ag(I) complexes being substantiated by the X-ray diffraction analysis [95–97]. The results obtained support the assumption of PCT complexes formed made on the basis of analysis of their ESR spectra.

It should be emphasized that the peaks at 460–500 nm characteristic of colloidal silver [98] are absent in the luminescence spectra of the complexes. Consequently, it may be stated that no silver nanoparticles are formed on interaction of Ag(I) ions with the compounds HL^I–HL^V. In the light of the physico-chemical characterization and DFT calculations the general mode of the ligating atoms in Ag(I) complexes can be represented as shown in Figure 4.

2. ANTIMICROBIAL ACTIVITY OF 1,2-DIHYDROXYBENZENE DERIVATIVES AND THEIR SILVER (I) COMPLEXES

Continuing our previous biological evaluation of sterically hindered *o*-diphenol derivatives and their transition metal complexes, we have carried out microbiological screening of newly synthesized compounds to assess how modification of composition and structure of phenolic ligands and complexation with Ag(I) ions affected antimicrobial activity of the complexes. Microbiological investigation was carried out *in vitro* for test cultures of Gram-positive and Gram-negative bacteria, yeasts and moulds, using the procedures described in our previous papers [40–43, 45, 46]. The antimicrobial activity of the compounds was determined as their lowest concentration which inhibits the visible microbial growth, i.e. a minimum inhibitory concentration (MIC, $\mu mol \cdot ml^{-1}$) [99, 100]. Commonly used antibacterial (streptomycin, tetracycline, chloramphenicol, isoniazid), antifungal (terbinafine, fluconazole, amphotericin B) and silver-containing (silver nitrate, silver sulphadiazine) pharmaceuticals were tested as positive controls. Tables 6, 7 and 8 give MICs for these ligands and Ag(I) complexes; some of them have demonstrated antimicrobial activity comparable to or higher than the inhibitory effect of the above-mentioned standard drugs and acceptable from the viewpoint of their possible practical application.

The Ag(I) complexes suppress growth of test cultures at very low concentrations (MIC=0.004÷0.008 $\mu mol \cdot ml^{-1}$), and they are characterized by comparable inhibiting action against the Gram-negative and Gram-positive bacteria tested (Table 6).

Their antibacterial activity exceeds not only the inhibiting action of the ligands (MIC=0.017÷0.320 $\mu mol \cdot ml^{-1}$), but also that of some standard antibiotics (MIC=0.005÷0.172 $\mu mol \cdot ml^{-1}$) as well as silver-containing pharmaceuticals (MIC=0.018÷0.294 $\mu mol \cdot ml^{-1}$) (Table 6). It should be emphasized that the lowest MIC value (MIC≤0.004 $\mu mol \cdot ml^{-1}$) is characteristic of Ag(I) complexes for *Mycobacterium smegmatis*; it is lower than that of the first-line anti-tubercular medication isoniazid (MIC=0.009 $\mu mol \cdot ml^{-1}$).

This finding could be of significance because *Mycobacterium smegmatis* is a fast growing test-mycobacterium commonly used in the antimycobacterial assay of antitubercular agents by several workers [55, 101, 102].

Table 6. Antibacterial activity of the ligands and their Ag(I) complexes evaluated by minimum inhibitory concentration*

Compound	Ps. aeruginosa	S. marcescens	E. coli	B. subtilis	S. lutea	St. aureus	M. smegmatis
HL^{I}	>0.320	>0.320	>0.320	0.160	0.080	0.080	0.160
[AgH(L^{I})$_2$]	<0.004	<0.004	<0.004	<0.004	<0.004	<0.004	<0.004
HL^{II}	>0.306	>0.306	>0.306	>0.306	0.153	0.153	0.076
[AgH(L^{II})$_2$]	0.008	0.004	0.004	0.008	0.004	0.008	0.004
HL^{III}	>0.305	>0.305	>0.305	>0.305	0.305	0.305	0.305
[AgH(L^{III})$_2$]	0.008	0.008	0.008	0.008	0.008	0.008	0.008
HL^{IV}	>0.270	>0.270	>0.270	0.017	0.017	0.034	0.017
[Ag(HL^{IV})$_2$]NO$_3$	<0.004	<0.004	<0.004	0.004	<0.004	0.004	<0.004
HL^{V}	>0.309	>0.309	>0.309	0.077	0.077	0.077	0.077
[Ag(HL^{V})$_2$]NO$_3$	<0.004	0.004	<0.004	0.004	0.004	0.004	<0.004
AgNO$_3$	0.147	0.147	0.294	0.147	0.147	0.294	0.073
Silver sulphadiazine	0.018	0.018	0.018	0.018	0.018	0.070	0.070
Streptomycin	0.172	0.011	0.005	0.011	0.021	0.011	0.011
Tetracycline	0.056	NA**	0.007	0.014	0.014	0.007	N***
Chloramphenicol	0.039	NA	0.019	0.009	NA	0.019	0.039
Isoniazid	NA	NA	NA	NA	NA	NA	0.009

*MIC values are given in $\mu mol \cdot ml^{-1}$.

**NA – not applicable.

***N – unreceptive to antibiotic.

Table 7. Antifungal activity of the ligands and their Ag(I) complexes against yeasts evaluated by minimum inhibitory concentration*

Compound	C. laurentii	L. lipofer	C. albicans	C. boidinii	C. utilis	S. cerevisiae
HL^I	>0.320	0.040	0.160	0.160	0.160	0.080
[AgH(L^I)$_2$]	<0.004	<0.004	<0.004	<0.004	<0.004	<0.004
HL^{II}	>0.306	0.153	0.153	>0.306	0.306	0.076
[AgH(L^{II})$_2$]	0.008	0.004	0.004	0.008	0.008	0.004
HL^{III}	>0.305	0.153	0.305	0.305	0.305	0.305
[AgH(L^{III})$_2$]	0.004	0.004	0.008	0.008	0.008	0.004
HL^{IV}	0.068	0.034	0.017	0.034	0.017	0.034
[Ag(HL^{IV})$_2$]NO$_3$	<0.004	<0.004	<0.004	<0.004	<0.004	<0.004
HL^V	0.155	0.155	0.077	0.077	0.077	0.155
[Ag(HL^V)$_2$]NO$_3$	0.004	0.004	0.004	0.008	0.004	0.004
AgNO$_3$	0.147	0.073	0.147	0.147	0.147	0.147
Silver sulphadiazine	0.140	0.070	0.070	0.140	0.140	0.070
Terbinafine	0.009	NA**	0.019	0.019	0.019	0.076
Fluconazole	0.020	NA	0.010	0.040	0.040	0.020
Amphotericin B	0.003	NA	0.003	0.003	0.003	0.003

*MIC values are given in μmol·ml^{-1}.

**NA – not applicable.

Table 8. Antifungal activity of the ligands and their Ag(I) complexes against moulds evaluated by minimum inhibitory concentration*

Compound	Aspergillus niger	Fusarium spp.	Mucor spp.	Penicillium lividum	Botrytis cinerea	Sclerotinia sclerotiorum	Alternaria alternata
HL^I	0.160	0.080	0.080	0.160	0.080	0.080	0.080
[AgH(L^I)$_2$]	<0.004	<0.004	<0.004	<0.004	<0.004	<0.004	<0.004
HL^{II}	0.153	0.153	0.153	0.153	0.076	0.076	0.076
[AgH(L^{II})$_2$]	0.008	0.004	0.008	0.008	<0.004	<0.004	<0.004
HL^{III}	0.152	0.152	0.152	0.152	0.152	0.152	0.152
[AgH(L^{III})$_2$]	0.016	0.008	0.008	0.004	0.004	0.004	0.004
HL^{IV}	0.270	0.136	0.270	0.136	0.068	0.068	0.068
[Ag(HL^{IV})$_2$]NO$_3$	0.004	0.004	<0.004	0.004	<0.004	<0.004	<0.004
HL^V	0.155	0.077	0.077	0.155	0.077	0.077	0.077
[Ag(HL^V)$_2$]NO$_3$	0.008	0.004	0.004	0.008	<0.004	<0.004	<0.004
AgNO$_3$	0.018	0.018	0.073	0.073	0.036	0.036	0.018
Silver sulphadiazine	0.018	0.140	0.070	0.018	NA	NA	0.035
Terbinafine	0.009	0.076	0.076	0.019	NA	NA	0.152
Fluconazole	>0.327	>0.327	>0.327	>0.327	NA	NA	NA
Amphotericin B	0.003	0.003	0.003	0.003	NA	NA	0.003

*MIC values are given in $\mu mol \cdot ml^{-1}$.

**NA – not applicable.

Among the results of pharmacological screening characterizing the antifungal activity of the compounds against yeasts and moulds (Tables 7 and 8) the highest activity of the Ag(I) complexes (MIC$\leq$0.004 μmol·ml^{-1}) comparable with that of the broad-spectrum antibiotic amphotericin B (MIC=0.003 μmol·ml^{-1}) deserves special emphasis, because effective means for their control are extremely limited [103].

An increased activity of Ag(I) complexes as compared to silver nitrate is known, and it is associated, according to Meyer-Overton theory, with an increase in compound lipophilicity owing to Ag(I) complexation with organic ligands [4]. Among silver-containing pharmaceuticals it is the complex of Ag(I) with sulphadiazine that is in most common use as antibacterial agent for treatment of wounds and burns [4–6]. The chief drawbacks of pharmaceuticals containing this complex as an active substance are system side effects characteristic of sulphanilamides (leucopenia, headache, dyspepsia) as well as burning pain, itch, brownish-grey skin coloration, allergic reactions [4]. Besides, in patients of burns departments bacteria resistant to silver sulphadiazine are not infrequently encountered [104]. In this connection a pressing problem is to develop novel effective broad-spectrum drugs for external application with no side effects and microbial resistance. To solve this problem, the Ag(I) complexes synthesized may be promising, as they are characterized by a broad spectrum of antimicrobial activity, the level of the latter against most of the test cultures being higher than that of silver sulphadiazine (Tables 6, 7 and 8).

Microbiological tests show that Ag(I) complexes are more active than the respective ligands. These effects can be due to higher lipophilicity of the complexes (Table 3). Changing lipophilicity is likely to result in bringing down the solubility and permeability of cell barriers, which in turn enhances the bioavailability of antimicrobial agents [99].

The complexes [AgH(L^I)$_2$] and [Ag(L^{IV})$_2$]NO$_3$ with the highest reducing ability among the complexes synthesized are the most active ones against bacteria, yeasts and moulds (Tables 6, 7 and 8). This result could be expected considering our previous data [45–50] about the correlation between redox properties of o-diphenol derivatives and their antibacterial activity. MIC (μmol·ml^{-1}) values of the compounds were found to follow the order:

i)   HL^{IV}$\geq$HL^V>HL^I>HL^{II}>HL^{III};

ii)   [AgH(L^I)$_2$]>[Ag(HL^{IV})$_2$]NO$_3$$\geq$[Ag(HL^V)$_2$]NO$_3$>[AgH(L^{II})$_2$]>
       [AgH(L^{III})$_2$];

the reducing ability (determined electrochemically) of the three most active Ag(I) complexes followed the same order (Figure 3).

Based on the literature and our experimental data several explanations for the effect observed can be offered. First, the complex-forming ion is bound with an oxygen atom in coordination cores of the Ag(I) complexes and thus, according to [12], is able to take part in exchange reactions with bioligands, interacting with more soft bases (nitrogen, sulphur atoms) in the composition of target biomolecules of a microbial cell. Second, the newly synthesized Ag(I) complexes are effective antioxidants owing to a special state of silver in their molecules resulting from PCT complex being formed, and for redox-active complexes, which are active reductants, the antimicrobial activity can be related to their action on electron-transport systems of a microbial cell [26, 105]. The toxic effect is believed to result generally from the catalytic production of reactive radical species that arise *via* electron transfer and destroy the cell. Alternatively, there may be interference with normal electron transport chains.

3. REDUCION OF CYTOCHROME *C* WITH 1,2-DIHYDROXYBENZENE DERIVATIVES AND THEIR SILVER(I) COMPLEXES

On the basis of our data on the properties of sterically hindered phenolic derivatives and their transition metal complexes it may be suggested that biological properties of these compounds (including their antimicrobial activity) in no small measure are due to their participation in redox processes in the cells of microorganisms and man. Processes of this kind being catalyzed by oxidoreductase, these enzymes may be possible macromolecular targets of the sterically hindered phenolic derivatives and their transition metal complexes.

Mammalian mitochondrial Cyt *c* is often used in various investigations as a model target oxidoreductase or as a prototype of various structurally-similar oxidoreductases [106]. It is known [59] that *ortho-* and *para-*diphenol derivatives are able to reduce mammalian Cyt *c*. As noted above, we have studied the interaction of sterically hindered phenolic derivatives and their transition metal complexes with bovine Cyt *c* [47–50]. The choice of Cyt *c* as a model target to study its interaction with potential antimicrobials synthesized is based on the literature data on the structure of mammalian Cyt *c*, its redox properties and biological functions as well as on the information about a number of microorganisms' Cyt *c* with structural-functional properties similar to those of bovine Cyt *c* used in our investigations.

Mammalian Cyt *c* is a small (about 12–15 kDa) cationic (its isoelectric point being about 10 [107]) protein with the single heme, which is covalently linked to the protein molecule via thioester bonds with two conservative cysteine residues. It has methionine and histidine residues as ligands of the heme's iron (so-called class I *c*-type cytochrome). Approximately 25 % of the heme of mammalian Cyt *c* is exposed from the polypeptide globule into medium, and its edge is surrounded by positively charged amino acid residues. On the whole, homology and similarity of 3D-structures among Cyt *c* of mammals and other eukaryotes (fishes, yeast etc.) are very high [108, 109].

Eukaryotic cytochromes *c* localize in inner mitochondrial space, where they transfer electrons from the complex III (coenzyme Q-cytochrome *c* reductase) to the complex IV (cytochrome *c* oxidase) of the mitochondrial respiratory chain and re-oxidize superoxide into dioxygen, controlling formation of reactive oxygen species (ROS) [57, 110–112]. Liberation of mammalian Cyt *c* from mitochondria into cytosol is an essential step of apoptosis, and redox chemistry of the protein also plays an important role in programmed cell death. For example, mammalian Cyt *c* controls ROS level [113], the complex of cardiolipin with Cyt *c* acts as peroxidase and cardiolipin oxygenase phospholipid [114], the oxidized form of the Cyt *c* can induce activation of caspases *via* apoptosome, while the reduced form cannot do it [115].

At pH 7.0 the midpoint redox potential of mammalian (bovine, horse *etc.*) Cyt *c* is reported to be about 0.265 V *versus* normal hydrogen electrode [109, 116] and is known to vary with temperature, electrolyte composition and ionic strength [117, 118]. In general, *c*-type cytochromes with a histidyl-methionyl coordination of iron have redox potentials about from 0 to 0.360 V [109].

Mammalian Cyt *c* is reported to be reduced by the following ions and low molecular weight compounds: Cr(II) [119], Fe(II) complex with EDTA [120], some complexes of Co(II) [121] and Ru(II) [122], and reduced mammalian Cyt *c* is oxidized by Cu(II)-(bis)histidine complex [123]. The protein is also reduced by superoxide-ion [122], ascorbate [124], thiols [125, 126] as well as by catechols, quinols, hydroquinon and *o*-aminophenols [47–50, 58, 59, 112]. All these redox interactions take place close to the solvent accessible heme edge, and the mechanism of outer sphere electron transfer has been proven in many kinetics experiments.

In artificial systems mammalian Cyt c can be reduced by various enzymes, among which are, for instance, mammalian microsomal diflavin NADPH:cytochrome P450 reductase (P450R) [127] as well as mitochondrial [Fe$_2$S$_2$]-ferredoxins (adrenodoxin (Adx) [128] and hepatoredoxin) and cytochrome b5.

Table 9. Redox characteristics of P450R, Adx and Cyt c

Compound (enzyme (organism) or low molecular weight compound)*	Redox pair	E_{mp}, V	References
Cyt c (bovine)	Fe^{3+}/Fe^{2+}	+0.265	[116]
P450R (human)	FMN/ FMNH*	−0.066	[130]
Pyrocatechol	QH*/QH$_2$	−0.100	[129]
P450R (human)	FMNH*/ FMNH$_2$	−0.270	[130]
Adx (bovine)	[Fe$_2$S$_2$] $^{2+}$/[Fe$_2$S$_2$] $^{1+}$	−0.270	[131]
P450R (human)	FAD/FADH*	−0.290	[130]
P450R (human)	FADH*/FADH$_2$	−0.380	[130]
Pyrocatechol	Q/QH*	−0.530	[129]

Abbreviations: E_{mp} – midpoint redox-potential versus the standard hydrogen electrode, FMN – flavin mononucleotide, FAD – flavin adenine dinucleotide, Adx – adrenodoxin, FMN, FMNH and FMNH$_2$ – quinone, semiquinone and quinol forms of flavin mononucleotide, respectively; FAD FADH* and FADH$_2$ – quinone, semiquinone and quinol forms of flavin adenine dinucleotide, respectively; Q – quinone (completely oxidized), QH* – semiquinone, QH$_2$ – pyrocatechol (completely reduced).

There are numerous data testifying that the interaction of Cyt c with its reductases and oxidases is to a large extent of an electrostatic type involving positively charged ε-amino groups of the surface lysine residues of Cyt c molecule and negatively charged free carboxyl groups of corresponding electron transfer proteins. Dissociation constants have been determined for complexes of adrenodoxin, hepatoredoxin, cytochrome b5 heme-containing tryptic fragment and myoglobin with Cyt c preparations immobilized *via* lysine residues (Cyt c-Sepharose I) or *via* histidine residues (Cyt c-Sepharose II). The latter adsorbent possesses a 2−3 times higher affinity to adrenodoxin and hepatoredoxin that the former one. Affinity to Cyt c-Sepharose II for the proteins studied increases in the following sequence: Adx ≥ hepatoredoxin > cytochrome b5 heme-containing tryptic fragment > myoglobin [129−132].

Thus, the affinity and selectivity of formation of protein-protein Cyt c complexes are a prerequisite to effective electron transfer between the above-mentioned protein redox partners.

Previously we showed that the rate of Cyt c reduction with some thiocatechols and o-aminophenols increased on adding P450R, but not Adx [47–49]. This experimental fact is consistent with the literature data on redox characteristics of the proteins mentioned (Table 9) and allows one to suggest that P450R is able to catalyze the oxidation of catechols into semiquinones, probably creating an additional route of transferring electrons to Cyt c (Figure 5).

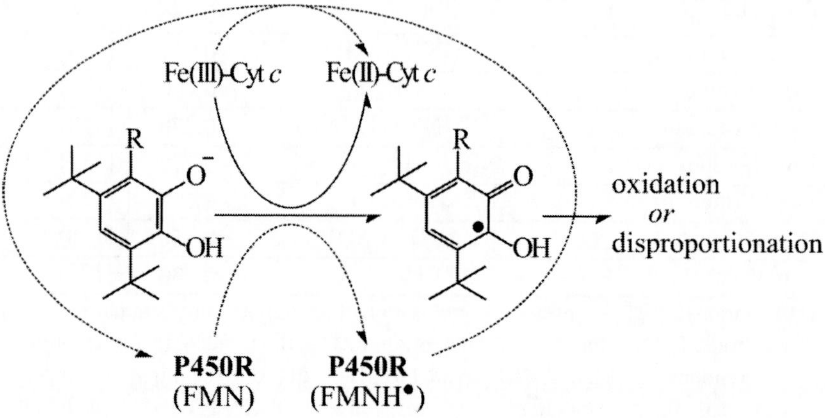

Figure 5. Plausible scheme of catalysis by P450R of reduction bovine (mammalian) Cyt c with catechols (QH_2) in anaerobic conditions (Q – quinone (completely oxidized), QH^* – semiquinone). Fe(III)-Cyt c and Fe(II)-Cyt c are respectively the oxidized and reduced forms of Cyt c.

It should be noted that dioxygen can also act as a catalyst of this process, as it can accept an electron from semiquinone forms (QH^*) of the compounds being oxidized, transforming into superoxide which reduces the Cyt c [112]. Figure 5 shows the scheme of catalysis by P450R of bovine (mammalian) Cyt c reduction with sterically hindered phenolic derivatives, which we carried out in argon-saturated solutions [47–49], but *in vivo* dioxygen is an important participant of processes in Cyt c-containing enzymatic systems. It is likely that catalysis of this kind can take place also in natural respiration electron transport systems including Cyt c and its reductive partners with suitable value of redox potential (i.e. quinol:Cyt c reductases like bc_1-complex). But it is more likely that in the case of natural systems in their innocent state the direct reduction of Cyt c with their intrinsic quinols (ubiquinol, menaquinol etc.) is prohibited. However, in the case of external attack by quinol-(catechol)-based bioactive compounds (in particular, sterically hindered phenolic derivatives) the number of direct interactions of quinols with Cyt c will increase.

Bacteria possess various c-type cytochromes: multi-heme, water-soluble or membrane-bound ones as well as those with hystydyl-methionyl (as for eukaryotic Cyt c) or, less often, hystydyl-hystydyl axial ligands, etc., and they play an important part in vital functions of microorganisms. Usually, a c-type cytochrome (quite often, monoheme Cyt c) acts as a fast electron shuttle between quinol oxidases and terminal oxidoreductases in various bacterial electron transport chains. Bacterial Cyt c oxidases, Cyt c peroxidases, Cyt c nitrite reductases are the terminal oxidoreductases for these cytochromes [108, 109, 132, 133]. Cyt c oxidases are essential for aerobic respiration and protection from reactive oxygen species [111, 134]. Cyt c peroxidases are thought to play a role in resistance to exogenous H_2O_2 [135]. In particular, they are found in bacteria *Neisseria gonorea* [136], *Pseudomonas aeruginosa* [137]. Cyt c nitrite reductases catalyze the reduction of nitrite, nitrous oxide and hydroxylamine to ammonia as an important step of the nitrogen assimilation, anaerobic nitrate (nitrite) respiration and protection against nitrogen reactive species [138]. For example, bacteria *E. coli* [139], *Pseudomonas aeruginosa* [140], *Salmonella typhimurium* [141] have got Cyt c nitrite reductases of this type.

In the literature there are data pointing to an intimate connection between some of bacterial Cyt c and virulence as well as viability of microorganisms. In particular, two similar monoheme small c-type cytochromes, CccA (Mw 13 kDa, His-Met ligation, midpoint redox potential about 195 mV) and CccB (Mw 10 kDa), located on the extracellular surface of the cytoplasmic membrane, regulate the major toxin gene expression of *Bacillus anthracis* (the etiologic agent of anthrax) [142]. This and other functions of CccA and CccB are most likely redox-related and associated with electron transfer. These findings are essential not only to virulence regulation in *Bacillus anthracis*, but also to analysis of virulence regulation in many pathogenic Gram-positive bacteria [143]. Cytochromes c of the same type are found also in *Bacillus cereus* and *Bacillus subtilis*. Moreover, maturation of type I Cyt c has recently been shown to contribute to virulence in *Legionella pneumophila* [144] as well as *Mycobacterium tuberculosis* [145]. Two genes (nirM and nirC) of *Pseudomonas aeruginosa* encode two Cyt c (13 and 15 kDa, respectively; both monoheme with His-Met ligation) which have been reported to be physiological electron donors for the Cyt c nitrite reductase of the pathogen

[140]. In *Legionella pneumophila* cytochrome *c*1 (28 kDa, one heme, His-Met ligation) and cytochrome *c*5 (15 kDa, one heme, His-Met ligation) promote intracellular infection. Moreover, cytochrome *c*4 (a 21 kDa protein, containing two *c*-type hemes, both with His-Met iron ligation) is required for biosynthesis of legiobactin that is an untypical iron-sequestering siderophore of the bacterium, which is important for lung infection by *Legionella pneumophila* [146, 147]. Electron-transferring monoheme Cyt *c* with His-Met ligation is also presented in bacteria genera *Mycobacterium, Helicobacter, Campylobacter, Wolinella, Serratia* [108].

Mycobacterium tuberculosis virulence correlates with release of mammalian Cyt *c* from mitochondria which are disrupted by the pathogen in infected macrophages [148, 149]. Taking into consideration the data [115], reduction of the Cyt *c* liberated with a pharmacological agent may offer promise for preventing damage to the cells in the case of *Mycobacterium tuberculosis* infection.

A relationship between virulence and Cyt *c* is found also for mould *Aspergillus fumigatus* containing Cyt *c* in mitochondria. According to [150], Cyt *c* CycA of this mould is required for virulence of the microorganism, but the controversial data from an earlier source are also presented [151]. Yeast and mould mitochondrial Cyt *c* are very similar to mammalian enzymes. Notice that *Saccharomyces cerevisiae* expresses two isoforms of Cyt *c*, which share 80 % identity and are encoded by the genes *CYC1* and *CYC7* [152]. In yeast Cyt *c* is involved in scavenging hydrogen peroxide by delivering electrons to the yeast enzyme *b*-type heme-containing Cyt *c* peroxidase [108, 153].

Thus, it is quite reasonable to use mammalian Cyt *c* as a plausible model of *c*-type cytochromes to investigate the interaction of potential redox-active antimicrobials (including sterically hindered *o*-diphenol derivatives and their metal complexes) with their probable macromolecular targets – oxidoreductases.

We have carried out a spectrophotometrical investigation of reduction of bovine heart Cyt *c* with the compounds HL^I–HL^V and their Ag(I) complexes; the results obtained are given in Table 10. Using the procedure developed by us [48], it was found that all the compounds under study can reduce Cyt *c*. The higher rate of Cyt *c* reduction with the compounds HL^{IV} and HL^V compared to that with the compounds HL^I–HL^{III} can be due first of all to the higher reducing ability (determined electrochemically) of the former. Almost equal rates of Cyt *c* reduction with HL^I–HL^{III} can be due to similar reducing abilities of these compounds (Figure 3). Furthermore, attention should be paid to the ionization constant values of HL^I–HL^V characterizing their ability to form anions by hydroxyls being deprotonated, which differ but slightly (pK=9.0÷11.0 [36]).

Table 10. Rates of reduction of Cyt c (υ) with the ligands HL^I–HL^V and their Ag(I) complexes*

Compound	υ**, nmol·min^{-1}	Compound	υ, nmol·min^{-1}
HL^I	1.0	$[AgH(L^I)_2]$	3.0
HL^{II}	1.1	$[AgH(L^{II})_2]$	2.5
HL^{III}	1.0	$[AgH(L^{III})_2]$	2.3
HL^{IV}	1.5	$[Ag(HL^{IV})_2]NO_3$	2.7
HL^V	1.3	$[Ag(HL^V)_2]NO_3$	2.5

*The final concentrations of Cyt c and the compound tested were respectively 7 and 35 μmol·l^{-1}.

**The absolute error doesn't exceed 0.1 nmol·min^{-1}.

Taking into account the findings presented in our previous publications [47–50] as well as the results of our electrochemical investigation (see Section 1), it may be suggested that the most probable route of oxidation of the above-mentioned compounds upon interacting with Cyt c *in vitro* under anaerobic conditions can include two successive one-electron steps of oxidation of their anionic forms to yield *o*-benzoquinones via intermediate *o*-benzosemiquinone formation (Figure 6). This scheme of the reduction of Cyt c with the anion form of the sterically hindered 1,2-dihydroxybenzene derivatives HL^I–HL^V is substantiated by the fact that isoniazid, possessing a reducing ability [69, 71], nevertheless doesn't reduce Cyt c (υ<0.1 nmol·min^{-1}), being essentially unable to form the above-mentioned ionic forms (phenolate).

It is known [59] that metal complexes can interact with Cyt c both in their molecular form as well as via phenolate ligand formed upon their dissociation. All the Ag(I) complexes under study reduce Cyt c at a rate several times higher than that of the redox process involving the compounds HL^I–HL^V (Table 10). The rate of Cyt c reduction with the Ag(I) complexes varies in a very narrow range (Table 10) and correlates with their reducing ability determined electrochemically (Figure 3). Among these complexes it is the complex $AgH(L^I)_2$ that is characterized by the highest rate of Cyt c reduction.

According to electrochemical data, this complex is the strongest reductant in the series of Ag(I) complexes (Figure 3).

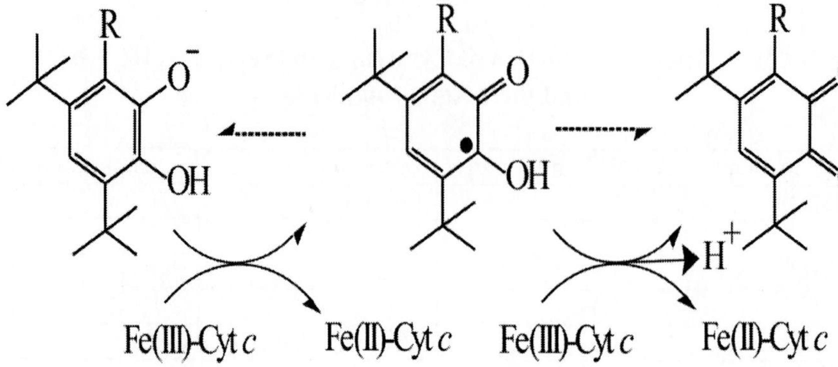

Figure 6. Scheme of the reduction of Cyt *c* with the anion form of 1,2-dihydroxy-benzene derivatives; Fe(III)-Cyt *c* and Fe(II)-Cyt *c* are respectively the oxidized and reduced forms of Cyt *c* (disproportionation of the ligand is depicted by a dashed line).

In summary, the sequences characterizing the decrease of the rates of Cyt *c* reduction with the ligands and their Ag(I) complexes are the same as those characterizing their antibacterial activity (Tables 5, 6 and 7) and reducing ability determined electrochemically (Figure 3):

i) $HL^{IV} > HL^{V} \geq HL^{I} \sim HL^{II} \sim HL^{III}$;
ii) $[AgH(L^{I})_2] > [Ag(HL^{IV})_2]NO_3 > [Ag(HL^{V})_2]NO_3 \sim [AgH(L^{II})_2] > [AgH(L^{III})_2]$.

Nevertheless, the reduction of Cyt *c* with sterically hindered 1,2-dihydroxybenzene derivatives and their Ag(I) complexes cannot be due solely to their capacity for oxidation, and it depends on physicochemical properties (ionization, lipophilicity etc.) in more intricate way.

In this connection attention should be paid to the values of stability and ionization constants of the compounds under investigation as well as their *n*-octanol/water partition coefficient: these constants vary in a very narrow range (see Section 1).

Global analysis of correlations "property–activity" obtained by us not only for the series of compounds presented in this manuscript, but also upon examining several tens of mono- and di-substituted derivatives of sterically hindered 1,2-dihydroxybenzene as well as their metal complexes, showed that it is correct to consider these correlations only in a limited series of chemically similar compounds, that is, separately for ligands and metal complexes, the chemical nature of compounds belonging to these classes being radically different [47–50].

CONCLUSION

1,2-Dihydroxybenzene derivatives and their silver complexes may present a promising field of a search for compounds to develop new effective antimicrobials. Our study provides the basis for the synthesis and investigation of physicochemical properties of these compounds. The results are presented of physicochemical investigation of Ag(I) ion complexation with some sterically hindered 1,2-dihydroxybenzene derivatives, which made it possible to determine ionic and redox ligand forms with high nucleophilicity of silver-ion binding sites as well as the peculiarities of the structural organization of the coordination cores of the newly synthesized Ag(I) complexes.

Based on the pharmacological screening results, the selection is justified of hit-compounds – the Ag(I) complexes with 2-[4,6-di(*tert*-butyl)-2,3-dihydroxyphenylsulphanyl]-acetic acid and 4,6-di-*tert*-butyl-2,3-dihydroxy-benzaldehyde isonicotinoyl hydrazone, possessing antibacterial and antifungal activity higher than those of some standard antibiotics, to develop effective drugs for combination therapy of mixed infections. The correlation between antimicrobial activity of the compounds and their reducing ability deserves a particular attention. Relying on these results, an assumption can be made that redox interaction with oxidoreductases as macromolecular targets can be essential for realizing antimicrobial and antioxidant activity of the compounds studied.

Oxidation of 1,2-dihydroxybenzene derivatives and their metal complexes by the oxidized form of Cyt c results in formation of semiquinone species of these compounds and Cyt c reduction. Hypothetically, on the level of the electron transport chain of cellular respiration under aerobic conditions it will benefit superoxide production due to oxygen interacting with exogenous semiquinones as well as "leakage" of electrons from a quinol:Cyt c reductase (bc$_1$-complex) on dioxygen because of the main pool of Cyt c being reduced, and hence, normal electron transfer from this reductase will be disrupted.

According to the results of our investigations, transition metal complexes of 1,2-dihydroxybenzene derivatives, in particular, those with silver ions, possess a substantial antimicrobial activity *in vitro*, while the ligands are characterized by a relatively low activity, although both the ligands and their metal complexes can reduce Cyt *c*. Thus, the presence of the metal ion is extremely important for realization of the antimicrobial effect. In the frame of the hypothesis described above, a transition metal ion may promote formation of hydrogen peroxide and hydroxyl radical from superoxide, increasing cell damage, but this invites further investigation. Moreover, other reasons also have to be invoked to explain the antimicrobial effects of the metal complexes under study.

REFERENCES

[1] Farrell, N. P. (Ed.). (1999). Uses of inorganic chemistry in medicine, Cambridge, UK: *Royal Society of Chemistry*.

[2] Gielen, M. and Tiekink, E.R.T. (Eds.). (2005). Metallotherapeutic drugs and metal-based diagnostic agents. The use of metals in medicine. Weinheim, Germany: *Wiley-VCH*.

[3] Leeb, M. (2004). Antibiotics: a shot in the arm. *Nature*, Vol. 431, 892–893.

[4] Lansdown, A.B.G. (2010). Silver in health care: antimicrobial effects and safety in use, Cambridge, UK: *Royal Society of Chemistry*.

[5] Carr, H.S., Wlodkowski, Th.J. and Rosenkranz, H.S. (1973). Silver sulfadiazine: in vitro antibacterial activity. *Antimicrob. Agents Chemother.*, Vol. 4, 585–587.

[6] Clement, J.L. and Jarrett, P.S. (1994). Antibacterial silver. *Met.-Based Drugs*, Vol. 1, 467–482.

[7] Kazachenko, A.S., Legler, A.V., Per'yanova, O.V. and Vstavskaya, Yu.A. (2000). Synthesis and antimicrobial activity of silver complexes with histidine and tryptophan. *Pharm. Chem. J.*, Vol. 34, 257–258.

[8] Legler, A.V., Kazachenko, A.S., Kazbanov, V.I., Per'yanova, O.V. and Veselova, O.F. (2001). Synthesis and antimicrobial activity of silver complexes with arginine and glutamic acid. *Pharm. Chem. J.*, Vol. 35, 501–503.

[9] Nomiya, K. and Yokoyama, H. (2002). Syntheses, crystal structures and antimicrobial activities of polymeric silver(I) complexes with three amino-acids [aspartic acid (H_2asp), glycine (Hgly) and asparagine (Hasn)]. *J. Chem. Soc., Dalton Trans.*, № 12, 2483–2490.

[10] Nomiya, K., Noguchi, R. and Oda, M. (2000). Synthesis and crystal structure of coinage metal(I) complexes with tetrazole (Htetz) and triphenylphosphine ligands, and their antimicrobial activities. A helical polymer of silver(I) complex [Ag(tetz)(PPh3)2]n and a monomeric gold(I) complex [Au(tetz)(PPh3)]. *Inorg. Chim. Acta,* Vol. 298, 24–32.

[11] Abuskhuna, S., Briody, J., McCann, M., Devereux, M. and Kavanagh, K. (2004) Synthesis, structure and anti-fungal activity of dimeric Ag(I) complexes containing bis-imidazole ligands. *Polyhedron,* Vol. 23, 1249–1255.

[12] Nomiya, K., Tsuda, K., Sudoh, T. and Oda, M. (1997). Ag(I)-N-bond-containing compound showing wide spectra in effective antimicrobial activities: polymeric silver(I) imidazolate. *J. Inorg. Biochem.,* Vol. 68, 39–44.

[13] Coyle, B., Kinsella, P., McCann, M., Devereux, M. and O'Connor, R. (2004) Synthesis, X-ray structure, anti-fungal and anti-cancer activity of [Ag(NH$_3$)$_2$(salH)$_2$] (salH$_2$=salicylic acid). *J. Inorg. Biochem.,* Vol. 98, 1361–1366.

[14] Nomiya, K., Tsuda, K. and Kasuga, N.C. (2000) Synthesis and crystal structure of hexanuclear silver(I) cluster [Ag(Hmna)]$_6$·4H$_2$O(H$_2$mna=2-mercaptonicotinic acid) and a supramolecular gold(I) complex H[(Au(Hmna)$_2$] in solid state, and their antimicrobial activities. *J. Chem. Soc., Dalton Trans.*, № 13, 2091–2097.

[15] Nomiya, K., Onoue, K.-I., Kondoh, Y., Kasuga, N.C., Nagano, H., Oda, M. and Sakuma, S. (1995). Synthesis and characterization of oligomeric, anionic thiomalato-silver(I) complexes with biological activities. *Polyhedron*, Vol. 14, 1359–1367.

[16] Melaiye, A., Hindi, K.M., Durmus, S., Panzner, M.J. and Hogue, L.A. (2004). Formation of water-soluble pincer silver(I) –carbene complexes: a novel antimicrobial agent. *J. Med. Chem.*, Vol. 47, 973–977.

[17] Nomiya, K., Takahashi, S. and Noguchi, R. Water-soluble silver(I) complexes of (R)-(+)- and (S)-(-)-2-pyrrolidone-5-carboxylic acid and their antimicrobial activities. Chiral helical polymer and polymer sheet structures in the solid-state formed by self-assembly of dimeric [Ag(Hpyrrld)]$_2$ cores. (2000). *J. Chem. Soc., Dalton Trans.*, № 23, 4369–4373.

[18] Liu, W., Bensdorf, K., Hagenbach, A., Abram, U., Niu, B., Mariappan, A. and Gust, R. (2011). Synthesis and biological studies of silver N-heterocyclic carbene complexes derived from 4,5-diarylimidazole. *Eur. J. Med. Chem.*, Vol. 46, 5927–5934.

[19] Hemmert, C., Fabié, A., Fabre, A., Benoit-Vical, F. and Gornitzka, H. (2013). Synthesis, structures, and antimalarial activities of some silver(I), gold(I) and gold(III) complexes involving N-heterocyclic carbene ligands. *Eur. J. Med. Chem.*, Vol. 60, 64–75.

[20] Percival, S.L., Bowler, P.G. and Russel, D. (2005). Bacterial resistance to silver in wound care. *J. Hospital Infect.*, Vol. 60, 1–7.

[21] Gupta, A., Matsui, K., Lo, J.F. and Silver, S. (1999). Molecular basis for resistance to silver cation in Salmonella. *Nature Medicine*, Vol. 5, 183–188.

[22] Silver, S. (2003). Bacterial silver resistance: molecular biology and uses and misuses of silver compounds. *FEMS Microbiology Rev.*, Vol. 27, 341–353.

[23] Nomiya, K., Takahashi, S. and Noguchi, R. (2000). Synthesis and crystal structure of silver(I) complexes with (S)-(+)-5-oxo-2-tetrahydro-furancarboxylic acid (S-Hothf) and its isomeric forms showing wide spectra of effective antibacterial and antifungal activities. Chiral helical polymers in the solid state formed by self-assembly of the dimeric [Ag(othf)]$_2$ cores. *J. Chem. Soc., Dalton Trans.*, № 8, 1343–1348.

[24] Nomiya, K., Yoshizawa, A., Tsukagoshi, K., Kasuga, N.C., Hirakawa, S. and Watanabe, J. (2004). Synthesis and structural characterization of silver(I), aluminium(III) and cobalt(II) complexes with 4-isopropyltropolone (hinokitiol) showing noteworthy biological activities. Action of silver(I)-oxygen bonding complexes on the antimicrobial activities. *J. Inorg. Biochem.*, Vol. 98, 46–60.

[25] Nomiya, K., Takahashi, S., Noguchi, R., Nemoto, S., Takayama, T. and Oda, M. (2000). Synthesis and characterization of water–soluble silver(I) complexes with L-histidine and (S)-(–)2-pyrrolidone-5-carboxylic acid showing a wide spectrum of effective antibacterial and antifungal activities. *Inorg. Chem.*, Vol. 39, 3301–3311.

[26] Ames, J.R., Ryan, M.D. and Kovacic, P. (1986). Mechanism of antibacterial action: electron transfer and oxy radicals. *J. Free Radic. Biol. Med.*, Vol. 2, 371–391.

[27] Reisner, E., Arion, V.B., Keppler, B.K. and Pombeiro, A.J.L. (2008). Electron-transfer activated metal-based anticancer drugs. *Inorg. Chim. Acta,* Vol. 361, 1569–1583.

[28] Kowol, C.R., Reisner, E., Chiorescu, I., Arion, V.B., Galanski, M., Deubel, D. V. and Keppler, B.K. (2008). An electrochemical study of antineoplastic gallium, iron and ruthenium complexes with redox

noninnocent α-N-heterocyclic chalcogensemicarbazones. *Inorg. Chem.*, Vol. 47, 11032–11047.

[29] Jakupec, M.A., Reisner, E., Eichinger, A., Pongratz, M., Arion, V.B., Galanski, M., Hartinger, C.G. and Keppler, B.K. (2005). Redox-active antineoplastic ruthenium complexes with indazole: correlation of in vitro potency and reduction potential. *J. Med. Chem.*, Vol. 48, 2831–2837.

[30] Von Sengbusch, P. (1979). Molekular und Zellbiologie, Berlin-Heidelberg-New York: Springer-Verlag.

[31] Coyle, B., Kinsella, P., McCann M., Devereux, M., O'Connor, R., Clynes, M. and Kavanagh, K. (2004) Induction of apoptosis in yeast and mammalian cells by exposure to 1,10-phenanthroline metal complexes. Toxicol. In Vitro, Vol. 18, 63–70.

[32] Coyle, B., Kavanagh, K., McCann, M. and Devereux, M. (2003). Mode of anti-fungal activity of 1,10-phenanthroline and its Cu(II), Mn(II) and Ag(I) complexes. *BioMetals,* Vol. 16, 321–329.

[33] Creaven, B.S., Egan, D.A., Karcz, D., Kavanagh, K., McCann, M., Mahon, M., Noble, A., Thati, B. and Walsh, M. (2007). Synthesis, characterization and antimicrobial activity of copper(II) and manganese(II) complexes of coumarin-6,7-dioxyacetic acid (cdoaH$_2$) and 4-methylcoumarin-6,7-dioxyacetic acid (4-MecdoaH$_2$): X-ray crystal structures of [Cu(cdoa)(phen)$_2$]·8.8H$_2$O and [Cu(4-Mecdoa)(phen)$_2$]·13H$_2$O (phen=1,10-phenanthroline). *J. Inorg. Biochem.,* Vol. 101, 1108–1119.

[34] McCann, M., Coyle, B., McKay, S., McCormack, P., Kavanagh, K., Devereux, M., McKee, V., Kinsella, P., O'Connor, R. and Clynes, M. (2004). Synthesis and X-ray crystal structure of [Ag(phendio)$_2$]ClO$_4$ (phendio = 1,10-phenanthroline-5,6-dione) and its effects on fungal and mammalian cells. *BioMetals,* Vol. 17, 635–645.

[35] Loginova, N.V., Chernyavskaya, A.A., Polozov, G.I., Koval'chuk, T.V., Bondarenko, E.V., Osipovich, N.P., Sheryakov, A.A. and Shadyro, O.I. (2005). Silver(I) interaction and complexation with sterically hindered sulfur-containing diphenol derivatives. *Polyhedron,* Vol. 24, 611–618.

[36] Chernyavskaya, A.A. (2008). Complexation and redox interaction of silver(I) with derivatives of sterically hindered diphenols and aminophenols. Ph.D. Thesis, Belarusian State University, Minsk.

[37] Chernyavskaya, A.A., Loginova, N.V., Polozov, G.I., Shadyro, O.I., Sheryakov, A.A. and Bondarenko, E.V. (2006). Synthesis and antimicrobial activity of silver(I) and copper(II) complexes with 2-(4,6-

di-tert-butyl-2,3-dihydroxyphenylsulfanyl) acetic acid. *Pharm. Chem. J.,* Vol. 40, 413–415.

[38] McDonnell, G., Russgell, A.D. (1999). Antiseptics and disinfectants: activity, action, and resistance. *Clin. Microbiol. Rev.,* Vol. 12, 14–179.

[39] Loginova, N.V., Koval'chuk, T.V., Polozov, G.I., Osipovich, N.P., Chernyavskaya, A.A., Sorokin, V.L. and Shadyro, O.I. (2010). Redox-active antimicrobial metal complexes with sterically hindered o-diphenol and o-aminophenol derivatives. In G. Blanc, and D. Moreau (Eds.), Biometals: Molecular structures, binding properties (pp. 59–90). Hauppauge, New York: Nova Science Publisher's.

[40] Loginova, N.V., Koval'chuk, T.V., Zheldakova, R.A., Chernyavskaya, A.A., Osipovich, N.P., Glushonok, G.K., Polozov, H.I., Sorokin, V.L. and Shadyro, O.I. (2006). Copper(II) complexes of sterically hindered diphenol derivatives: synthesis, characterization and microbiological studies. *Centr. Eur. J. Chem.,* Vol. 4, № 3, 440–457.

[41] Loginova, N.V., Chernyavskaya, A.A., Parfenova, M.S., Osipovich, N.P., Polozov, G.I., Fedutik, Yu.A., Koval'chuk, T.V. and Shevchenko, G.P. (2006). Complex of silver(I) with 2-[4,6-di(tert-butyl)-2,3-dihydroxyphenylsulfanyl]acetic acid as a precursor of silver nanoparticles. *Polyhedron,* Vol. 25, 1723–1728.

[42] Loginova, N.V., Koval'chuk, T. V., Zheldakova, R.A., Chernyavskaya, A.A., Osipovich, N.P., Glushonok, G.K., Polozov, H. I., Povalishev, V.N., Sorokin, V.L. and Shadyro, O.I. (2006). Synthesis, characterization and antifungal activity of copper (II) complexes of sterically hindered diphenol derivatives. *Polyhedron,* Vol. 25, 3603–3610.

[43] Loginova, N.V., Koval'chuk, T.V., Zheldakova, R.A., Osipovich, N.P., Sorokin, V.L., Polozov, G.I., Ksendzova, G.A., Glushonok, G.K., Chernyavskaya, A.A. and Shadyro, O.I. (2006). Synthesis and biological evaluation of copper (II) complexes of sterically hindered o-aminophenol derivatives as antimicrobial agents. *Bioorg. Med. Chem. Lett.,* Vol. 16, 5403–5407.

[44] Koval'chuk, T.V. (2007). Synthesis and characterization of bioactive copper(II), cobalt(II), nickel(II) and zinc(II) complexes with derivatives of sterically hindered diphenols and aminophenols. Ph.D. Thesis, Belarusian State University.

[45] Loginova, N.V., Koval'chuk, T.V., Polozov, G.I., Osipovich, N.P., Rytik, P.G., Kucherov, I.I., Chernyavskaya, A.A., Sorokin, V.L. and Shadyro, O.I. (2008). Synthesis, characterization, antifungal and anti-

HIV activities of metal(II) complexes of 4,6-di-tert-butyl-3-[(2-hydroxyethyl)thio]benzene-1,2-diol. *Europ. J. Med. Chem.*, Vol. 43, 1536–1542.

[46] Loginova, N.V., Koval'chuk, T.V., Osipovich, N.P., Polozov, G.I., Sorokin, V.L., Chernyavskaya, A.A. and Shadyro, O.I. (2008). Redox-active antifungal cobalt(II) and copper(II) complexes with sterically hindered o-aminophenol derivatives. *Polyhedron*, Vol. 27, 985–991.

[47] Loginova, N.V., Faletrov, Y.V., Koval'chuk, T.V., Osipovich, N.P., Polozov, G.I., Chernyavskaya, A.A., Zheldakova, R.A., Azarko, I.I., Gres, A.T., Shadyro, O.I. and Shkumatov, V.M. (2010). Redox-active metal(II) complexes of sterically hindered phenolic ligands: antibacterial activity and reduction of cytochrome c. *Polyhedron*, Vol. 29, 1646–1652.

[48] Loginova, N.V., Koval'chuk, T.V., Faletrov, Y.V., Halauko, Y.S., Osipovich, N.P., Polozov, G.I., Zheldakova, R.A., Gres, A.T., Halauko, A.S., Azarko, I.I., Shkumatov, V.M. and Shadyro, O.I. (2011). Redox-active metal(II) complexes of sterically hindered phenolic ligands: antibacterial activity and reduction of cytochrome c. Part II. Metal(II) complexes of o-diphenol derivatives of thioglycolic acid. *Polyhedron,* Vol. 30, 2581–2591.

[49] Loginova, N.V., Polozov, G.I., Koval'chuk, T.V., Faletrov, Y.V., Osipovich, N.P., Gres, A.T., Zheldakova, R.A. and Shadyro, O.I. (2012). Pharmacologically active benzene derivatives: Synthesis, complexation with biometals, and biological evaluation of sterically hindered 1,2-dihydroxybenzene and o-aminophenol derivatives. In G. Tranfo (Ed.), Benzene and its derivatives: New uses and impacts on environment and human health (pp. 23–68). Hauppauge, New York: Nova Science Publisher's.

[50] Loginova, N.V., Gres, A.T., Polozov, G.I., Koval'chuk, T.V., Osipovich, N.P., Zheldakova, R.A., Faletrov, Y.V., Strakha, I.S. and Azarko, I.I. (2013). Redox-active metal(II) complexes of sterically hindered phenolic ligands: Antibacterial activity and reduction of cytochrome c. Part III. Copper(II) complexes of cycloaminomethyl derivatives of o-diphenols. *Polyhedron,* Vol. 57, 39–46.

[51] Loginova, N., Chernyavskaya, A., Polozov, G., Osipovich, N., Koval'chuk, T., Gres, A., Halauko, Y., Halauko, A., Zheldakova, R., Faletrov, Y. and Azarko, I. (2013). Bioactive silver(I) complexes with phenolic derivatives of thioglycolic and thiopropionic acids. *Mini-Rev. Org. Chem.*, Vol. 10, 227–240.

[52] Rollas, S. and Güniz Küçükgüzel, Ş. (2007). Biological activities of hydrazone derivatives. *Molecules,* Vol. 12, 1910–1939.

[53] Hearn, M.J., Cynamon, M.H., Chen, M.F., Coppins, R., Davis, J., Joo-On Kang, H., Noble, A., Tu-Sekine, B., Terrot, M.S., Trombino, D., Thai, M., Webster, E.R. and Wilson, R. (2009). Preparation and antitubercular activities in vitro and in vivo of novel Schiff bases of isoniazid. *Eur. J. Med. Chem.,* Vol. 44, 4169–4178.

[54] Hu, W., Zhou, W., Xia, Ch. and Wen, X. (2006). Synthesis and anticancer activity of thiosemicarbazones. *Bioorg. Med. Chem. Lett.,* Vol. 16, 2213–2218.

[55] Patole, J., Sandbhor, U., Padhye, S., Deobagkar, D.N., Anson, Ch.E. and Powell, A. (2003). Structural chemistry and in vitro antitubercular activity of acetylpyridine benzoyl hydrazone and its copper complex against Mycobacterium smegmatis. *Bioorg. Med. Chem. Lett.,* Vol. 13, 51–55.

[56] Muller, F.L., Liu, Y. and van Remmen, H. (2004). Complex III releases superoxide to both sides of the inner mitochondrial membrane. *J. Biol. Chem.,* Vol. 279, 49064–49073.

[57] Maneg, O., Malatesta, F., Ludwig, B., and Drosou, V. (2004). Interaction of cytochrome c with cytochrome oxidase: two different docking scenarios. *Biochim. Biophys. Acta,* Vol. 1655, 274–281.

[58] Nagasawa, H.T., Gutmann, H.R. and Morgan, M.A. (1959). The oxidation of o-aminophenols by cytochrome c and cytochrome oxidase. *J. Biol. Chem.,* Vol. 234, 1600–1604.

[59] Saleem, M.M.M. and Wilson, M.T. (1982). Reduction of cytochrome c and other haem proteins by catechol(s) and quinol(s). *Biochem. J.,* Vol. 201, 433–444.

[60] Samuni, A.M., Chuang, E.Y., Krishna, M.C., Stein, W., DeGraff, W., Russo, A. and Mitchell, J.B. (2003). Semiquinone radical intermediate in catecholic estrogen-mediated cytotoxicity and mutagenesis: Chemoprevention strategies with antioxidants. *Proc. Nat. Acad. Sci. USA,* Vol. 100, 5390–5395.

[61] Cavalieri, E.L., Li, K-M., Balu, N., Saeed, M., Devanesan, P., Higginbotham, S., Zhao, J., Gross, M.L. and Rogan, E.G. (2002). Catechol ortho-quinones: the electrophilic compounds that form depurinating DNA adducts and could initiate cancer and other diseases. *Carcinogenesis,* Vol. 6, 1071–1077.

[62] Koppenol, W.H., van Buuren, K.J., Butler, J. and Braams, R. (1976). The kinetics of the reduction of cytochrome c by the superoxide anion radical. *Biochim. Biophys. Acta*, Vol. 449, 157–168.

[63] Wilming, M. and Johnsson, K. (1999). Spontaneous formation of the bioactive form of the tuberculosis drug isoniazid. *Angew. Chem. Int. Ed. Engl.*, Vol. 38, 2588–2590.

[64] Nguyen, M., Claparols, C., Bernadou, J. and Meunier, B. (2001). A fast and efficient metal-mediated oxidation of isoniazid and identification of isoniazid–NAD(H) adducts, *Chem. Bio. Chem.*, Vol. 2, 877–883.

[65] Wheeler, D.E., Rodriguez, J.H. and McCusker, J.K. (1999). Density functional theory analysis of electronic structure variations across the orthoquinone/semiquinone/cathecol redox series. *J. Phys. Chem.* A, Vol. 103, 4101–4112.

[66] Berberova, N.T., Smolyaninov, I.V., Okhlobystin, A.O., Letichevskaya, N.N. and Shinkar, E.V. (2005). Structural features and electrochemical characteristics of transition metal complexes (Pt, Pd, Ni, Co) with non-innocent ligands. *Mendeleev Chemistry Journal,* Vol. 59, № 5, 67–74.

[67] Buchanan, R.M. and Pierpont, C.G. (1980). Tautomeric catecholate-semiquinone interconversion via metal-ligand electron transfer. Structural, spectral, and magnetic properties of (3,5-di-tert-butylcatecholato)(3,5-di-tert-butylsemiquinone)(bipyridyl)-cobalt(III), a complex containing mixed-valence organic ligands. *J. Am. Chem. Soc.*, Vol. 102, № 15, 4951–4957.

[68] Zippel, F., Ahlers, F., Werner, R., Haase, W., Nolting, H.-F. and Krebs, B. (1996). Structural and functional models for the dinuclear copper active site in catechol oxidases: Syntheses, X-ray crystal structures, magnetic and spectral properties, and X-ray absorption spectroscopic studies in solid state and in solution. *Inorg. Chem.*, Vol. 35, 3409–3419.

[69] Lund, H. and Hammerich, O. (Eds.). (2001). Organic electrochemistry (4th ed.). New York, Basel: Marcel Dekker.

[70] Pessôa, M.M.B., Andrade, G.F.S., dos Santos, M.R. and Temperini, M.L.A. (2003). The electrochemical reduction of 2-formylpyridine thiosemicarbazone monitored by SERS and UV-vis spectroscopies. *J. Electroanal. Chem.*, Vol. 545, 117–122.

[71] Mairanovskii, S.G., Stradyn', Ya.P. and Bezuglyi, V.D. (1975). Polarography in organic chemistry. Leningrad, USSR: Chemistry (In Russian).

[72] Kitaev, Yu.P. and Buzykin, B.I. (1974). Hydrazones. Moscow, USSR: Science (In Russian).

[73] Brown, M.E. (2001). Introduction to thermal analysis. London: Kluwer Academic Publisher.

[74] Powder diffraction file JCPDS INT 65–3178. (1989). Swarthmore, PA: International Center for Diffraction Data.

[75] Leo, A., Hansch, C. and Elkins, D. (1971). Partition coefficients and their uses. *Chem. Rev.,* Vol. 71, № 6, 525–616.

[76] Geary, W.J. (1971). The use of conductivity measurements in organic solvents for the characterization of coordination compounds. *Coord. Chem. Rev.*, Vol. 7, 81–122.

[77] Lever, A.B.P. and Solomon, E.I. (Eds.). (2006). Inorganic electronic structure and spectroscopy. New York: John Wiley & Sons.

[78] Roy, S., Mondal, T.K., Mitra, P., Torres, E.L. and Sinha, C. (2011). Synthesis, structure, spectroscopic properties, electrochemistry, and DFT correlative studies of N-[(2-pyridyl)methyliden]-6-coumarin complexes of Cu(I) and Ag(I). Polyhedron, Vol. 30, № 6, 913–922.

[79] Dennehy, M., Ferullo, R.M., Quinzani, O.V., Mandolesi, S.D., Castellani, N. and Jennings, M. (2008). Unusual coordination in a silver thionate complex. Synthesis, structural characterization and theoretical calculations of dinuclear and polynuclear silver(I) thiosaccharinates with pyridine and 1,10-phenanthroline. *Polyhedron*, Vol. 27, № 11, 2243–2250.

[80] Frisch, M.J., Trucks, G.W., Schlegel, H.B., Scuseria, G.E., Robb, M.A., Cheeseman, J.R., Montgomery, J.A., Jr., Vreven, T., Kudin, K.N., Burant, J.C., Millam, J.M., Iyengar, S.S., Tomasi, J., Barone, V., Mennucci, B., Cossi, M., Scalmani, G., Rega, N., Petersson, G.A., Nakatsuji, H., Hada, M., Ehara, M., Toyota, K., Fukuda, R., Hasegawa, J., Ishida, M., Nakajima, T., Honda, Y., Kitao, O., Nakai, H., Klene, M., Li, X., Knox, J. E., Hratchian, H.P., Cross, J.B., Adamo, C., Jaramillo, J., Gomperts, R., Stratmann, R.E., Yazyev, O., Austin, A. J., Cammi, R., Pomelli, C., Ochterski, J.W., Ayala, P.Y., Morokuma, K., Voth, G.A., Salvador, P., Dannenberg, J.J., Zakrzewski, V.G., Dapprich, S., Daniels, A.D., Strain, M.C., Farkas, O., Malick, D.K., Rabuck, A.D., Raghavachari, K., Foresman, J.B., Ortiz, J.V., Cui, Q., Baboul, A.G., Clifford, S., Cioslowski, J., Stefanov, B.B., Liu, G., Liashenko, A., Piskorz, P., Komaromi, I., Martin, R.L., Fox, D.J., Keith, T., Al-Laham, M.A., Peng, C.Y., Nanayakkara, A., Challacombe, M., Gill, P.M.W., Johnson, B., Chen, W., Wong, M.W., Gonzalez, C. and Pople, J.A. (2003). Gaussian 03, revision C.01. Pittsburgh, PA: Gaussian, Inc.

[81] Hay, P.J. and Wadt, W.R. (1985). Ab initio effective core potentials for molecular calculations. Potentials for K to Au including the outermost core orbitals. *J. Chem. Phys.,* Vol. 82, № 1, 299–310.

[82] Young, D.C. (2001). Computational chemistry: A practical guide for applying techniques to real-world problems. New York: Wiley Interscience.

[83] Nakamoto, K. (1997). Infrared and Raman spectra of inorganic and coordination compounds: theory and applications in inorganic chemistry. New York: John Wiley & Sons.

[84] Bellamy, L.J. (1958). The infrared spectra of complex molecules. London: Methuen.

[85] Shevchenko, L.L. (1963). Infrared spectra of salts and complexes of carboxylic acids and some of their derivatives. *Russ. Chem. Rev.,* Vol. 32, № 4, 201–206.

[86] Umland, F., Janssen, A., Thierig, D. and Wunsch, G. (1971). Theorie und Practische Anwendung von Komplexbildnern in der Analytik. Weinheim: Verlag Chemie.

[87] Gutmann, V. (1978). The donor-acceptor approach to molecular interaction. New York: Plenium Press.

[88] Belicchi-Ferrari, M., Bisceglie, F., Cavalieri, C., Pelosi, G. and Tarasconi, P. (2007). Bis(triphenylphosphine)4-fluorobenzaldehyde thiosemicarbazone copper(I): Forcing chelation through oxoanions. *Polyhedron,* Vol. 26, 3774–3782.

[89] Lange, C.W. and Pierpont, C.G. (1997). Nickel complexes containing catecholate, benzoquinone and semiquinone radical ligands. *Inorg. Chim. Acta,* Vol. 263, 219–224.

[90] Shultz, D.A., Bodnar, S.H., Lee, H. and Gwaltney, K.P. (2002). Singlet-triplet gap in triplet ground-state biradicals is modulated by substituent effects. *J. Am. Chem. Soc.,* Vol. 124, 10054–10061.

[91] Kawabato, A. (1979). Electronic properties of fine metallic particles. III ESR absorption line shape. *J. Phys. Soc. Jpn.,* Vol. 29, № 4, 975–986.

[92] Dmitryuk, A.V., Paramzina, S.E., Perminov, A.S., Solov'eva N.D. and Timofeev, N.T. (1996). The influence of glass composition on the properties of silver-doped radiophotoluminescent phosphate glasses. *J. Non-Cryst. Solids,* Vol. 202, 173–177.

[93] Michalik, J., Sadlo, J.; Yu, J.-S. and Kevan, L. (1996). Tetrameric silver clusters in rho-zeolite stable above room temperature – ESR studies. Colloids Surf., A: Physicochem. *Eng. Aspects,* Vol. 115, 239–247.

[94] Kozlova, N.B.; Skurlatov, Yu.I. (1989). Activation of oxygen by metalloenzymes and their models. *Russ. Chem. Rev.*, Vol. 58, 138–147.

[95] Liu, B., Xu, L., Guo, G.C. and Huang, J.-S. (2006). The first discrete tetranuclear silver(I) complex containing 4-substituted (m-phenol)-1,2,4-triazole: synthesis, structure and fluorescence. *Inorg. Chem. Commun.*, Vol. 9, 687–690.

[96] Borsella, E., Gonella, F., Mazzoldi, P. Quaranta, A., Battaglin, G. and Polloni, R. (1998). Spectroscopic investigation of silver in soda-lime glass. *Chem. Phys. Lett.* Vol. 284, 429–434.

[97] Bisht, K.K., Kathalikkattil, A.C. and Suresh, E. (2012). Structure modulation, argentophilic interactions and photoluminescence properties of silver(I) coordination polymers with isomeric N-donor ligands. *RSC Advances,* Vol. 2, 8421–8428.

[98] Treguer, M., Rocco, F., Lelong, G., Le Nestour, A., Cardinal, T., Maali, A. and Lounis, B. (2005). Fluorescent silver oligomeric clusters and colloidal particles. *Solid State Sciences,* Vol. 7, 812–818.

[99] Lancini, G. and Parenti, F. (1982). Antibiotics. An integrated view. New York: Springer-Verlag.

[100] Lorian, V. (Ed.). (2005). Antibiotics in laboratory medicine. Philadelphia: Lippincott Williams & Wilkins.

[101] Saha, D.K., Sandbhor, U., Shirisha, K., Padhye, S., Deobagkar, D., Anson, Ch.E. and Powell, A.K. (2004). A novel mixed-ligand antimycobacterial dimeric copper complex of ciprofloxacin and phenanthroline. *Bioorg. Med. Chem. Lett.,* Vol. 14, 3027–3032.

[102] Chacon, O., Feng, Z., Harris, N.B., Caceres, E., Adams, L.G. and Barletta, R.G. (2002). Mycobacterium smegmatis d-alanine racemase mutants are not dependent on d-alanine for growth. *Antimicrob. Agents Chemther.,* Vol. 46, 47–54.

[103] Carrillo-Muñoz, A.J., Quindós, G. and Lopez-Ribot, J.L. (2004). Current developments in antifungal agents. *Curr. Med. Chem. – Anti-Infective Agents,* Vol. 3, 297–323.

[104] Silver, S., le Phung, T. and Silver, G. (2006). Silver as biocide in burn and wound dressings and bacterial resistance to silver compounds. *J. Ind. Microbiol. Biotechnol.,* Vol. 33, 627–634.

[105] Kappus, H. (1986). Overview of enzyme systems involved in bioreduction of drugs and in redox cycling. *Biochem. Pharmacol.*, Vol. 35, 1–6.

[106] Stevens, J.M. (2011). Cytochrome c as an experimental model protein. *Metallomics,* Vol. 3, 319–322.

[107] Nakashima, T., Higa, H., Matsubara, H., Benson, A.M. and Yasunobu, K.T. (1966). The amino acid sequence of bovine heart cytochrome c. *J. Biol. Chem.*, Vol. 241, 1166–1177.

[108] Bertini, I., Cavallaro, G., Rosato, A. (2006). Cytochrome c: occurrence and functions. *Chem. Rev.*, Vol. 106, 90–115.

[109] Dolla, A., Blanchard, L., Guerlesquin, F. and Bruschi, M. (1994). The protein moiety modulates the redox potential in cytochromes c. *Biochimie*, Vol. 76, 471–479.

[110] Muller, F.L. , Liu, Y. and Van Remmen, H. (2004). Complex III Releases Superoxide to Both Sides of the Inner Mitochondrial Membrane. *J. Biol. Chem.*, Vol. 279, 49064–49073.

[111] Pereverzev, M.O., Vygodina, T.V., Konstantinov, A.A. and Skulachev, V.P. Cytochrome c, an ideal antioxidant. (2003). *Biochem. Soc. Trans.*, Vol. 31 (Pt. 6), 1312–1315.

[112] Butler, J., Koppenol, W.H. and Margoliash, E. (1982). Kinetics and mechanism of the reduction of ferricytochrome c by the superoxide anion. *J. Biol. Chem.*, Vol. 257, 10747–10750.

[113] Cai, J and Jones, D.P. (1998). Superoxide in apoptosis. Mitochondrial generation triggered by cytochrome c loss. *J. Biol. Chem.*, Vol. 273, 11401–11404.

[114] Kagan, V.E., Tyurin, V.A., Jiang, J., Tyurina, Y.Y., Ritov, V.B., Amoscato, A.A., Osipov, A.N., Belikova, N.A., Kapralov, A.A., Kini, V., Vlasova, I.I., Zhao, Q., Zou, M., Di, P., Svistunenko, D.A., Kurnikov, I.V. and Borisenko, G.G. (2005). Cytochrome c acts as a cardiolipin oxygenase required for release of proapoptotic factors. *Nat. Chem. Biol.*, Vol. 1, 223–232.

[115] Brown, G.C. and Borutaite, V. (2008). Regulation of apoptosis by the redox state of cytochrome c. *Biochim. Biophys. Acta.*, Vol. 1777, 877–881.

[116] Gopal, D., Wilson, G.S., Earl, R.A. and Cusanovich, M.A. (1988). Cytochrome c: ion binding and redox properties. Studies on ferri- and ferro-forms of horse, bovine, and tuna cytochrome c. *J. Biol. Chem.*, Vol. 263, 11652–11656.

[117] Battistuzzi, G., Borsari, M., Sola, M. and Francia, F. (1997). Redox thermodynamics of the native and alkaline forms of eukaryotic and bacterial class I cytochromes c. *Biochemistry*, Vol. 36, 16247–16258.

[118] Cruanes, M.T., Rodgers, K.K. and Sligar S.G. (1992). Protein electrochemistry at high pressure. *J. Am. Chem. Soc.*, Vol. 114, 9660–9661.

[119] Kowalsky, A. (1969). A study of the mechanism of electron transfer in cytochrome c. Chromium as a probe. *J. Biol. Chem.*, Vol. 244, 6619–6625.

[120] Kurihara, M and Sano, S. (1970). Reduction of cytochrome c by ferrous ions and ethylenediaminetetraacetic acid in acid solution. *J. Biol. Chem.*, Vol. 245, 4804–4806.

[121] Scholten, U., Merchán, A.C. and Bernauer, K. (2005). Electron-transfer-mediated binding of optically active cobalt (III) complexes to horse heart cytochrome c. *J. R. Soc. Interface.*, Vol.2, 109–112.

[122] Speh, S. and Elias, H. (1994). The effect of electrostatic and hydrophobic interactions on the rate of cytochrome c reduction by ruthenium (II) complexes. *J. Biol. Chem.*, Vol. 269, 6370–6375.

[123] Davison, A.J. (1968). Kinetics of the copper-histidine catalysis of ferrocytochrome c oxidation. *J. Biol. Chem.*, Vol. 243, 6064–6067.

[124] Mathews, A.J. and Brittain, T. (1987). Some electron-transfer reactions involving carbodi-imide-modified cytochrome c. *Biochem. J.*, Vol. 243, 379–384.

[125] Ginsburgh, C.L. and Everse, J. (1978). Studies on the reduction of cytochrome c by thiols: A preliminary report. *Bioorg. Chem.*, Vol. 7, 481–492.

[126] Hu, T.-M. and Ho, S.-C. (2011). Kinetics of redox interaction between cytochrome c and thiols. *J. Med. Sci.*, Vol. 31, 109–115.

[127] Yasukochi, Y. and Masters, B.S. (1976). Some properties of a detergent-solubilized NADPH-cytochrome c (cytochrome P-450) reductase purified by biospecific affinity chromatography. *J. Biol. Chem.*, Vol. 251, 5337–5344.

[128] Worrall, J.A., Reinle, W., Bernhardt, R. and Ubbink, M. (2003). Transient protein interactions studied by NMR spectroscopy: the case of cytochrome c and adrenodoxin. *Biochemistry,* Vol. 42, 7068–7076.

[129] Shkumatov, V.M., Gilevich, S.N., Chashchin, V.L. and Akhrem, A.A. (1983). Immobilized cytochrome c – an effective ligand for affinity chromatography of electron transport proteins. *Bioorg. Khim.*, Vol. 9, P. 1237–1247.

[130] Shkumatov, V.M., Gilevich, S.N., Chashchin, V.L. and Akhrem, A.A. (1983). The C27-steroid hydroxylating system from bovine liver

mitochondria. Isolation of ferredoxin (hepatoredoxin) by affinity chromatography on cytochrome-c-sepharose. *Bioorg. Khim.,* Vol. 9, P. 1231–1236.

[131] Akhrem, A.A., Gilevich, S.N., Shkumatov, V.M. and Chashchin, V.L. (1984). Selectively immobilized cytochrome c as an effective affinity ligand for electron transfer proteins. *Biomed. Biochim. Acta,* Vol. 43, P. 165–177.

[132] Chashchin, V.L., Shol'kina, L.V., Lapko, V.N., Shkumatov, V.M. and Akhrem, A.A. (1983). Structural organization of adrenodoxin using limited proteolysis. *Biokhimiia,* Vol. 48, P. 1697–1704.

[133] Schweigert, N., Zehnder, A.J.B. and Eggen, R.I.L. (2001). Chemical properties of catechols and their molecular modes of toxic action in cells, from microorganisms to mammals: *Minireview. Env. Microbiol.,* Vol. 3, 81–91.

[134] Munro, A.W., Noble, M.A., Robledo, L., Daff, S.N. and Chapman, S.K. (2001). Determination of the redox properties of human NADPH-cytochrome P450 reductase. *Biochemistry,* Vol. 40, 1956–1963.

[135] Hannemann, F., Rottmann, M., Schiffler, B., Zapp J. and Bernhard, R. (2001). The loop region covering the iron-sulfur cluster in bovine adrenodoxin comprises a new interaction site for redox partners *J. Biol. Chem.,* Vo. 276, 1369–1375.

[136] Thöny-Meyer, L. (1997). Biogenesis of respiratory cytochromes in bacteria. *Microbiol. Mol. Biol. Rev.,* Vol. 61, 337–376.

[137] Pettigrew, G.W., Echalier, A. and Pauleta, S.R. (2006). Structure and mechanism in the bacterial di-heme cytochrome c peroxidases. *J. Inorg. Biochem.,* Vol. 100, 551–567.

[138] Iwata, S. (1998). Structure and function of bacterial cytochrome c oxidase. *J. Biochem.,* Vol. 123, 369–375.

[139] Atack, J.M. and Kelly, D.J. (2007). Structure, mechanism and physiological roles of bacterial cytochrome c peroxidases. *Adv. Microb. Physiol.,* Vol. 52, 73–106.

[140] Turner, S., Reid, E., Smith, H. and Cole, J. (2003). A novel cytochrome c peroxidase from Neisseria gonorrhoeae: a lipoprotein from a Gram-negative bacterium. *Biochem. J.,* Vol. 373 (Pt. 3), 865–873.

[141] Fülöp, V., Ridout, C.J., Greenwood, C. and Hajdu, J. (1995). Crystal structure of the di-heme cytochrome c peroxidase from Pseudomonas aeruginosa. *Structure,* Vol. 3, 1225–1233.

[142] Stach, P., Einsle, O., Schumacher, W., Kurun, E. and Kroneck, P.M. (2000). Bacterial cytochrome c nitrite reductase: new structural and functional aspects. *J. Inorg. Biochem.*, Vol. 79, 381–385.

[143] Clarke, T.A., Mills, P.C., Poock, S.R., Butt, J.N., Cheesman, M.R., Cole, J.A., Hinton, J.C., Hemmings, A.M., Kemp, G., Söderberg, C.A., Spiro, S., Van Wonderen, J. and Richardson, D.J. (2008). Escherichia coli cytochrome c nitrite reductase NrfA. *Methods Enzymol.*, Vol. 437, 63–77.

[144] Hasegawa, N., Arai, H. and Igarashi, Y. (2001). Two c-type cytochromes, NirM and NirC, encoded in the nir gene cluster of Pseudomonas aeruginosa act as electron donors for nitrite reductase. *Biochem. Biophys. Res. Commun.*, Vol. 288, 1223–1230.

[145] Mills, P.C., Rowley, G., Spiro, S., Hinton, J.C. and Richardson, D.J. (2008). A combination of cytochrome c nitrite reductase (NrfA) and flavorubredoxin (NorV) protects Salmonella enterica serovar Typhimurium against killing by NO in anoxic environments. *Microbiology*, Vol. 154 (Pt. 4), 1218–1228.

[146] David, P.S., Morrison, M.R., Wong, S.L. and Hill, B.C. (1999). Expression, purification, and characterization of recombinant forms of membrane-bound cytochrome c-550nm from Bacillus subtilis. *Protein Expr. Purif.*, Vol. 15, 69–76.

[147] Wilson, A.C., Hoch, J.A. and Perego, M. (2009). Two small c-type cytochromes affect virulence gene expression in Bacillus anthracis. *Mol. Microbiol.*, Vol. 72, 109–123.

[148] Naylor, J. and Cianciotto, N.P. (2004). Cytochrome c maturation proteins are critical for in vivo growth of Legionella pneumophila. *FEMS Microbiol. Lett.*, Vol. 15, 249–256.

[149] Small, J.L., Park, S.W., Kana, B.D., Ioerger, T.R., Sacchettini, J.C. and Ehrt, S. (2013). Perturbation of cytochrome c maturation reveals adaptability of the respiratory chain in Mycobacterium tuberculosis. *mBio*, Vol. 4, e00475–13.

[150] Allard, K.A., Dao, J., Sanjeevaiah, P., McCoy-Simandle, K., Chatfield, C.H., Crumrine, D.S., Castignetti, D. and Cianciotto, N.P. (2009) Purification of legiobactin and importance of this siderophore in lung infection by Legionella pneumophila. *Infect. Immun.*, Vol. 77, 2887–2895.

[151] Yip, E.S., Burnside, D.M. and Cianciotto, N.P. (2011). Cytochrome c4 is required for siderophore expression by Legionella pneumophila, whereas

cytochromes c1 and c5 promote intracellular infection. *Microbiology,* Vol. 157, 868–878.

[152] Abarca-Rojano, E., Rosas-Medina, P., Zamudio-Cortéz, P., Mondragón-Flores, R. and Sánchez-García, F.J. (2003). Mycobacterium tuberculosis virulence correlates with mitochondrial cytochrome c release in infected macrophages. *Scand. J. Immunol.,* Vol. 58, 419–427.

[153] Chen, M., Gan, H. and Remold, H.G. (2006). A mechanism of virulence: virulent Mycobacterium tuberculosis strain H37Rv, but not attenuated H37Ra, causes significant mitochondrial inner membrane disruption in macrophages leading to necrosis. J. Immunol., Vol. 176, 3707–3716.

[154] Grahl, N., Dinamarco, T.M,, Willger, S.D., Goldman, G.H. and Cramer, R.A. (2012). Aspergillus fumigatus mitochondrial electron transport chain mediates oxidative stress homeostasis, hypoxia responses and fungal pathogenesis. *Mol. Microbiol.,* Vol. 84, 383–999.

[155] Bradshaw, R.E., Bird, D.M., Brown, S., Gardiner, R.E. and Hirst, P. (2001). Cytochrome c is not essential for viability of the fungus Aspergillus nidulans. *Mol. Genet. Genomics*, Vol. 266, 48–55.

[156] Dumont, M.D., Mathews, A.J., Nall, B.T., Baim, S.B., Eustice, D.C. and Sherman, F. (1990). Differential stability of two apo-isocytochromes c in the yeast Saccharomyces cerevisiae. *J. Biol. Chem.*, Vol. 265, 2733–2739.

[157] Erman, J.E. and Vitello, L.B. (2002). Yeast cytochrome c peroxidase: mechanistic studies via protein engineering. *Biochim. Biophys. Acta*, Vol. 1597, 193–220.

Reviewed by
V.I. Potkin, Professor, Dr. Sci. (Chem.),
Institute of Physical Organic Chemistry of the National Academy of Sciences of Belarus, Surganov str. 13, Minsk 220072, Belarus;
e-mail: potkin@ifoch.bas-net.by

In: Cytochromes *b* and *c*
Editor: Rurik Thom

ISBN: 978-1-63117-467-4
© 2014 Nova Science Publishers, Inc.

Chapter 6

STRUCTURAL ASPECTS OF CYTOCHROME *C*-CARDIOLIPIN INTERACTIONS: FÖRSTER RESONANCE ENERGY TRANSFER STUDY

Valeriya M. Trusova[1,], Julian G. Molotkovsky[2],*
Paavo K. J. Kinnunen[3] and Galyna P. Gorbenko[1]
[1]Department of Nuclear and Medical Physics,
V. N. Karazin Kharkov National University, Kharkov, Ukraine
[2]Shemyakin–Ovchinnikov Institute of Bioorganic Chemistry,
Russian Academy of Sciences, Moscow, Russia
[3]Department of Biomedical Engineering and Computational Science,
School of Science and Technology, Aalto University,
Espoo, Finland

ABSTRACT

Cytochrome *c* (cyt *c*) is a mitochondrial membrane hemoprotein of high physiological importance. Fisrt, cyt *c* is one of the key elements of respiration chain transferring electrons from cyt *c* reductase (*bc*1 complex) to cyt *c* oxidase. Second, release of cyt c from the intermembrane space of mitochondria into the cytosol triggers the apoptotic pathway. The idea that specific interactions between cyt *c* and

* Address for correspondence: Valeriya M.Trusova, 19-32 Geroyev Truda St., Kharkov 61144, Ukraine. E-mail: valtrusova@yahoo.com.

cardiolipin (CL), the main lipid component of mitochondrial membrane, are crucial to the protein biological activities, constantly receives further corroboration from both theoretical and experimental studies. Despite considerable progress achieved in the field of cyt c – CL biophysics, the detailed structural description of protein-lipid complexation is still lacking. In the present study we applied Förster resonance energy transfer (RET) technique to give comprehensive characterization of cyt c binding to the model lipid membranes composed of the mixtures of zwitterionic lipid phosphatidylcholine (PC) with anionic lipids phosphatidylglycerol (PG), phosphatidylserine (PS) or cardiolipin (CL) in different molar ratios. The donor-acceptor pairs were represented by either anthrylvinyl-labeled PC (AV-PC) or anthrylvinyl-labeled CL (AV-CL) incorporated in trace amounts in lipid vesicles, and heme moiety of cyt c. Association of the protein with the lipid bilayers led to the decrease in donor fluorescence reflecting energy transfer from AV fluorophore to heme. The most effective RET was found for CL-containing membranes. This observation has been interpreted in terms of higher affinity of cyt c to CL as compared to other anionic lipids. In order to get understanding of protein specificity to CL, RET was measured as a function of CL content and ionic strength. Monte Carlo analysis of multiple datasets revealed a complex interplay between several processes, namely i) lipid demixing; ii) CL transition into extended conformation; iii) formation of hexagonal phase. The switch between these states was found to be controlled by CL content and salt concentration. These characteristics of cyt c – CL interaction are of great interest not only in the context of regulating cyt c electron transfer and apoptotic propensities, but also from the viewpoint of the protein biogenesis.

1. INTRODUCTION

Cytochrome c (cyt c) is a small mitochondrial membrane metalloprotein, which delicately holds the balance between cell functioning (respiration) and cell death (apoptosis) [1-3]. Fulfilling its canonical function in the electron-transport chain, this protein employs its prosthetic group as a redox intermediate to shuttle electrons from cyt c reductase (complex III) to cyt c oxidase (complex IV) [4]. Electron transfer occurs via the redox cycling between the ferric and ferrous state of His18/Met80 – coordinated heme. The reaction of cyt c reduction by cyt c reductase proceeds at the outer side of cytosolic surface of the inner membrane. Then ferrocytochrome c is donates four electrons to cyt c oxidase which, in turn, catalyzes the reduction of molecular oxygen to two water molecules. Hydrophobic and charged amino acid residues adjacent to and/or constituting the heme pocket of cyt c are thought to be responsible for the formation of cyt c – cyt c oxidase complex. While charged residues (Glu4, Lys13, Lys86, Lys87, Lys88, Glu89, and Glu90) ensure the proper orientation of cyt c, thereby facilitating electron movement, the nonpolar cluster (Cys17, Ile9, Ile11, and Ile81) partakes in the formation of the direct contacts with Cu_A site, the electron entry point of cyt c oxidase [5]. One of the key determinants of cyt c electron transfer ability is related to association of this protein with anionic membrane lipid cardiolipin (CL), which i) *per se* or in complex with cyt c oxidase constitutes mitochondrial binding site for the protein, ii) increases its local concentration in the membrane vicinity, and iii) promotes cyt c conformational transitions affecting its electron transfer activity.

The second important implication of cyt c relates to the programmed cell death, or apoptosis [6-8]. It is already generally recognized that release of cyt c from mitochondria represents the milestone in the induction of apoptotic cascade. Accordingly, dissociation of cyt c from the inner mitochondrial membrane is thought to precede the protein translocation into the cytosol [8]. Current theories of apoptosis assume that oxidative damage of CL alters its interactions with cyt c and results in the detachment of this protein from the membrane. Further events include the transient opening of the mitochondrial permeability transition pores and pore formation in the outer membrane by apoptosis regulator proteins such as BAX or BAK [9]. These processes mediate the passage of unbound protein through the outer membrane. The released cyt c then forms an apoptosome with Apaf-1 and pro-caspase-9 resulting eventually in triggering of the cell death [10].

All the above rationales strongly suggest that crucial role in cyt c retention, stability and normal physiological activity belongs to CL, a major lipid component of mitochondrial membranes ($\sim$ 25% of the total amount of lipids), representing the physiological binding site for this protein. In view of this, the nature and specificity of interactions between cyt c and lipid membranes remain for a long time in a focus of extensive research, and a bunch of important conclusions have been reached to date. The process of cyt c – lipid complexation has been shown to include several important stages, viz. i) cyt c adsorption onto the lipid bilayer surface driven by electrostatic interactions, ii) protein conformational changes coupled with membrane structural perturbations, iii) cyt c insertion into the lipid bilayer nonpolar core controlled by hydrophobic interactions [11-13]. Furthermore, a number of specific features of cyt c – CL association have been uncovered. Particularly, the existence of two distinct acidic phospholipid binding sites on protein surface nominated as A-site and C-site has been proposed [14-18]. The former one accounts for electrostatic contacts between positively charged protein patches and CL anionic headgroups while the latter one is involved in hydrophobic interactions between cyt c and lipid fatty acyl chains. Peculiar structural features of CL together with the existence of hydrophobic crevice in cyt c tertiary structure provide the basis for hypothesis of so-called extended lipid conformation, in which lipid acyl chains point to the opposite directions from the headgroup producing the angle of ca. 180° [17, 18]. In such an orientation one acyl chain remains within the bilayer interior, while another extends outwards filling the protein hydrophobic channel located near heme crevice. Recently, it was supposed that this anchorage represents an abnormal state of cyt c that might facilitate its exit from mitochondria [18]. Specifically, this mode of lipid binding was suggested to trigger the peroxidase activity of cyt c resulting from the dissociation of the axial Met80 − heme iron ligand [19]. The subsequent peroxidation of CL affects the stability of mitochondrial membrane culminating with a detachment of the protein into the cytoplasm.

Another intriguing aspect of cyt c − CL interactions involves modification of lipid lateral distribution and physicochemical properties. A vast majority of studies indicate that cyt c is capable of gathering CL molecules into highly dynamic microdomains and/or hexagonal (H_{II}) phases [20, 21]. Moreover, a number of experimental and theoretical works suggests that cyt c − induced formation of lipid domains and H_{II} configurations are interdependent processes − domains may represent the intermediate states of non-bilayer structures [22].

The fact that CL-enriched areas, as a means of structural and functional modulation of cyt c and other membrane proteins, are involved in a wide variety of physiological and pathological processes, together with the finding that cyt c may per se act as inducer of CL assembling, strongly emphasize the necessity of further in-depth exploration of this process. Specifically, the following questions still remain open: i) what factors initiate and regulate lipid sequestration upon protein-membrane binding; ii) what parameters control the domain-to-hexagonal phase transition; iii) what are the prerequisites for extended lipid conformation. To address these issues and gain further insights into molecular details of cyt c − induced structural reorganization of CL-containing lipid membranes, in the present contribution we employed the Förster resonance energy transfer technique in combination with Monte Carlo simulation.

MATERIALS AND METHODS

1.1. Materials

Bovine heart cardiolipin, horse heart cyt *c* (oxidized form), NaCl, HEPES and EDTA were purchased from Sigma (St. Louis, MO, USA). 1-Palmitoyl-2-oleoyl-*sn*-glycero-3-phosphocholine (PC), 1-palmitoyl-2-oleoyl-*sn*-glycero-3-phospho-*rac*-glycerol (PG) and 1-palmitoyl-2-oleoyl-*sn*-glycero-3-phospho-*rac*-phosphatidylserine (PS) were from Avanti Polar Lipids (Alabaster, AL). Fluorescent lipids, 1-acyl-2-(12-(9-anthryl)-11*E*-dodecenoyl)-*sn*-glycero-3-phosphocholine (AV-PC), and 1-(1,2-diacyl-*sn*-glycero-3-phospho)-3-{1'-[12-(9-anthryl)-11*E*-dodecenoyl]-2'-acyl-*sn*-glycero-3-phospho}glycerol (AV-CL) were synthesized as described in detail elsewhere [23, 24]. All other chemicals were of analytical grade and used without further purification.

1.2. Preparation of Lipid Vesicles

Large unilamellar vesicles were made by extrusion technique from PC mixtures with PG, PS or CL, as indicated [25]. Appropriate amounts of lipid stock solutions were mixed in chloroform, evaporated to dryness under a gentle nitrogen stream, and then left under reduced pressure for 1.5 h to remove any residual solvent. The dry lipid residues were subsequently hydrated with 20 mM HEPES, 0.1 mM EDTA, pH 7.4 at room temperature to yield lipid concentration of 1 mM. Thereafter, the sample was subjected to 15 passes through a 100 nm pore size polycarbonate filter (Millipore, Bedford, USA), yielding the liposomes of desired composition. AV-PC or AV-CL (0.26 and 0.13 mol% of total lipid, respectively) were added to the mixture of PC or CL prior to the solvent evaporation. The presence of AV probe did not influence the apparent particle size controlled by dynamic light scattering. The concentration of fluorescent lipid was determined spectrophotometrically using anthrylvinyl extinction coefficient $\varepsilon_{367} = 9 \times 10^3$ M^{-1}cm^{-1} [23].

Hereafter, liposomes with different composition were referred to using general abbreviation, in which first two letters represent the type of anionic lipid and the number denotes the molar content of this lipid. For example, CL5 stands for the lipid vesicles with 5 mol% of CL, while PG40 means PC/PG membranes with 40 mol% of PG. The datasets obtained at different ionic strengths are referred to as CL2.5/I20 or CL5/I40, where the figure after slash stands for the salt concentration in mM. Lipid membranes containing different fluorescent lipid analog abbreviated as $CL2.5_{AV-PC}$ or $CL20_{AV-CL}$, with the subscript denoting the type of energy donor (AV-PC or AV-CL).

2.3. Fluorescence Measurements

Fluorescence measurements were performed at 25 °C using 10-mm path-length quartz cuvettes using spectrofluorimeter equipped with a magnetically stirred, thermostated cuvette holder (LS-50B, Perkin-Elmer Ltd., Beaconsfield, UK). AV-PC or AV-CL emission spectra were recorded with 367 nm excitation wavelength. Excitation and emission slit widths were set at 5 nm. RET experiments have been conducted with either anthrylvinyl-labeled PC (AV-PC) or CL (AV-CL) as donors and heme group of cyt c as acceptor. Fluorescence intensity measured in the presence of cyt c at the maximum of AV emission (434 nm) was corrected for reabsorption and inner filter effects using the following coefficients [26]:

$$k = \frac{\left(1 - 10^{-A_o^{ex}}\right)\left(A_o^{ex} + A_a^{ex}\right)\left(1 - 10^{-A_o^{em}}\right)\left(A_o^{em} + A_a^{em}\right)}{\left(1 - 10^{-\left(A_o^{ex} + A_a^{ex}\right)}\right)A_o^{ex}\left(1 - 10^{-\left(A_o^{em} + A_a^{em}\right)}\right)A_o^{em}} \qquad (1)$$

where A_o^{ex}, A_o^{em} are the donor optical densities at the excitation and emission wavelengths in the absence of acceptor, A_a^{ex}, A_a^{em} are the acceptor optical densities at the excitation and emission wavelengths, respectively. The efficiency of energy transfer was determined by measuring the decrease of AV fluorescence upon addition of cyt c:

$$E = 1 - \frac{Q_{DA}}{Q_D} = 1 - Q_r \qquad (2)$$

where Q_D, Q_{DA} are the donor quantum yields in the absence and presence of acceptor, respectively, Q_r is the relative quantum yield.

2. THEORETICAL BACKGROUND

2.1. Binding Model

Binding of cyt *c* to CL-containing phospholipid membranes (Section 4.2) was analyzed in terms of the adsorption model allowing for area exclusion and electrostatic effects. The employed approach is based on Gouy-Chapman double-layer theory and scaled particle (SPT) model developed by Chatelier and Minton [27] and further extended by Minton [28] to take into account the possibility of multiple adsorbate conformations. SPT formalism is currently regarded as providing the most adequate description of excluded area interactions between the adsorbing protein molecules. Importantly, SPT expressions derived for the case of multiple conformations of bound protein appear to be applicable to treating protein association with heterogeneous surfaces where binding sites differ in their size and free energy of adsorption. In other words, if a protein adsorbs onto lipid bilayer surface containing two types of binding sites (i.e., there exist two populations of bound protein), the activity coefficient of a spherical ligand adsorbed in a particular conformation *i* or associated with the site of *i-th* type is given by:

$$\gamma_{1,2} = \frac{1}{1-\langle\rho a\rangle}\exp\left(\frac{a_{1,2}\langle\rho\rangle + s_{1,2}\langle\rho s\rangle/2\pi}{1-\langle\rho a\rangle} + \frac{a_{1,2}}{4\pi}\left[\frac{\langle\rho s\rangle}{1-\langle\rho a\rangle}\right]^2\right)$$

(3)

$$a_{1,2} = n_{1,2}S_L, \quad \rho_{1,2} = \frac{B_{1,2}}{L_a S_L}, \quad s_{1,2} = 2\sqrt{\pi n_{1,2}S_L}$$

(4)

$$\langle\rho\rangle = \frac{B_1+B_2}{L_a S_L}, \quad \langle\rho a\rangle = \frac{n_1 B_1 + n_2 B_2}{L_a}, \quad \langle\rho s\rangle = \frac{2\sqrt{\pi}\left(B_1\sqrt{n_1} + B_2\sqrt{n_2}\right)}{L_a\sqrt{S_L}}$$

(5)

where $\rho_{1,2}$, $a_{1,2}$, $s_{1,2}$ are the surface number density, area and circumference of the footprint of species *i*, $B_{1,2}$ – concentration of bound protein, $n_{1,2}$ – number of lipid molecules per binding site.

The adsorption isotherm can be described by the following equations:

$$K_{a1}(P - B_1 - B_2) = \rho_1 \gamma_1, \ K_{a2}(P - B_1 - B_2) = \rho_2 \gamma_2 \tag{6}$$

where P – total protein concentration, $K_{a1,2}$ – association constant.

The choice of the model assuming two types of binding sites was dictated by the fact that at neutral pH there exist two CL populations, viz. deprotonated (DP) and partially protonated (HP). These species represent two distinct binding sites for cyt c with different energy of binding and association constant (K_{a1}^0 and K_{a2}^0, respectively) [13]. Peculiar protonation behavior of CL stems from its unique structure with two acyl chains and glycerol-phosphate per each monomer linked through a single glycerol head.

The equilibrium binding constant is generally represented as consisting of electrostatic (K_{el}) and non-electrostatic or intrinsic (K^0) terms: $K_a = K_{el}K^0$. Electrostatic component of binding constant, dependent on electrostatic surface potential, environmental conditions (pH, ionic strength), and degree of surface coverage by a protein is given by [29]:

$$K_{el} = \exp\left(-\frac{d}{dN_P}\left[\frac{\Delta F_{el}(N_P)}{k_B T}\right]\right) \tag{7}$$

where T is the temperature, k_B is Boltzmann's constant, and ΔF_{el} is the total gain in electrostatic free energy, being a function of the number of adsorbed protein molecules, $N_P = B_a N_A$:

$$\Delta F_{el}(N_P) = F_{el}^s(N_P) - F_{el}^s(0) - N_P F_{el}^P \tag{8}$$

where F_{el}^s and F_{el}^P are the electrostatic free energies of a membrane and a protein, respectively. The electrostatic free energy of a spherical protein molecule with effective charge $+ze$ and uniform charge distribution can be written as [30]:

$$F_{el}^{P} = \frac{z^2 e^2}{2\varepsilon r_{cyt}(1 + \kappa_d r_{cyt})} \tag{9}$$

with r_{cyt} standing for the protein radius, e the elementary charge, N_A Avogadro's number, ε the dielectric constant, c the molar concentration of monovalent ions, and κ_d the reciprocal Debye length.

$$\kappa_d = \sqrt{\frac{8\pi e^2 N_A c}{\varepsilon k_B T}} \tag{10}$$

In terms of the Gouy-Chapman double layer theory, the electrostatic free energy of a membrane of area $S_m = S_L L_{out}$ (L_{out} is the concentration of accessible lipids related to total lipid concentration (L) as $L_{out} = 0.5L$) is given by [31]:

$$F_{el}^{s} = \frac{2k_B T S_m}{e}\left(\sigma \sinh^{-1}\left(\frac{\sigma}{a}\right) - \sqrt{a^2 + \sigma^2} + a\right);$$

$$a = \sqrt{2\pi^{-1}\varepsilon c N_A k_B T} \tag{11}$$

where S_L is the mean area per lipid molecule taken here as 0.65 nm^2 for PC and 1.2 nm^2 for CL [32], σ is the surface charge density determined by the mole fraction of CL (f_{CL}), the degree of its ionization (α), and the extent of neutralization of membrane charge by the adsorbed protein:

$$\sigma = \frac{-e}{S_m}\left(\alpha f_{CL} L_{out} - z B_a\right) \tag{12}$$

Considering CL as a dibasic acid, α can be written as:

$$\alpha = 2\alpha_P + \alpha_{HP} \tag{13}$$

where α_P and α_{HP} are the fractions of deprotonated and partially protonated species, respectively:

$$\alpha_P = \frac{K_1 K_2}{K_1 K_2 + K_1 [H^+]_b \exp\left(\frac{-e\psi_0}{k_B T}\right) + \left([H^+]_b \exp\left(\frac{-e\psi_0}{k_B T}\right)\right)^2},$$

$$\alpha_{HP} = \frac{\alpha_P [H^+]_b \exp\left(\frac{-e\psi_0}{k_B T}\right)}{K_2} \tag{14}$$

here K_1 are K_2 are CL ionization constants, $[H^+]_b$ is the bulk proton concentration, ψ_0 is electrostatic surface potential of a membrane related to the surface charge density as:

$$\psi_o = \frac{2k_B T}{e} \sinh^{-1}\left(\frac{\sigma}{a}\right) \tag{15}$$

Numerical solution of the set of Eqs. 3 – 10 yields theoretical isotherms that were fitted to the experimental data.

2.2. Resonance Energy Transfer Model

The results of RET measurements were quantitatively analyzed in terms of the model of energy transfer in 2D systems formulated by Fung & Stryer [33] and extended in our previous studies to allow for distance dependence of the orientation factor [34, 35]. Cyt c – lipid systems were treated as containing one donor plane and two acceptor planes located at distances d_1 and d_2 from membrane center. Anthrylvinyl fluorophores employed here as donors are attached to terminal methyl groups of acyl chains of both outer and inner monolayers. Due to the high mobility of these groups, AV moieties located at the outer and inner bilayer leaflets seem to be indistinguishable, so that the donor plane can be regarded as coinciding with the bilayer midplane while two populations of the bound protein (i.e., associated either with deprotonated or partially protonated CL species) were considered as being confined to two acceptor planes. In this case, relative quantum yield of the donor is given by:

$$Q_r = \int_0^\infty \exp(-\lambda)\exp\left[-\left(\frac{B_1}{S_m}S_1(\lambda) + \frac{B_2}{S_m}S_2(\lambda)\right)\right]d\lambda \qquad (16)$$

$$S_1(\lambda) = \int_{d_1}^\infty \left[1 - \exp\left(-\lambda\kappa_1^2(R)\left(\frac{R_o^r}{R}\right)^6\right)\right]2\pi R dR$$

$$(17)$$

$$S_2(\lambda) = \int_{d_2}^\infty \left[1 - \exp\left(-\lambda\kappa_2^2(R)\left(\frac{R_o^r}{R}\right)^6\right)\right]2\pi R dR$$

$$(18)$$

where R is the donor-acceptor separation, $\lambda = t/\tau_d$; τ_d is the lifetime of excited donor in the absence of acceptor. By representing Förster radius as $R_o = \left[\kappa^2(R)\right]^{1/6} \cdot R_o^r$, it follows that

$$R_o^r = 979\left(n_r^{-4}Q_D J\right)^{1/6} \quad J = \frac{\int_0^\infty F_D(\lambda)\varepsilon_A(\lambda)\lambda^4 d\lambda}{\int_0^\infty F_D(\lambda)d\lambda} \qquad (19)$$

here n_r is the refractive index of the medium (n_r=1.37), Q_D is the donor quantum yield (0.8), J is the overlap between the donor emission ($F_D(\lambda)$) and acceptor absorption ($\varepsilon_A(\lambda)$) spectra [26]. When the donor emission and acceptor absorption transition moments are symmetrically distributed within the cones about certain axes D_x and A_x, distance-dependent orientation factor is given by:

$$\kappa_{1,2}^2(R) = d_D d_A \left(3\left(\frac{d_c \mp 0.5d_t}{R}\right)^2 - 1\right) + \frac{1-d_D}{3} + \frac{1-d_A}{3} + \left(\frac{d_c \mp 0.5d_t}{R}\right)^2 (d_D - 2d_D d_A + d_A)$$

$$(20)$$

$$d_{D,A} = \left\langle d_{D,A}^x \right\rangle \left(\frac{3}{2}\cos^2\alpha_{D,A} - \frac{1}{2}\right) \quad \left\langle d_{D,A}^x \right\rangle = \left(\frac{3}{2}\cos^2\psi_{D,A} - \frac{1}{2}\right) \quad (21)$$

where $\psi_{D,A}$ are the cone half-angles, $\alpha_{D,A}$ are the angles made by D_x and A_x with the bilayer normal N. The axial depolarization factors $\left\langle d_D^x \right\rangle$ and $\left\langle d_A^x \right\rangle$ are related to the experimentally measurable steady-state (r) and fundamental (r_0) anisotropies of donor and acceptor [36]:

$$d_{D,A}^x = \pm\left(r_{D,A}/r_{0D,A}\right)^{1/2}$$

$$(22)$$

2.3. Monte Carlo Simulation

The results of RET measurements suggesting lateral redistribution of CL and PC molecules upon cyt c binding were treated using a Monte Carlo (MC) approach. Positions of donors and acceptors were generated randomly in a square cell assuming periodic boundary conditions to avoid edge effects. The relative quantum yield averaged over all donors was calculated from fluorophore coordinates as:

$$Q_r = \frac{1}{N_D}\sum_{j=1}^{N_D}\left[1 + \sum_{i=1}^{N_{AC}}\left(\frac{R_o^r \kappa^2(r_{ij})}{r_{ij}}\right)^6\right]^{-1}$$

$$(23)$$

where N_D, N_{AC} stand for the number of donors and acceptors, respectively, r_{ij} represents the distance between jth donor and ith acceptor. The simulation procedure was repeated for at least 1000 fluorophore configurations until the standard deviation in Q_r was < 2%. The simulation algorithm was tested by comparing the data acquired from Fung & Stryer and the Monte Carlo calculation schemes. The results from analytical and numerical simulation approaches turned out to be in good agreement [37].

While analyzing the case of protein-induced domain formation we assumed that total number of disk-shaped domains (N_{dm}) is equal to the number of membrane-bound protein molecules (B_a), i.e. $N_{dm} = B_a N_A$, N_A is Avogadro's number. Total number of lipid molecules and the number of CL (N_{CL}^{dm}) and PC (N_{PC}^{dm}) molecules in domains can be calculated as:

$$N_L^{dm} = N_{CL}^{dm} + N_{PC}^{dm} = \frac{B_a N_A \pi r_{dm}^2}{S_L}; \quad N_{CL}^{dm} = f_{CL} k N_L^{dm};$$

$$N_{PC}^{dm} = (1 - f_{CL} k) N_L^{dm} \tag{24}$$

where k is the ratio of CL concentrations in the protein-affected region (adsorption disk-shaped domain of radius r_{dm}) at nonrandom and random distribution of charged lipids, $B_a = B_1 + B_2$. For molar fraction f_D of donors (AV-PC or AV-CL), total number of AV-PC or AV-CL molecules in outer monolayer is given by:

$$N_{AV-PC}^{tot} = N_{AV-CL}^{tot} = L_{out} f_D N_A \tag{25}$$

Given that the fraction of CL (f_{CL}^{dm}) and PC (f_{PC}^{dm}) in domains is equal to

$$f_{CL}^{dm} = \frac{B_a N_A f_{CL} k \pi r_{dm}^2}{L_{out} N_A f_{CL} S_L} = \frac{B_a k \pi r_{dm}^2}{L_{out} S_L};$$

$$f_{PC}^{dm} = \frac{B_a \pi r_{dm}^2 (1 - f_{CL} k)}{L_{out} S_L (1 - f_{CL})} \tag{26}$$

the number of AV-CL molecules in domain (N_{AV-CL}^{dm}) and non-domain (N_{AV-CL}^{ndm}) regions can be expressed as:

$$N_{AV-CL}^{dm} = N_{AV-CL}^{tot} f_{CL}^{dm} = \frac{B_a k \pi r_{dm}^2 N_A f_D}{S_L} \; ;$$

$$N_{AV-CL}^{ndm} = L_{out} N_A f_D - N_{AV-CL}^{dm} \tag{27}$$

Surface densities of AV-CL in domain (δ_{AV-CL}^{dm}) and non-domain (δ_{AV-CL}^{ndm}) regions are given by:

$$\delta_{AV-CL}^{dm} = \frac{N_{AV-CL}^{dm}}{B_a N_A \pi r_{dm}^2} = \frac{f_D k}{S_L} \; ;$$

$$\delta_{AV-CL}^{ndm} = \frac{N_{AV-CL}^{ndm}}{L_{out} S_L N_A - B_a N_A \pi r_{dm}^2} = \frac{f_D \left(L_{out} S_L - k B_a \pi r_{dm}^2 \right)}{S_L \left(L_{out} S_L - B_a \pi r_{dm}^2 \right)} \tag{28}$$

Analogously, for AV-PC one obtains:

$$N_{AV-PC}^{dm} = N_{AV-PC}^{tot} f_{PC}^{dm} = \frac{B_a \pi r_{dm}^2 N_A f_D \left(1 - f_{CL} k \right)}{S_L \left(1 - f_{CL} \right)} \; ;$$

$$N_{AV-PC}^{ndm} = L_{out} N_A f_D - N_{AV-PC}^{dm} \tag{29}$$

$$\delta_{AV-PC}^{dm} = \frac{N_{AV-PC}^{dm}}{B_a N_A \pi r_{dm}^2} = \frac{f_D \left(1 - f_{CL} k \right)}{S_L \left(1 - f_{CL} \right)} \; ;$$

$$\delta_{AV-PC}^{ndm} = \frac{f_D}{S_L \left(1 - f_{CL} \right)} \left(1 - \frac{f_{CL} \left(L_{out} S_L - k B_a \pi r_{dm}^2 \right)}{L_{out} S_L - B_a \pi r_{dm}^2} \right) \tag{30}$$

Eqs. 28 and 30 were used to calculate the number of donors in domain and non-domain regions for a square cell with the side length taken as $10 R_o$ (here $R_o = 0.67 R_o^r$). The number of acceptors was determined by multiplying protein surface density (C_a^s) by the cell square (S_c) ($N_{AC} = C_a^s S_c$). The simulation program was scripted in Mathcad 2001 Professional.

3. RESULTS

3.1. Anionic Phospholipid Specificity of Cyt *c*

The first step of our study was directed towards evaluating the specificity of cyt *c* to anionic phospholipids. For this purpose, we measured RET between AV-PC and heme moiety of cyt *c* in lipid vesicles containing PG, PS or CL as an anionic lipid component. Association of the protein with lipid bilayers was followed by the decrease in donor fluorescence reflecting energy transfer from AV group to heme. As shown in Figure 1, in weakly charged membranes, the most effective energy transfer was observed in CL-containing vesicles, while the least effective RET was in PC/PG vesicles. Notably, the rise in anionic lipid content resulted in disappearance of this effect over the whole range of lipid concentrations employed here (5, 10, 20 and 40 μM). To explain these findings, cyt *c*-lipid binding data were quantitatively interpreted using global analysis approach [38, 39]. In brief, this methodology allows simultaneous resolution of both structural and binding parameters of protein-lipid association through coupling of the analytical model of RET in membrane systems with the appropriate binding model and analyzing 2D datasets acquired upon varying both protein and lipid concentrations. To compare the overall specificities of cyt *c* to the examined anionic lipids, RET model described by Eqs. (16)-(22) was streamlined by the simplest Langmuir adsorption model ignoring possible heterogeneity of cyt c-lipid binding centers:

$$K_d = \frac{B_a}{(P - B_a)(L_{acs}/n - B_a)},$$

$$B_a = \frac{1}{2}\left[P + \frac{L_{acs}}{n} + K_d - \sqrt{\left(P + \frac{L_{acs}}{n} + K_d\right)^2 - 4\frac{PL_{acs}}{n}}\right], \quad (31)$$

where B_a is the amount of bound acceptor (that is actually equal to the concentration of bound protein), P is the total protein concentration, L_{out} – concentration of lipids accessible to protein binding, K_d – dissociation constant, n – binding stoichiometry.

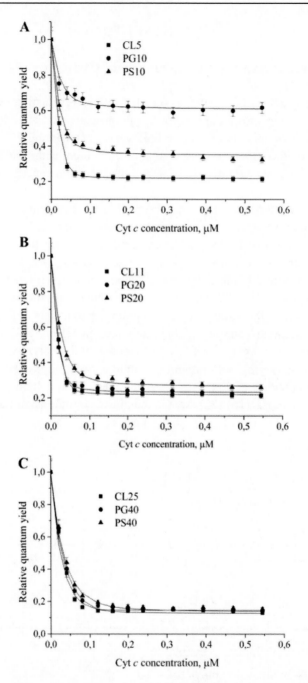

Figure 1. Relative quantum yield of AV-PC in different lipid systems. Solid lines show theoretical curves providing the best global fit of RET data.

Table 1. Structural and binding parameters derived for cyt *c* - lipid systems

System	d_c, nm	K_d, µM	n
CL5	$3.22^{\pm0.17}$	$0.81^{\pm0.04}$	$62^{\pm3.2}$
PG10	$3.53^{\pm0.21}$	$1.23^{\pm0.06}$	$54^{\pm2.9}$
PS10	$3.47^{\pm0.18}$	$0.94^{\pm0.05}$	$61^{\pm3.3}$
CL11	$3.51^{\pm0.19}$	$0.54^{\pm0.03}$	$47^{\pm2.5}$
PG20	$3.86^{\pm0.18}$	$0.91^{\pm0.05}$	$50^{\pm2.7}$
PS20	$3.68^{\pm0.22}$	$0.78^{0.04}$	$53^{\pm2.9}$
CL25	$3.85^{\pm0.21}$	$0.47^{\pm0.03}$	$42^{\pm2.2}$
PG40	$3.91^{\pm0.21}$	$0.51^{\pm0.03}$	$49^{\pm2.6}$
PS40	$3.93^{\pm0.22}$	$0.52^{\pm0.03}$	$41^{\pm2.2}$

Figure 1 shows the relative quantum yield of AV-PC as a function of total protein concentration, with solid lines representing the best fit of the combined RET-binding model to the experimental data. Global analysis of RET profiles obtained at varying P and L_{out} yielded the set of structural (d_c, the distance between lipid bilayer midplane and heme moiety of cyt *c*) and binding (K_d and n) parameters. As seen from Table 1, the depth of cyt *c* membrane penetration strongly depends on lipid bilayer composition, with the deepest protein embedment being observed for CL5 vesicles. Furthermore, protein complexation with CL5 liposomes is characterized by the lowest dissociation constant reflecting the strongest affinity of cyt *c* to this type of model membranes. Notably, these findings are in line with the results reported by Stepanov et al. who showed the highest specificity of cyt *c* to CL compared to other phospholipids [40]. The authors hypothesized that there is a strong correlation between protein affinity for phospholipids and lipid ability to modify cyt *c* active site.

Interestingly, increase in anionic lipid content up to the highest percentage resulted in apparent similarity of the derived parameters for CL-, PG- or PS-containing vesicles (Table 1). The fact that headgroup specificity of cyt *c* manifests itself only at the lowest content of anionic lipids can be explained as follows. In weakly charged lipid vesicles, only a part of protein molecules are bound to the bilayer. Indeed, as illustrated in Figure 2, A, only 44%, 36% and 22% of total cyt *c* added are associated with CL5, PS10 and PG10 membranes.

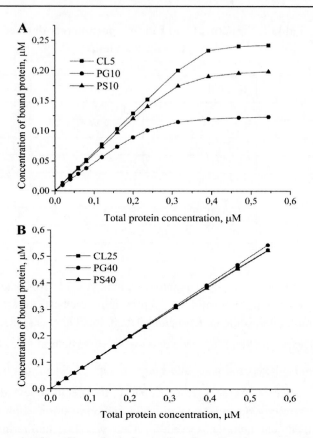

Figure 2. Concentration of bound protein as a function of total cyt c concentration in weakly (A) and highly (B) charged lipid vesicles.

The amount of bound protein is determined by the mode and molecular-level details of protein-lipid complexation. Thus, experimental $Q_r(P)$ curves, that actually reflect the behavior of $B(P)$ dependencies, appeared to be distinct for CL-, PG- and PS-containing lipid vesicles, pointing to different affinity of cyt c for the above anionic lipids. In contrast, at highly charged vesicles due to strong electrostatic cyt c – lipid interactions gives rise to almost complete protein association with lipid bilayer, so that $B(P)$ plots become virtually indistinguishable for CL25, PG40 and PS40 membranes (Figure 2, B), and, as a consequence, no differences are observed in the corresponding RET profiles. All the above considerations pose the question of what molecular events lie behind specific interactions between cyt c and CL. This issue was addressed at the next step of our study.

3.2. Cyt *c* Binding to CL-containing Membranes

Pursuing a comprehensive picture of cyt *c* – CL interactions, our experimental strategy was directed towards collecting multiple data sets. RET experiments have been conducted with either anthrylvinyl-labeled PC (AV-PC) or CL (AV-CL) as donors and heme group of cyt *c* as acceptor. More specifically, the relative quantum yield (Q_r) of donor was measured as a function of acceptor concentration upon varying the following experimental parameters:

A) CL content – 2.5, 5, 10 and 20 mol%;
B) lipid concentration (L) – 20 and 50 µM;
C) ionic strength (I) – 20, 40 and 60 mM.

The acquired data and their analysis are organized as follows. First, we briefly overview the main qualitative effects of the above variables on the characteristics of the measured RET. Subsequently we focus on the quantitative treatment of the obtained results using adsorption, RET and Monte Carlo models as described in Theoretical background section. Finally, we discuss the observed processes in detail. Notably, while the RET experiments were performed with a range of liposomes (CL2.5, CL5, CL10 and CL20), and two types of donors, due to the very large number of data (around 100 curves) collected we will in the following discuss only the representative ones.

A. *Features of RET Profiles Depending on Liposome Composition and Donor Type*

Figure 3 represents a set of RET curves obtained for different donors (either AV-PC or AV-CL) at varying CL mole fraction. The following salient features of RET profiles are noteworthy:

- *the absence of a definite dependence of energy transfer efficiency on CL content* suggesting that cyt *c* – lipid complexes are stabilized not only by electrostatic forces but also, presumably, by hydrophobic interactions;

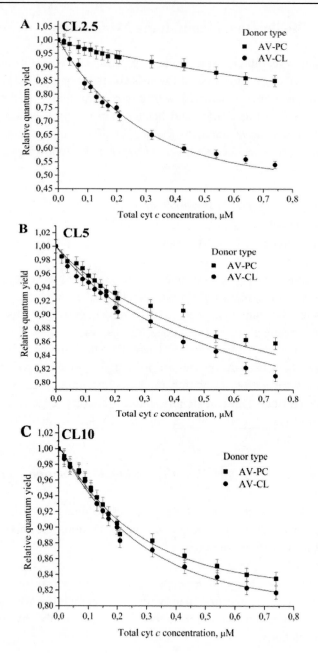

Figure 3. (Continued).

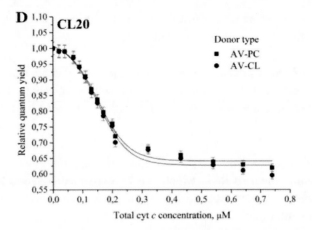

Figure 3. AV-PC and AV-CL quenching profiles in different types of lipid membranes. Measurements were performed under the conditions of low ionic strength (20 mM). Lipid concentration was 20 µM. Solid lines are presented to guide the reader's eye.

- *marked enhancement of energy transfer from anionic donor AV-CL* compared to the zwitterionic AV-PC in CL2.5 model membranes (Figure 3, A), a hallmark of accumulation of anionic lipids in the vicinity of bound protein;
- *inverted S-shape of the RET curves* in CL20 systems for both AV-PC and AV-CL donors which cannot be explained by the lateral movement of lipids and is attributable to the changes in cyt *c* transverse location. More specifically, given that the increment of acceptor concentration at the initial points of titration was rather small (~ 0.02 µM), the sigmoidality of the experimental plots is most likely the result of superposition of two curves with different saturation levels which correspond to two populations of membrane bound cyt *c* – surface-residing (saturation level is reached at the third titration point) and bilayer-inserted (saturation level coincides with the that of the overall curve). Furthermore, the sigmoidal curves are characterized by initial "lag region" (protein concentrations ≤ 0.1 µM) which presumably reflects the protein accumulation at the lipid-water interface prior to approaching a certain critical surface coverage efficient to overcome the energy barrier for protein insertion into the membrane. Interestingly, S-shape dependency of RET efficiency on acceptor concentration were also observed by Bacalum and Radu while investigating energy transfer from Trp residues of the bacterial

outer membrane porin to diphenylhexatriene, and the conclusion about donor insertion was made [41].

B. Effect of Lipid Concentration on the Behavior of RET Curves

At the next stage of the study, we addressed the question of whether the surface coverage could affect the RET profiles. Focusing on Figure 4, it is evident that:

- *decreasing lipid concentration is coupled with significant enhancement of RET*, which can be explained by an increase in the surface concentration of the acceptor upon lowering the lipid concentration;

- *lag period of sigmoidal RET curves* observed for CL20 membranes *depends on L* (Figure 4, B). For example, at $L = 20\,\mu M$ initial plateau ends at $P \approx 0.1\,\mu M$ while at $L = 50\,\mu M$ this value is about 0.15 µM. Such behavior most likely arises from the different modes of cyt c – lipid binding depending on surface coverage or, in other words, on L:P ratio. As was hypothesized by Oellerich et al., at high L:P values, in excess of lipid, a lot of binding sites for the protein are available, and electrostatic association of cyt c with the membrane surface seems to be predominant. Lowering the L:P ratio increases the surface coverage and weakens the electrostatic forces due to the neutralization of the protein and membrane charges because of the formation of protein-lipid complexes. As a result, cyt c insertion into the hydrophobic part of the membrane effectively competes with peripheral, electrostatically-controlled protein binding [42]. Determining roughly the completion of lag region as the beginning of protein embedment, the shift of "retardation" phase towards higher P at elevating lipid concentration indicates that, at $L = 50\,\mu M$ cyt c concentration, $0.1\,\mu M$ is insufficient for protein insertion to start. Analogous mechanism may explain the conversion of $Q_r(P)$ dependencies from sigmoidal to hyperbolic upon decreasing CL content (Figure 3). With CL20 lipid membranes within the same protein concentration range (from 0 to ~0.1 µM), where electrostatic interactions more efficiently compete with hydrophobic ones compared to CL2.5 due to higher membrane surface potential, the process of cyt c insertion into the bilayer seems to be slower and can be detected by RET. Importantly, all above considerations require further verification and will be the subject of more detailed analysis. Since in the present work, our attention was concentrated mainly on lipid segregation induced by cyt *c*, while analyzing the experimental data we ignored the deviations of RET curves from typical hyperbolic shape for liposomes with 20 mol% CL.

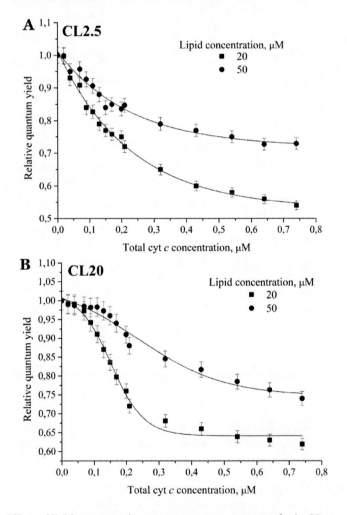

Figure 4. Effect of lipid concentration on resonance energy transfer in CL_{AV-CL} model membranes. Ionic strength was 20 mM. Solid lines are presented to guide the reader's eye.

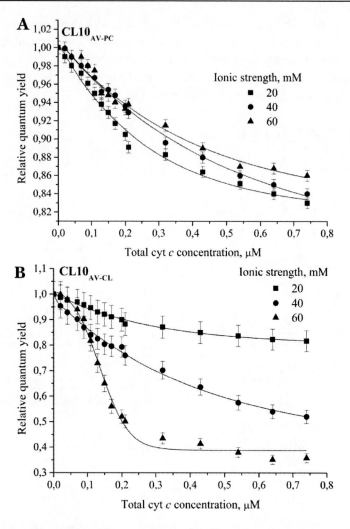

Figure 5. Concentration dependence of AV-PC and AV-CL fluorescence quenching by cyt c in PC/CL liposomes under conditions of varying ionic strength. Lipid concentration was 20 µM. Solid lines are presented to guide the reader's eye.

C. AV–cyt c Energy Transfer at Varying Ionic Strength

The last step of the study was aimed at exploring the impact of solvent conditions on energy transfer from the AV-lipids to the heme moiety. Elevating ionic strength turned out to have anomalous consequences for cyt c – lipid association. Conceptually, rise in monovalent ion concentration would attenuate electrostatic protein-lipid interactions thereby resulting in overall decrease of energy transfer efficiency. This was the case for AV-PC containing liposomes (Figure 5, A), but not for those with AV-CL where RET exhibited an unexpected enhancement with increasing ionic strength (Figure 5, B). As a consequence, difference between the relative quantum yields of AV-PC and AV-CL (ΔQ_r) did increase with ionic strength, this effect being most pronounced in weakly charged CL2.5 membranes (Figure 6).

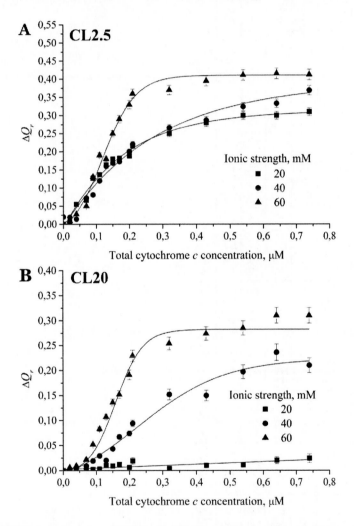

Figure 6. Difference between AV-PC and AV-CL relative quantum yields as a function of total protein concentration. Lipid concentration was 20 µM. Solid lines are presented to guide the reader's eye.

Table 2. Structural and binding parameters of cyt c association with PC/CL membranes

Parameter	CL2.5			CL5			CL10			CL20		
	I=20	I=40	I=60	I=20	I=40	I=60	I=20	I=40	I=60	I=20	I=40	I=60
K_1^0, μM^{-1}	$120^{\pm32}$	$500^{\pm145}$	$2000^{\pm564}$	$14^{\pm3.1}$	$50^{\pm10.5}$	$200^{\pm48}$	$10^{\pm2.6}$	$30^{\pm7.4}$	$50^{\pm10.5}$	$10^{\pm2.7}$	$30^{\pm7.2}$	$30^{\pm8.4}$
K_2^0, μM^{-1}	$900^{\pm262}$	$820^{\pm234}$	$740^{\pm212}$	$50^{\pm12}$	$39^{\pm15.2}$	$27^{\pm12}$	$10^{\pm2.6}$	$8.2^{\pm2.2}$	$7^{\pm2.1}$	$9^{\pm2.7}$	$7.1^{\pm2.4}$	$5.8^{\pm2.8}$
d_1, nm	$3.5^{\pm0.97}$	$3.0^{\pm0.89}$	$2.9^{\pm0.91}$	$4.1^{\pm0.94}$	$3.3^{\pm0.66}$	$3.0^{\pm0.72}$	$4.1^{\pm1.1}$	$3.5^{\pm0.77}$	$3.0^{\pm0.63}$	$4.1^{\pm1.1}$	$3.8^{\pm0.9}$	$3.5^{\pm0.9}$
d_2, nm	$3.2^{\pm0.91}$	$2.9^{\pm0.82}$	$2.7^{\pm0.75}$	$3.9^{\pm0.82}$	$3.0^{\pm0.6}$	$2.7^{\pm0.65}$	$3.9^{\pm1}$	$3.1^{\pm0.68}$	$2.8^{\pm0.59}$	$3.9^{\pm1.05}$	$3.6^{\pm0.8}$	$3.1^{\pm0.8}$

I is in mM, K_1^0, d_1 – DPS; K_2^0, d_2 – HPS.

After brief outlining of the obtained results and highlighting the main findings, we will now turn to quantitative data processing. As illustrated in Figure 6 energy transfer from the anionic donor was much more pronounced compared to the zwitterionic donor, except for CL5, CL10 and CL20 vesicles at $I = 20$ mM where RET curves obtained for either AV-PC or AV-CL as energy donors were virtually indistinguishable (data not shown for CL5 and CL10 systems). Among possible reasons for this phenomenon, the most probable seems to involve local lipid demixing upon cyt *c* adsorption onto the surface of oppositely charged membranes – CL molecules moving towards the membrane bound protein to minimize the electrostatic free energy of complexation. To account for this effect and to extract the morphology of cyt *c*-induced lipid domains, we developed Monte Carlo simulation procedure, the validity of which has been demonstrated in our previous study [37]. Overall, data treatment algorithm was based on three main steps: i) determination of structural (heme distance from the bilayer center, d) and binding (intrinsic association constants, K_1^0 and K_2^0, and stoichiometry, n) characteristics of cyt *c* – lipid association within the framework of SPT-based adsorption and 2D RET models (see Theoretical background section); ii) estimation of concentration of bound protein (B_a), iii) determination of domain size using MC simulation.

Optimization of the results obtained in terms of the combined RET-adsorption model revealed that the best quality fit was achieved with the parameters presented in Table 2. It appeared that i) intrinsic binding constants decrease with increasing CL content, and ii) K_1^0 rises with ionic strength while K_2^0 exhibits the opposite behavior. While interpreting these results, it is necessary to stress that the adsorption of peripheral proteins to membranes is a complex process implicating a range of interrelated events. Formation of electrostatic, hydrogen bonding and hydrophobic protein-lipid contacts is accompanied by mutually-dependent conformational changes of the protein and structural reorganizations of a lipid bilayer. Furthermore, modification of bilayer electrostatic characteristics by varying CL content or ionic strength may also influence the membrane structural properties (e.g., packing density of lipid molecules, free volume, acyl chain order etc.). All these phenomena together with other important contributors such as steric factors, hydrogen bonding, hydrophobic mismatch, surface complementarity, bilayer elastic deformation, the depth of protein bilayer penetration, the strength of confinement of a polypeptide chain to a surface membrane hydration etc., may underlie nonmonotonous character of K^0 dependence on liposome type and ambient conditions.

The recovered values of intrinsic constant were further used for evaluating the concentration of bound cyt c, and calculating the number of donors and acceptors (Eqs. 27, 29), required for implementing the MC simulation. Noteworthy, for $CL_{AV\text{-}PC}$ systems, the number of donors in domains N_{AV-PC}^{dm} proved to take on nonzero value ($N_{AV-PC}^{dm} = 1$) only at the highest surface densities of cyt c, thereby rendering RET profiles insensitive to variations in domain radius (r_{dm}) and the extent of CL segregation in the interaction zone (k). Therefore, the RET data obtained for $CL_{AV\text{-}PC}$ liposomes were treated using the MC approach with d_1 and d_2 being the only optimized parameters. Next, the recovered d_1 and d_2 values were fixed and (r_{dm}, k) sets providing the best agreement between simulated and experimental data were derived from the MC analysis of $CL_{AV\text{-}CL}$ RET curves.

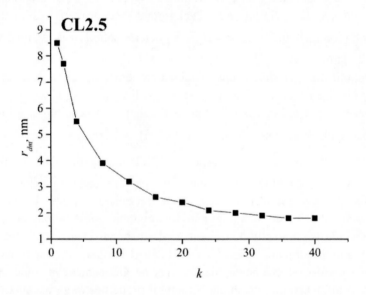

Figure 7. Dependence of lipid domain radius (r_{dm}) on the factor by which CL mole fraction increases in the protein-membrane interaction zone (k) obtained by the Monte-Carlo simulations for CL2.5/I20 vesicles.

It should be noted that the basic MC algorithm turned out to be successful only in fitting the RET data obtained for the lowest ionic strength ($I = 20$ mM) (δ, the relative difference between experimental and theoretical Q_r values, did not exceed 2%). Remarkably, MC modeling of RET in CL2.5 systems at $I = 20$ mM demonstrated that the radius of CL-enriched zone upon varying k from 1 to 40 (the value corresponding to complete replacement of PC by CL) does not exceed 8.5 nm (Figure 7) highlighting the local pattern of cyt *c* − induced lipid lateral redistribution. On the contrary, while trying to fit the results of RET measurements acquired at ionic strengths 40 and 60 mM using the basic MC procedure, we failed to achieve satisfactory agreement between theory and experiment (δ was > 15%). This implies that the behavior of all other sets of RET measurements cannot be explained in terms of the simple assumption about lateral segregation of PC and CL upon cyt *c* binding. Evidently, the observed RET profiles reflect complex interplay between a number of interfering processes, which may involve lipid demixing, aggregation of interfacially-adsorbed protein, and CL morphological changes (extended lipid conformation, non-bilayer structures).

4. DISCUSSION

Cyt *c* − CL interactions have been investigated with a variety of experimental techniques including SPR [43], atomic force microscopy [12, 44], NMR [45], electron paramagnetic resonance [46], FTIR spectroscopy [47] etc., and a wealth of data has been obtained up to date. Of these, fluorescence techniques have superiority due to their extraordinary sensitivity, relative simplicity, high selectivity, and experimental convenience. Among different modifications of fluorescence spectroscopy, the utility and versatility of RET for examining the different facets of protein-lipid association, especially those concerning the resolution of spatial details of cyt *c* − CL complexes, are indubitable. In our previous study, we applied RET from AV-PC to the heme moiety of cyt *c* to extend the model of two distinct acidic phospholipid binding sites in the protein (A- and C-site) with a special attention to the effects of CL protonation [13]. In the present work, the use of two energy donors, viz. AV-PC and AV-CL, allowed us to contribute further to the understanding of cyt *c* − CL biophysics, by putting the examination of cyt *c* ability to control membrane morphology in the focus of our research. The observation that at

$I = 20$ mM in CL5, CL10 and CL20 systems the efficiencies of energy transfer from neutral (AV-PC) and anionic (AV-CL) donor are identical suggest that in these types of lipid vesicles cyt c exerts no influence on lipid lateral distribution. In contrast, in CL2.5 membranes strong lipid demixing, determined by segregation-favoring screening of lipid charges by adsorbing cyt c molecules, was observed. This finding is in line with the results of May et al., who showed that the most effective clustering of anionic lipids occurs for a weakly charged membrane and highly charged protein [48]. Importantly, preferably electrostatic nature of lipid domains and the small size of AV fluorophore (ca. 0.3 nm) relative to the length of lipid molecules provide strong grounds for believing that AV-PC and AV-CL resemble their non-labeled counterparts in the partitioning into the lipid domains.

As mentioned above, the radius of CL domains was found not to exceed 8.5 nm implicating molecular scale deviation from the average lipid composition within and around the protein-membrane interaction zone [49-51]. Higher ionic strengths seem to enhance CL propensity to segregate, since the discrepancy in RET profiles from AV-PC and AV-CL was revealed for all types of the model membranes investigated here. This phenomenon was explained by the assumption that along with protein binding, accumulation of monovalent ions near the bilayer surface may heavily contribute to membrane charge compensation. However, as evidenced from our results, the formation of regular planar CL domains is not the finite stage of cyt c association with all types of membranes at $I = 40$ mM and $I = 60$ mM because basic MC procedure which accounts only for lipid demixing turned out to be inapplicable for satisfactory fitting of experimental curves. Therefore, we scrutinized several hypotheses concerning the possible factors which could explain the observed enhancement of energy transfer at increasing salt concentrations.

Hypothesis I. Imperfection of Theoretical Models

Extraction of quantitative information from RET data requires the knowledge of the surface acceptor concentration (B_a). Here this parameter was found using combined RET-adsorption model. A question arises if the inherent imperfection of this model associated with ignoring factors such as cyt c insertion into the lipid bilayer, protein conformational change, nonuniform charge distribution on cyt c surface etc., may influence the validity of the data analysis. To probe this question, we modeled two threshold situations – complete protein binding, i.e., $B_a = P$ (Case I in Figure 8), and protein location in the bilayer center, i.e., $d_1 = 0$ and $d_2 = 0$ (Case II in Figure 8). We considered only these cases since mathematically increasing B_a and decreasing d yield Q_r reduction. However, as seen in Figure 8, theoretical curves calculated by MC for these limiting cases still lie far above the experimental plot suggesting that underestimation of B_a or overestimation of d cannot explain the discrepancy between simulation and experiment. Additional proof in favor of this viewpoint comes from the mimicking of cyt c adsorption behavior in terms of SPT and 2D RET models which showed that if $B_a = P$, then d_1 and d_2 attain unrealistic magnitude of about 10 nm, while the maximum reasonable d value for our systems is $ca. \sim 4.5$ nm.

Based on the above rationales, we concluded with a high degree of confidence that disagreement between experimental data and theoretical predictions is not a consequence of inherent uncertainties of the experimental and optimization procedures.

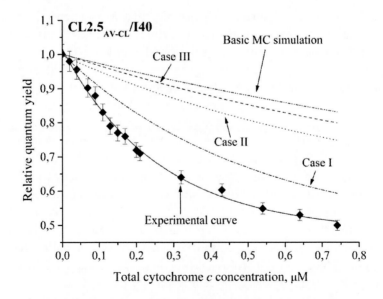

Figure 8. Monte Carlo calculations of AV-CL relative quantum yield for the cases of basic lipid demixing model (*dash dot dot line*), basic demixing model allowing for complete protein binding (*dash dot line*), cyt c location in the lipid bilayer center (*dot line*), and aggregation of membrane-bound protein (*dash line*).

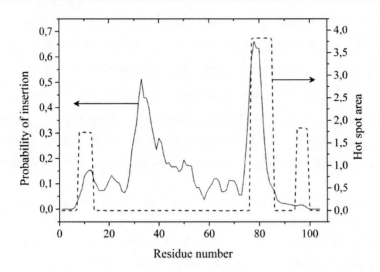

Figure 9. Correlation between aggregation and membrane insertion abilities of cyt c.

Hypothesis II. Aggregation of Membrane-bound Cyt c

A vast majority of studies demonstrates that association of cyt c with anionic lipids evokes protein conformational changes consistent with loosening of its tertiary structure and partial unfolding [19, 52-54]. Lipid bilayer can lower the activation energy barrier for protein unfolding providing an environment with reduced pH and decreased dielectric constant whose concerted action enhances side chain charge repulsion, thereby giving rise to a more open structure with exposed aggregation-prone areas. According to our calculations, pH decrease compared to the bulk phase can be as large as 0.6, 0.9, 1.3 and 1.8 pH units for CL2.5, CL5, CL10 and CL20 vesicles, respectively. Further, sophisticated theoretical analysis made by Heimburg and Marsh coupled with elegant electron spin resonance experiments revealed that at ionic strengths higher than 40 mM surface-denatured protein monomers exhibit strengthened tendency for self-association [55]. Analysis of cyt c structure by the web-based software AGGRESCAN, an online server for prediction of "hot" spots of self-association in polypeptides [56, 57], identified 3 aggregation-prone regions in protein molecule: $Lys_7 - Cys_{14}$, $Pro_{76} - Lys_{86}$, and $Leu_{94} - Lys_{100}$, with the second one possessing the highest aggregation propensity (Figure 9, dashed line). In the same time, examination of cyt c crystal structure by MemBrain online resource [58-60], developed for prediction of transmembrane protein structure, revealed two main protein regions with highest probability of bilayer insertion: His_{26} – Tyr_{48}, Lys_{73} – Lys_{86} (Figure 9, solid line). These findings suggest that the fragment Lys_{73} – Lys_{86} represents both aggregation-prone and membrane-penetrating region. Furthermore, a part of this region along with the His_{26} – Tyr_{48} segment are adjacent to the protein prosthetic group. The above considerations indicate that the heme moiety of cyt *c* (energy acceptor in our studies) may be involved into the aggregation and its embedment into the lipid bilayer. These processes may affect the RET curves, resulting in their deviation from the RET profiles corresponding to a random acceptor distribution. Assuming that lipid domains are formed around protein oligomers adsorbed/immersed into the bilayer, the total number of domains can be defined as $N_{dm} = B_a N_A / z_p$, where z_p is the degree of protein oligomerization. However, as judged from Figure 8 (Case III), this assumption didn't improve the data fitting, thereby invalidating this hypothesis. Indeed, if the demixing occurs locally, i.e. in the vicinity of singly adsorbed protein or peptide, there is no thermodynamical incentive for adsorbate aggregation [48].

Hypothesis III. Transition of CL into Extended Lipid Conformation

The nature and specificity of interactions between cyt *c* and CL have remained for a long time at the kernel of extensive research [11-20, 61-63]. Despite some contradictions in molecular-level details, a consensus regarding the general picture of cyt *c* – lipid complexation has been achieved, postulating the existence of two distinct acidic phospholipid binding sites on protein surface nominated as A-site and C-site [14-18]. A-site involves electrostatic interactions of deprotonated CL species with cyt *c*, while C-site is featured by hydrogen bonding to protonated phosphate coupled with the formation of electrostatic contacts with deprotonated phosphate. At low pH, protein-lipid interactions occur via C-site, around neutrality – via both sites. Increasing ionic strength dissociates cyt *c* bound to membrane via A-site thus shifting the equilibrium towards C-site-associated protein. Peculiar structural features of CL together with the existence of hydrophobic crevice in cyt *c* tertiary structure led to hypothesis of so-called extended lipid conformation in which lipid acyl chains point to the opposite directions from the headgroup producing straight angle of 180° [17, 18]. In such an orientation, one acyl chain remains within the plane of lipid bilayer while the other extends outwards and accommodates in the protein hydrophobic channel located near the heme crevice. This phospholipid frustration is specific for CL and is dictated by amphiphile tendency to minimize the bending stress created by high negative curvature. It was supposed that accommodation of lipid acyl chain in protein groove is stabilized by two types of interactions: i) strong electrostatic contacts between a network of positively charged amino acid residues (Lys_{72}, Lys_{73} and Lys_{86}) and DP cardiolipin in the case of A-site, and ii) H-bonds between Asn_{52} and HP lipid in the case of C-site [15, 18]. If one assumes that CL adopts such a conformation and acyl tail bearing the AV chromophore protrudes out of a membrane entering the hydrophobic cavity of cyt c, the enhancement of energy transfer might be expected due to the reduction of donor-acceptor separation distance. Indeed, allowing for this phenomenon in MC simulation by varying the zeta coordinate of donor and introducing the additional parameter D_{CE} standing for the distance between bilayer center and the plane of donors adopting the extended conformation, had partially beneficial effect and provided satisfactory fit of experimental results for CL10 and CL20 liposomes (Figure 10).

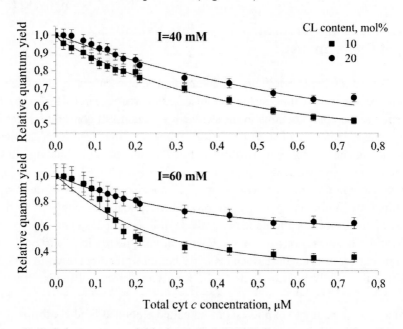

Figure 10. Relative quantum yield of AV-CL in PC/CL liposomes containing 10 mol% CL (■) or 20 mol% CL (●) as a function of cytochrome c concentration at $I = 40$ mM (upper panel) and $I = 60$ mM (lower panel). Solid lines show theoretical curves derived from Monte Carlo simulation.

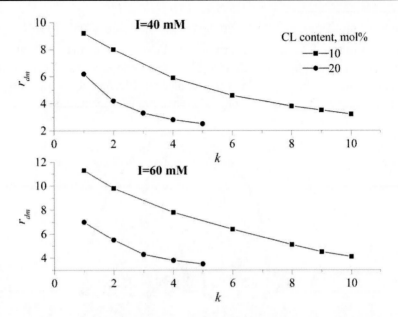

Figure 11. Parameters of membrane domains recovered from the combined "lipid demixing + extended lipid anchorage" Monte-Carlo model for CL10 (■) and CL20 (●) systems at ionic strengths 40 (upper panel) and 60 mM (lower panel).

Approximation of the experimental data by the combined "domain + extended lipid conformation" MC model yielded the radius of CL-enriched areas to fall in the ranges $3.2 - 9.2$ ($CL10_{AV-CL}/I40$), $2.5 - 6.2$ ($CL20_{AV-CL}/I40$), $4.1 - 11.3$ ($CL10_{AV-CL}/I60$) and $3.5 - 7$ nm ($CL20_{AV-CL}/I60$), depending on k (Figure 11). These estimates suggest that domain radius (taken at certain k) increases with ionic strength and decreases with CL content. Yet, for $CL2.5_{AV-CL}$ and $CL5_{AV-CL}$ systems, the above data treatment strategy proved unsuccessful suggesting the involvement of other factors.

Denoting the depth of protein penetration in the bilayer, the distance between membrane surface and plane of donor in the extended conformation, and membrane half-width by D_P, D_{SE} and D_m (Figure 12), respectively, the depth at which CL acyl chain impales cyt c (D_E) can be roughly estimated as $$D_E = D_P + D_{SE} = D_P + D_{CE} + D_m.$$ The bounds for the depth of protein insertion into lipid bilayer can be found by considering two cyt c orientations with the heme lying above or below the molecule center. Then, the lower and upper limits for D_P are given by $D_P^{min,max} = D_m - d_{1,2} + R_P \mp r_t$ where

$R_p \approx 2.1$ nm is protein effective radius in the lipid-bound state [64], $r_t \approx 0.7$ nm is displacement of heme group off the protein center. Notably, this expression may acquire more defined form if one addresses the recent work of Kalanxhi and Wallace [18] in which a mechanistic model for the extended lipid anchorage of cyt c to CL-containing membranes was proposed.

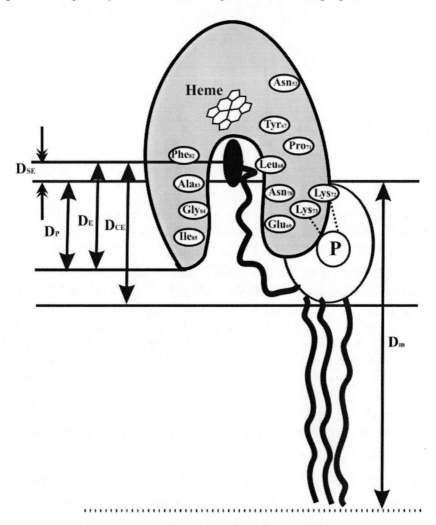

Figure 12. Schematic presentation of extended lipid conformation. Highlighted are amino acid residues constituting cyt c hydrophobic channel. P stands for CL phosphate. Black oval represents AV moiety. See text for explanation.

This model supposes that ionic contacts between phosphate group and Lys_{72}, Lys_{73} anchor CL in cyt *c* hydrophobic channel created by two non-polar polypeptide patches (residues Tyr_{67} – Pro_{71} and Phe_{82} – Ile_{85}). Such cyt *c* alignment, represented schematically in Figure 12, implies that heme moiety is located above the center of protein molecule and thus the upper limit of D_P should be considered. Furthermore, the above orientation suggests that Asn_{52} is more than 1 nm distant from the phosphate group of the lipid. Given that the length of H-bond is typically ~0.2 nm, hydrogen bonding between the protein and HP lipid species (characteristic of C-site) is unlikely, suggesting that in extended lipid conformation CL binds to cyt *c* mainly via the A-site. Accordingly, the depth of cyt *c* membrane penetration can be calculated from equation $D_P = D_m - d_1 + R_P - r_t$, with $D_m \approx 2.3$ nm. Evaluated in such a way the sets of parameters characterizing cyt *c* disposition relative to lipid-water interface are summarized in Table 3. These quantitative estimates suggest that ionic strength – induced RET enhancement may arise from favoring of extended lipid conformation.

In the present context it is reasonable to refer to the recent work of Hanske et al. in which four dye-labeled variants of cyt *c* have been used to study conformational properties of CL-bound protein [19]. The authors suggested that elevating ionic strength does not fully diminish the interactions between cyt *c* and CL molecules but rather favors the formation of specific hydrophobic protein-lipid contacts. These contacts are distinct from traditional hydrophobic interactions between exposed protein nonpolar patches and lipid acyl chains since the populations of extended cyt *c* structures were found to decrease with the rise in salt concentration. It was hypothesized that alternative mode of hydrophobic protein-lipid contacts could involve the insertion of CL acyl chains into cyt *c* interior [19].

Table 3. Structural parameters of cyt *c* – CL complex in an extended lipid conformation

Parameter	I = 40 mM		I = 60mM	
	CL10	CL20	CL10	CL20
D_P, nm	$0.3^{\pm 0.02}$	$0.1^{\pm 0.007}$	$0.7^{\pm 0.04}$	$0.4^{\pm 0.03}$
D_{CE}, nm	$2.7^{\pm 0.4}$	$3^{\pm 0.7}$	$2.4^{\pm 0.4}$	$2.9^{\pm 0.1}$
D_E, nm	$0.7^{\pm 0.06}$	$0.8^{\pm 0.09}$	$0.8^{\pm 0.09}$	$1.0^{\pm 0.12}$

Hypothesis IV. Formation of Non-bilayer Structures

As follows from the above considerations, for CL10 and CL20 membranes, the unusual behavior of RET curves can be explained by reversal of CL acyl chain with covalently bound AV into the cyt c crevice. However, the question about the driving force of energy transfer amplification in CL2.5 and CL5 vesicles at increasing salt concentration still remains open. Last but not least putative mechanism that could provide an answer is the well-known ability of cyt c to trigger the formation of non-bilayer structures. It was demonstrated in the early fundamental work by de Kruijff and Cullis that strong and specific cyt c – CL interactions may result in hexagonal (H_{II}) lipid configuration [20]. The formation of protein-induced non-bilayer structures was postulated to proceed through the following steps: electrostatically-governed protein adsorption onto membrane surface → lipid demixing and formation of CL-enriched domains → local destabilization of bilayer structure involving bilayer invagination → adoption of the lower-energy H_{II} phase. In keeping with this concept, we anticipated that gathering of CL molecules in the regions with negative curvature, i.e., hexagonal cylinders around cyt c, would result in displacement of PC molecules from protein vicinity and enhancement of RET. In distance terms, this scenario means that the minimal donor-acceptor separation in such a configuration is $R_{min} = R_P + D_m \approx 4.4$ nm (Figure 13). Following the fundamental energy transfer law, it is evident that for H_{II} phase, relative quantum yield can be as low as $Q_r = 1 - \dfrac{1}{\left(\dfrac{R_{min}}{R_0}\right)^6 + 1} \approx 0.4$ where $R_0 \approx 4.7$ nm is the Förster radius. The most pronounced energy transfer was observed for CL2.5$_{AV\text{-}CL}$/I60 liposomes with the $Q_r = 0.44$ at the highest protein concentration lending support to the idea that formation of non-bilayer structures can represent the main pathway consistent with anomalous Q_r decrease in CL2.5$_{AV\text{-}CL}$ and CL5$_{AV\text{-}CL}$ membranes upon rising I.

Vladimirov et al. characterized hexagonal state of cyt c – CL complex as a spherical nanoparticle with a diameter of ~11 nm, in which protein is completely covered by polar headgroups of 35-40 CL molecules [65, 66]. Furthermore, it was shown that the assembly of such kind of nanostructures is accompanied by cyt c swelling, i.e. increase in its molecular volume. The authors assumed that this effect is associated with submerging of one acyl chain of CL molecule into the protein interior. This becomes possible due to conformational transition of cyt *c* into the molten globule state. Indeed, a good deal of works has shown that binding of cyt *c* to CL induces the formation of protein conformer with reduced thermal stability that conserves a native-like secondary structure [19, 65-69]. Likewise, it was supposed that transition of CL into extended conformation and hexagonal phase are interrelated processes. The ability of CL to form both these conformations (extended anchorage and H_{II}) is likely to originate from lipid conical shape which induces negative curvature strain in lipid bilayer [70]. In order to relieve the lateral pressure, CL molecules tend to adopt one of these states or both of them. In the light of these rationales we cannot exclude the possibility that in the systems examined here, CL is transformed into hexagonal phase where acyl chains of some lipid molecules protrude into cyt *c* matrix.

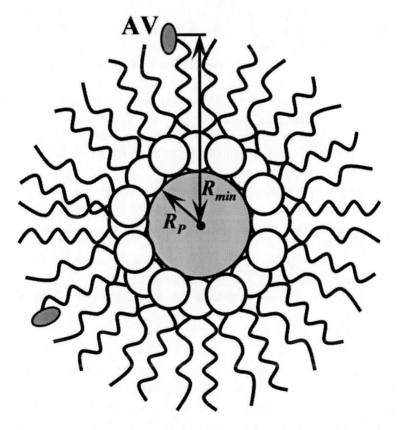

Figure 13. Geometry of inverted CL phase induced by cyt *c*. Protein molecule is shown as a grey sphere.

5. Tentative Model of Cyt C - Induced Structural Changes of Lipid Bilayer

Keeping in mind the knowledge on the processes occurring in our systems, we can now try to specify the ways by which salt concentration and CL content may control the switching between the regular CL-replete domains (CL2.5/I20), domains in which CL molecules adopt additionally extended conformation (CL10/I40, CL20/I40, CL10/I60 and CL20/I60) and H_{II} structures (CL2.5/I40, CL5/I40, CL2.5/I60 and CL5/I60) (Figure 11). A good deal of experimental and theoretical works has been invested into the studies on lipid morphological transformations induced by adsorption of oppositely charged cationic proteins [48-51, 71]. From these studies, a mechanism emerges according to which the fluid nature of lipid bilayer allows the lipid constituent with the higher protein affinity to migrate laterally towards the interaction zone, modulating locally the lipid composition. If the curvature radius of anionic lipid-enriched areas exceeds that of surrounding lipid, membrane can further lower the interaction energy by bending and stretching, thereby changing local curvature [48]. While the elasticity of membrane underlies the further possible structural transformations of the domains, initial crowding of specific lipids around the adsorbate is dictated by electrostatic protein-lipid interactions. Factors that would facilitate the preferential interactions of protein with anionic lipids can be identified as [50]:

a) presence of clusters of positively charged amino acid residues on the protein surface allowing one protein molecule to interact simultaneously with several anionic lipids;
b) conformational flexibility of a polypeptide chain to promote the formation of protein conformer in which the distance between positive charges and anionic lipid headgroups is minimal;
c) physiological stimuli providing the screening of electrostatic repulsion between charged lipids – increasing salt concentration and decreasing pH.

Returning to our systems, it is clear that at $I = 20$ mM strong lipid demixing occurs exclusively for CL2.5 membranes, which is determined by segregation-favoring screening of lipid charges by adsorbing cyt c molecules. This finding is in line with the results of May et al., who showed that the most effective clustering of anionic lipids is inherent for a weakly charged membrane and highly charged protein [48]. Higher ionic strengths seem to enhance CL propensity to segregate, since along with protein binding, accumulation of monovalent ions near the bilayer surface may heavily contribute to membrane charge compensation. However, as evidenced from our results, the formation of regular planar CL domains is not the finite stage of cyt *c* association with all types of membranes at $I = 40$ mM and $I = 60$ mM. Clustering of CL molecules creates gradients of curvature and line tension along the membrane surface. This results in membrane folding within CL domains (Figure 14, upper panel, *3*). For weakly charged vesicles, the sorption of every subsequent protein molecule would lead to further membrane bending in the same direction. It was hypothesized that thermally driven undulations within the soft lipid membrane enhance the probability of attraction between two segments of the same extended membrane placed in apposition with cyt *c* residing in this so-called lipid "pocket" [72]. The bilayer segments coming in contact may fuse, thereby favoring the formation of closed lipid structure around the protein molecule (Figure 14, upper panel, *4*). This structure is described as "bulging" and represents hydrophobic nanosphere integrated between two lipid monolayers [65, 66]. In this geometry electrostatic free energy reaches its minimum because all lipid charges are in contact with protein charges, while in lamellar phase only a fraction of anionic lipids appear to be vicinal to cyt *c*. Several lines of evidence indicate that phospholipid polymorphism can be electrostatically controlled, and a number of anionic lipids may adopt H_{II} configuration at low pH or at high concentrations of monovalent salts or divalent metal cations [70]. These observations are usually explained by neutralization of anionic headgroup charges which favors the formation of H_{II} over the lamellar phase. Apparently, on the one hand, elevating salt concentration enhances the demixing tendency of CL to such extent that the most stable state for lipid domains would be a highly curved monolayer bending around protein molecule. On the other hand, elevated ionic strength screens lipid charges thereby strengthening the polymorphic potential of CL.

In highly charged liposomes, the conversion into inverted hexagonal phase is somewhat hampered because of high initial surface potential of lipid bilayer. Moreover, due to the lower degree of demixing, the transition into hexagonal phase is not required for reaching a thermodynamic equilibrium, and the route by which the system further reduces the interaction energy seems to involve CL transition into extended conformation (Figure 14, lower panel, *3*). It's noteworthy in this regard that conditions facilitating the extended anchorage implicate increasing bilayer curvature and charge, and decreasing the headgroup size [64].

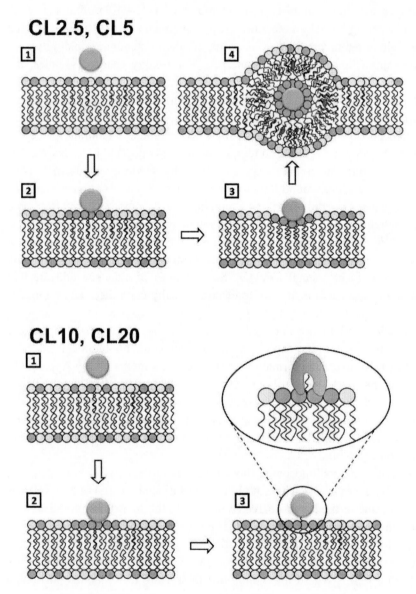

Figure 14. Tentative model for cyt c-induced structural reorganization of lipid bilayer.

These factors are believed to allow stronger electrostatic cyt *c* – lipid interactions resulting in more pronounced conformational changes of both protein (greater extent of unfolding and wider opening of a crevice) and lipid that facilitate the insertion of acyl chain in cyt *c* interior. Evidently, the above determinants readily explain why CL protrudes into protein only in the model membranes containing 10 and 20 mol% of anionic lipid – within the range of CL concentrations used here the highest curvature and charge, and the smallest average headgroup size are anticipated for CL10 and CL20 lipid bilayers. Meanwhile, the augmented ability of CL to adopt the extended conformation with lifting the concentration of monovalent ions originates, apparently, from the alterations in polarity near the membrane surface. From a thermodynamic point of view, to insert into the protein, lipid molecule should overcome the barrier associated with passage of acyl chain through the highly polar bilayer surface. Rising salt concentration brings about a drop in the dielectric constant at the lipid-water interface and, as a consequence, reduction in interfacial polarity which makes the accommodation of CL chain in cyt *c* groove more energetically favorable.

The formation of CL-enriched domains may have important physiological significance. First, the cristae of the inner mitochondrial membrane and contact sites between the inner and outer membranes are supposed to consist from the regions of hexagonal CL phase [73]. In view of crucial importance of cyt *c* in stabilization of such CL structures, and, as a consequence, stabilization of cristae folds, one hot question, that requires further investigation, is whether the cristae remodeling observed during apoptosis is initiated by the detachment of cyt *c* into cytosol? Second, CL structuring was shown to enhance the rate of electron transfer by cyt *c*. Furthermore, the formation of CL clusters was supposed to amplify the apoptotic signal, and plays a key role in energy channeling and opening the permeability transition pore, the early events of programmed cell death [74, 75]. In addition, CL domains can enhance ATP synthase function and serve as a membrane proton sink, particularly, when they are in close proximity to oxidative phosphorylation complexes [76, 77]. Finally, formation of CL-gathered zones is an important step in polar targeting of PIN proteins [72, 78]. Specifically, it was shown that elevated local concentrations of CL are highly required for targeting of an osmosensory transporter ProP [79, 80].

CONCLUSION

Cumulatively, using resonance energy transfer technique and Monte Carlo modelling, we have analyzed the formation of CL-enriched areas induced by the adsorption of cyt c onto PC/CL membranes under varying experimental conditions. The key findings are:

- at ionic strength 20 mM cyt c triggers the formation of lipid domains in CL2.5 vesicles with the radius of CL clusters not exceeding 8.5 nm;
- higher ionic strength (> 40 mM) enhances CL demixing propensity and generates lateral heterogeneity in all types of model membranes investigated here;
- the size of lipid domains increases with ionic strength and reduction of CL content, pointing to a significant role of electrostatic effects in controlling membrane lateral organization;
- at ionic strength 40 and 60 mM in lipid bilayers containing 10 and 20 mol% CL, segregation of CL into lipid domains with high negative curvature is followed by CL transition into the extended conformation tending to minimize the bending stress;
- for CL2.5 and CL5 membranes at ionic strength 40 and 60 mM, regular CL domains represent the intermediates in transition from lamellar to hexagonal phase.

Our results may have important implications for a wealth of cellular activities including fusion and fission of membranes, cell sporulation and division, functioning of cyt c in mitochondria as electron shuttle, its role in apoptosis, and overall biogenesis of the protein.

REFERENCES

[1]   Salemme, FR. Structure and functions of cytochromes c. *Annu. Rev. Biochem.*, 1977, *46*, 299-329.

[2]   Goodsell, DS. The molecular perspective: cytochrome c and apoptosis. *The Oncologist*, 2004, *9*, 226-227.

[3]   Diaz-Moreno, I; Garcia-Heredia, JM; Diaz-Quintana, A; De la Rosa, MA. Cytochrome c signalosome in mitochondria. *Eur. Biophys. J.*, 2011, *40*, 1301-1315.

[4]   Cusanovich, MA; Hazzard, JT; Meyer, TE; Tollin, G. Electron transfer mechanisms in heme proteins. *J. Macromol. Sci.-Chem.*, 1989, *A26*, 433-443.

[5]   Gray, HB; Winkler, JR. Electron flow through metalloproteins. *Biochim. Biophys. Acta*, 2010, *1797*, 1563-1572.

[6]   Ascenzi, P; Polticelli, F; Marino, M; Santucci, R; Coletta, M. Cardiolipin drives cytochrome c proapoptotic and antiapoptotic actions. *Life*, 2011, *63*, 160-165.

[7]   Orrenius, S; Gogvadze, V; Zhivotovsky, B. Mitochondrial oxidative stress: implications for cell death. *Annu. Rev. Pharmacol. Toxicol.*, 2007, *47*, 143-183.

[8]   Ow, YP; Green, DR; Hao, Z; Mak, TW. Cytochrome *c*: functions beyond respiration. *Nat. Rev. Mol. Cell. Biol.*, 2008, *9*, 532-542.

[9]   Huang, X; Zhai, D; Huang, Y. Dependence of permeability transition pore opening and cytochrome c release from mitochondria on mitochondria energetic status. *Mol. Cell. Biochem.* 2001, *224*, 1-7.

[10] Kumar, S; Baliga, B. Apaf-1/cytochrome *c* apoptosome: an essential initiator of caspase activation or just a sideshow? *Cell Death Differ.*, 2003, *10*, 16-18.

[11] Bernad, S; Oellerich, S; Soulimane, T; Noinville, S; Baron, MH; Paternostre, M; Lecomte, S. Interaction of horse heart and *Thermus thermophilus* type *c* cytochromes with phospholipid vesicles and hydrophobic surfaces. *Biophys. J.*, 2004, *86*, 3863-3872.

[12] Choi, EJ; Dimitriadis, EK. Cytochrome c adsorption to supported, anionic lipid bilayers studied via atomic force microscopy, *Biophys. J.*, 2004, *87*, 3234-3241.

[13] Gorbenko, GP; Molotkovsky, JG; Kinnunen, PKJ. Cytochrome *c* interaction with cardiolipin/phosphatidylcholine model membranes: effect of cardiolipin protonation. *Biophys. J.*, 2006, *90*, 4093-4103.

[14] Rytömaa, M; Mustonen, P; Kinnunen, PKJ. Reversible, nonionic, and pH-dependent association of cytochrome *c* with cardiolipin-phosphatidylcholine liposomes. *J. Biol. Chem.*, 1992, *267*, 22243-22248.

[15] Rytömaa, M; Kinnunen, PKJ. Evidence for two distinct acidic phospholipids-binding sites in cytochrome *c*. *J. Biol. Chem.*, 1994, *269*, 1770-1774.

[16] Rytömaa, M; Kinnunen, PKJ. Reversibility of the binding of cytochrome *c* to liposomes. *J. Biol. Chem.*, 1995, *270*, 3197-3202.

[17] Mattila, JPM, Sabatini, K; Kinnunen, PKJ. Interaction of cytochrome c with 1-palmitoyl-2-azelaoyl-sn-glycero-3-phosphocholine: evidence for acyl chain reversal. *Langmuir*, 2008, *24*, 4157-4160.

[18] Kalanxhi, E; Wallace, CJA. Cytochrome c impaled: investigation of the extended lipid anchorage of a soluble protein to mitochondrial membrane models. *Biochem. J.*, 2007, *407*, 179-187.

[19] Hanske, J; Toffey, JR; Morenz, AM; Bonilla, AJ; Schiavoni, KH; Pletneva, EV. Conformational properties of cardiolipin-bound cytochrome c. *Proc. Natl. Acad. USA*, 2012, *109*, 125-130.

[20] de Kruijff, B. Cullis, PR. Cytochrome c specifically induces non-bilayer structures in cardiolipin-containing model membranes. *Biochim. Biophys. Acta*, 1980, *602*, 477-490.

[21] Heimburg, T., Angerstein, B., Marsh, D. Binding of peripheral proteins to mixed lipid membranes: effect of lipid demixing upon binding. *Biophys. J.*, 1999, *76*, 2575-2586.

[22] Trusova, VM; Gorbenko, GP; Molotkovsky, JG; Kinnunen, PKJ. Cytochrome c – lipid interactions: new insights from resonance energy transfer. *Biophys. J.*, 2010, *99*, 1754-1763.

[23] Bergelson, L., Molotkovsky, JG; Manevich, Y. Lipid-specific probes in studies of biological membranes. *Chem. Phys. Lipids*, 1985, *37*, 165-195.

[24] Boldyrev, IA; Pavlova, YuA; Molotkovsky, JG. Synthesis and characteristics of new fluorescent probes based on cardiolipin. *Bioorg. Khim. (Moscow) (Engl. Transl.)*, 2009, *35*, 219-227.

[25] Mui, B; Chow, L; Hope, MJ. Extrusion technique to generate liposomes of defined size. *Meth. Enzymol.*, 2003, *367*, 3-14.

[26] Lakowicz, JR. *Principles of Fluorescent Spectroscopy*. Plenum Press, New York, 2006, 954 p.

[27] Chatelier, R; Minton, AP. Adsorption of globular proteins on locally planar surfaces: models for the effect of excluded surface area and aggregation of adsorbed protein on adsorption equilibria. *Biophys. J.*, 1996, *71*, 2367-2374.

[28] Minton, AP. Adsorption of globular proteins on locally planar surfaces. II. Models for the effect of multiple adsorbate conformations on adsorption equilibria and kinetics. *Biophys. J.*, 1999, *76*, 176-187.

[29] Heimburg, T; Marsh, D. Protein surface-distribution and protein-protein interactions in the binding of peripheral proteins to charged lipid membranes. *Biophys. J.*, 1995, *68*, 536-546.

[30] Tanford, C. The electrostatic free energy of globular protein ions in aqueous solution. *J. Phys. Chem.*, 1955, *59*, 788-793.

[31] Jähnig, F. Electrostatic free energy and shift of the phase transition for charged lipid membranes. *Biophys. Chem.*, 1976, *4*, 309-318.

[32] Wydro, P. The influence of cardiolipin on phosphatidylglycerol/ phosphatidylethanolamine monolayers − studies on ternary films imitating bacterial membranes. *Coll. Surf. B Biointerf.*, 2013, *106*, 217-223.

[33] Fung, BK; Stryer, L. Surface density determination in membranes by fluorescence energy transfer. *Biochemistry*, 1978, *17*, 5241-5248.

[34] Gorbenko, GP; Ioffe, VM; Molotkovsky, JG; Kinnunen, PKJ. Resonance energy transfer study of lysozyme-lipid interactions. *Biochim. Biophys. Acta*, 2008, *1778*, 1213-1221.

[35] Gorbenko, GP; Handa, T; Saito, H; Molotkovsky, JG; Tanaka, M; Egashira, M; Nakano, M. Effect of cholesterol on bilayer location of the class A peptide Ac-18A-NH$_2$ as revealed by fluorescence resonance energy transfer. *Eur. Biophys. J*, 2003, *32*, 703-709.

[36] Dale, R; Eisinger, J; Blumberg, W. The orientational freedom of molecular probes. The orientation factor in intramolecular energy transfer. *Biophys. J*, 1979, *26*, 161-194.

[37] Gorbenko, GP; Trusova, VM; Molotkovsky, JG; Kinnunen, PKJ. Cytochrome *c* induces lipid demixing in weakly charged phosphatidylcholine/phosphatidylglycerol model membranes as evidenced by energy transfer. *Biochim. Biophys. Acta*, 2009, *1788*, 1358-1365.

[38] Domanov, YA; Gorbenko, GP; Molotkovsky, JG. Global analysis of steady-state energy transfer measurements in membranes: resolution of structural and binding parameters. *J. Fluoresc.*, 2004, *14*, 49-55.

[39] Domanov, YA; Molotkovsky, JG; Gorbenko GP. Coverage-dependent changes of cytochrome *c* transverse location in phospholipid membranes revealed by FRET. *Biochim. Biophys. Acta*, 2005, *1716*, 49-58.

[40] Stepanov, G; Gnedenko, O; Mol'nar A; Ivanov, A; Vladimirov, Y; Osipov, A. Evaluation of cytochrome c affinity to anionic phospholipids by means of surface plasmon resonance. *FEBS Lett.*, 2009, *583*, 97-100.

[41] Bacalum, M; Radu, M. Insertion of proteins in the lipid bilayer of liposomes revealed by FRET. *Romanian J. Biophys.*, 2007, *17*, 129-138.

[42] Oellerich, S; Lecomte, S; Paternostre, M; Heimburg, T; Hildebrandt, P. Peripheral and integral binding of cytochrome *c* to phospholipids vesicles. *J. Phys. Chem. B*, 2004, *108*, 3871-3878.

[43] Salamon, Z; Tollin, G. Surface plasmon resonance studies of complex between cytochrome *c* and bovine cytochrome c oxidase incorporated into a supported planar lipid bilayer. I. Binding of cytochrome c to cardiolipin/phosphatidylcholine membranes in the absence of oxidase. *Biophys. J.*, 1996, *71*, 848-857.

[44] Domenech, O; Sanz, F; Montero, MT; Hernandez-Borrell, J. Thermodynamic and structural study of the main phospholipid components comprising the mitochondrial inner membrane. *Biochim. Biophys. Acta*, 2006, *1758*, 213-221.

[45] Brown, L; Wüthrich, K. NMR and ESR studies of the interactions of cytochrome *c* with mixed cardiolipin-phosphatidylcholine vesicles. *Biochim. Biophys. Acta,* 1977, *468*, 389-410.

[46] Kagan, VE; Tyurina, YY; Bayir, H; Chuh, CT; Kapralov, AA; Vlasova, I; Belikova, NA; Tyurin, VA; Amoscato, A; Epperly, M; Greenberger, J; DeKosky, S; Shvedova, AA; Jiang, J. The "pro-apoptotic genies" get out of mitochondria: oxidative lipidomics and redox activity of cytochrome *c*/cardiolipin complexes. *Chem. Biol. Interact.*, 2006, *163*, 15-28.

[47] Choi, S., and J. M. Swanson. Interaction of cytochrome *c* with cardiolipin: an infrared spectroscopic study. *Biophys. Chem.*, 1995, *54*, 271-278.

[48] May, S; Harries, D; Ben-Shaul, A. Lipid demixing and protein-protein interactions in the adsorption of charged proteins in mixed membranes. *Biophys. J.*, 2000, *79*, 1747-1760.

[49] Binder, WH; Barragan, V; Menger, FM. Domains and rafts in lipid membranes. *Angew. Chem. Int. Ed.*, 2003, *42*, 5802-5827.

[50] Mukherjee, S; Maxfield, FR. Membrane domains. *Annu. Rev. Cell Dev. Biol.*, 2004, *20*, 839-866.

[51] Mbamala, EC; Ben-Shaul, A; May, S. Domain formation induced by the adsorption of charged proteins on mixed lipid membranes. *Biophys. J.*, 2005, *88*, 1702-1714.

[52] Bradley, JM; Silkstone, G; Wilson, MT; Cheesman, MR; Butt, JN. Probing a complex of cytochrome *c* and cardiolipin by magnetic circular

dichroism spectroscopy: implications for the initial events in apoptosis. *J. Am. Chem. Soc.*, 2011, *133*, 19676-19679.

[53] Musatov, A; Fabian, M; Varhac, R. Elucidating the mechanism of ferrocytochrome *c* heme disruption by peroxidized cardiolipin. *J. Biol. Inorg. Chem.* 2013, *18*, 137-144.

[54] Pinheiro, TJT, Elöve, GA; Watts, A; Roder, H. Structural and kinetic description of cytochrome *c* unfolding induced by the interaction with lipid vesicles. *Biochemistry*, 1997, *36*, 13122-13132.

[55] Heimburg, T; Marsh, D. Protein surface-distribution and protein-protein interactions in the binding of peripheral proteins to charged lipid membranes. *Biophys. J.*, 1995, *68*, 536-546.

[56] Conchillo-Sole, O; de Groot, NS; Aviles, FX; Vendrell, J; Daura, X; Ventura, S. AGGRESCAN: a server for the prediction and evaluation of "hot spots" of aggregation in polypeptides. *BMC Bioinform.*, 2007, *8*, 65-82.

[57] de Groot, NS; Castillo, V; Grana-Montes, R; Ventura, S. AGGRESCAN: method, application, and perspectives for drug design. *Meth. Mol. Biol.*, 2012, *819*, 199-220.

[58] Yang, J; Jang, R; Zhang, J; Shen, HB. High-accuracy prediction of transmembrane inter-helix contacts and application to GPCR 3D structure modeling. *Bioinformatics*, 2013, *29*, 2579-2587.

[59] Shen, H; Chou, JJ; MemBrain: Improving the accuracy of predicting transmembrane helices, *PLoS ONE*, 2008, *6*, e2399.

[60] Shen, HB; Chou, KC; Signal-3L: a 3-layer approach for predicting signal peptides, *Biochem. Biophys. Res. Commun.*, 2007, *363*, 297-303.

[61] Sinibaldi, F; Fiorucci, L; Patriarca, A; Lauceri, R; Ferri, T; Coletta, M; Santucci, R. Insights into cytuchrome *c* – cardiolipin interaction. Role played by ionic strength. *Biochemistry*, 2008, *47*, 6928-6935.

[62] Shidoji, Y; Hayashi, K; Komura, S; Ohishi, N; Yagi, K. Loss of molecular interaction between cytochrome *c* and cardiolipin due to lipid peroxidation. *Biochem. Biophys. Res. Commun.*, 1999, *264*, 343-347.

[63] Belikova, NA; Vladimirov, YA; Osipov, AN; Kapralov, AA; Tyurin, VA; Potapovich, MV; Basova, LV; Peterson, J; Kurnikov, IV; Kagan, VE. Peroxidase activity and structural transitions of cytochrome *c* bound to cardiolipin-containing membranes. *Biochemistry*, 2006, *45*, 4998-5009.

[64] Akiyama, S; Takahashi, S; Kimura, T; Ishimori, K; Morishima, I; Nishikawa, Y; Fujisawa, T. Conformational landscape of cytochrome c folding studied by microsecond-resolved small-angle X-ray scattering. *Proc. Natl. Acad. Sci. USA*, 2002, *99*, 1329-1334.

[65] Vladimirov, YA; Proskurnina, EV; Alekseev, AV. Molecular mechanisms of apoptosis. Structure of cytochrome c – cardiolipin complex. *Biochemistry (Moscow) (Engl. Transl.)*, 2013, *78*, 1391-1404.

[66] Vladimirov, YA; Nol', YT; Volkov, VV. Protein-lipid nanoparticles that determine whether cells will live or die. *Crystallograph. Rep.*, 2011, *56*, 553-559.

[67] Miyamoto,S; Nantes, IL; Faria, PA; Cunha, D; Ronsein, GE; Medeiros, MHG; Mascio, PD. Cytochrome c – promoted cardiolipin oxidation generates singlet molecular oxygen. *Photochem. Photobiol. Sci.*, 2012, 11, 1536-1546.

[68] Abe, M; Niibayashi, R; Koubori, S; Moriyama, I; Miyoshi, H. Molecular mechanisms for the induction of peroxidase activity of the cytochrome c – cardiolipin complex. *Biochemistry*, 2011, *50*, 8383-8391.

[69] Bergstrom, CL; Beales, PA; Lv, Y; Vanderlick, TK; Groves, JT. Cytochrome c causes pore formation in cardiolipin-containing membranes. *Proc. Natl. Acad. Sci.*, 2013, *110*, 6269-6274.

[70] Cullis, PR; de Kruijff, B. Lipid polymorphism and the functional roles of lipids in biological membranes. *Biochim. Biophys. Acta*, 1979, *559*, 399-420.

[71] Rinia, HA; Boots, JW; Rijkers, DT; Kik, RA; Snel, MM; Demel, RA; Killian, JA; van der Eerden, JP; de Kruijff, B. Domain formation in phosphatidylcholine bilayers containing transmembrane peptides: specific effects of flanking residues. *Biochemistry*, 2002, *41*, 2814-2824.

[72] Beales, PA; Bergstrom, CL; Geerts, N; Groves, JT; Vanderlick, TK. Single vesicle observations of the cardiolipin – cytochrome c interaction: induction of membrane morphology changes. *Langmuir*, 2011, *27*, 6107-6115.

[73] Claypool, SM. Cardiolipin, a critical determinant of mitochondrial carrier protein assembly and function. *Biochim. Biophys. Acta*, 2009, *1788*, 2059-2068.

[74] Gonzalvez, F; Gottlieb, E. Cardiolipin: setting the beat of apoptosis. *Apoptosis*, 2007, *12*, 877-885.

[75] Ott, M; Zhivotovsky, B; Orrenius, S. Role of cardiolipin in cytochrome *c* release from mitochondria. *Cell Death Different.*, 2007, *14*, 1243-1247.

[76] Mileykovskaya, E; Dowhan, W. Cardiolipin membrane domains in prokaryotes and eukaryotes. *Biochim. Biophys. Acta*, 2009, *1788*, 2084-2091.

[77] Acehan, D; Malhotra, A; Xu, Y; Ren, M; Stokes, DL; Schlame, M. Cardiolipin affects the supramolecular organization of ATP synthase in mitochondria. *Biophys. J.*, 2011, 100, 2184-2192.

[78] Renner, LD; Weibel, DB. Cardiolipin microdomains localize to negatively curved regions of *Escherichia coli* membranes. *Proc. Natl. Acad. Sci. USA*, 2011, *108*, 6264-6269.

[79] Epand, RM; Epand, RF. Lipid domains in bacterial membranes and the action of antimicrobial agents. *Biochim. Biophys. Acta,* 2009, *1788*, 289-294.

[80] Mileykovskaya, E. Subcellular localization of *Escherichia coli* osmosensory transporter ProP: focus on cardiolipin membrane domains. *Mol. Microbiol.*, 2007, *64*, 1419-1422.

In: Cytochromes *b* and *c*   ISBN: 978-1-63117-467-4
Editor: Rurik Thom   © 2014 Nova Science Publishers, Inc.

Chapter 7

THE INVOLVEMENT OF CYTOCHROME *C* OXIDASE IN ALUMINIUM NEUROTOXICITY

Ankica Jelenković[1], Marina D. Jovanović[2] and Nataša Petronijević[3]*

[1]University of Belgrade, Institute for Biological Research "Siniša Stanković", Belgrade, Republic of Serbia
[2]Military Medical Academy, Institute for Medical Research, Belgrade, Republic of Serbia
[3]University of Belgrade, School of Medicine, Institute of Medical and Clinical Biochemistry, Belgrade, Republic of Serbia

ABSTRACT

The initial stage of a number of neurodegenerative diseases, including Alzheimer's disease (AD), is characterized by oxido-reductive imbalance leading towards free radicals production as well as towards the impaired respiration in mitochondria. Both the decreased activity of cytochrome *c* oxidase (COX), i.e. the Complex IV of the respiratory chain, and the altered cholinergic transmission are found in AD patients brain.

* Corresponding author: Ankica Jelenkovic, Institute for Biological Research "Sinisa Stankovic". Bulevar despota Stefana, 142; University of Belgrade, 11000 Belgrade; Republic of Serbia. Phone/fax: +381 11 3420606. E-mali:jelaka@yahoo.com.

Aluminium is a metal whose role in the etiology and/or pathogenesis of AD could not be rejected. It has multiple effects, such as cellular respiration damage and oxidative stress induction. In the experimental model we used in our study, aluminium chloride was applied intrahippocampally (i.h.) to the adult male Wistar rats. That was followed by the decreased activity of three enzymes in the brain regions that are most affected in AD, such as the forebrain cortex, hippocampus and basal forebrain. The activity of glucose-6-phosphate dehydrogenase (G6PDH) was more than halved, while the activity of COX and acetylcholinesterase (AChE) was almost exhausted. All this was accompanied by deteriorated learning and memory established by a two-way active avoidance test.

The intrahippocampal application of G6PDH, the enzyme of the pentose monophosphate pathway, just before aluminium, reverted the activity of COX to the control values. The rats were also i.h. pretreateated with fresh prepared green tea leaf extract, which primarily has strong antioxidant effects. Such pretreatment resulted in statistically significant improvement of the activity of COX and AChE in comparison with the aluminium treated rats, although these values did not achieve the levels of controls. Besides that, green tea leaf extract reverted the decreased learning and memory to control values, as well.

Conclusion: Neurotoxicity of aluminium was demonstrated through the decreased activity of G6PDH, COX and AChE, that was clinically expressed as impaired learning and memory. G6PDH and green tea leaf extract showed protective effects against this toxicity.

Keywords: Aluminium   neurotoxicity,   cytochrome c oxidase, acetylcholinesterase, Alzheimer's disease, active avoidance, oxidative stress

INTRODUCTION

The major source of energy supply for neurons and other cells is adenosine triphosphate (ATP), which is generated mainly in oxidative metabolism in mitochondria. A reliable and sensitive indicator of neurons capacity for oxidative metabolism is cytochrome c oxidase (COX). It is the terminal enzyme of the mitochondrial respiratory chain, which receives an electron from each of four cytochrome c molecules and transfers them to one oxygen molecule, converting molecular oxygen to two molecules of water.

The activity of COX is significantly reduced in the frontal, parietal and temporal cortex in Alzheimer's disease (AD) patients [1, 2, 3, 4]. Furthermore, COX activity is tightly coupled to neuronal activity, testifying to the presence of a hypometabolic process in AD and providing a possible explanation for the cognitive deficit, which is one of the main clinical features of AD. In addition, Luques et al. [5] recently demonstrated that chronic inhibition of COX in rat brain selectively alters hippocampal cholinergic innervations and impairs memory.

Alzheimer's disease is a progressive age-related neurodegenerative disease. It is the most common form of dementia, which could not be considered a part of the normal aging process. Together with other neurodegenerative diseases, AD is the focus of scientific community because of the increasing prevalence and the great medical, economic and social impairment it causes.

Multiple parts of the central nervous system are affected in AD sufferers. Neurodegeneration is evident in the so-called vulnerable, selective brain regions, such as the forebrain cortex, hippocampus and basal forebrain. The aggregation of amyloidal plaques of beta-amyloid peptide extracellularly or in the cerebral blood vessel walls, and the generation of neurofibrillary tangles in the neurons and glial cells are the two histopathological hallmarks of AD that are evident in these regions. These pathological changes are followed by the progressive death of neuronal cells, loss of synapses, especially synaptic mitochondria, selective depletion of neurotransmitters, and cerebral atrophy [6, 7]. The progressive reduction of memory and cognition as well as the changes in behavior and personality represent the basic clinical characteristics of this disease.

The etiology and pathogenesis of AD is not fully elucidated. While in the majority of patients the disease is sporadic, i.e. the etiology is not known, in some cases heritability is clear and is found in about 1-3% AD sufferers [8]. This is the reason why a number of theories (hypothesis) of the etiology and/or pathogenesis of AD has been developed [9]. Among them, the most prominent place belongs to mitochondrial and cholinergic hypothesis. Furthermore, a potential role of aluminum in the etiopathogenesis of AD can not be dismissed [10, 11].

HYPOTHESIS OF ALZHEIMER'S DISEASE

Mitochondrial Hypothesis

The primary cause of age-related neurological decline in AD is likely to be attributed to the to the brain oxidative stress as a leading disturbance on the molecular level of the disease [12]. Oxidative stress induced by oxidant species, which results in oxidative damage of all biomolecules, is developed under conditions when the balance between the production and the removal of reactive oxygen (ROS) and nitrogen species (RNS) is impaired [13]. In fact, ROS and RNS are constantly produced in mitochondria respiratory chain as byproducts of normal cellular functions as well as under pathological conditions. In addition to the principal site for endogenous ROS generation, electron transport chain in mitochondria is the main source of energy production, i.e. production of ATP. Cytochrome c is the subunit of this mitochondrial respiratory chain capable of oxidation and reduction, with regard to transferring electrons from Complex III to Complex IV.

The decreased activity of COX is found in both the peripheral tissue and the brain of AD patients. This alteration indicates that the mitochondrial respiration as well as the production of energy are reduced in AD, resulting in the increment of free radicals production [2]. Thus, the hypothesis of mitochondrial dysfunction in AD is quite reasonable [14].

Cholinergic Hypothesis

Cholinergic hypothesis is one of the earliest as to the cause of AD. It denotes a marked cholinergic dysfunction found in AD, especially the degeneration of anatomical pathways, primarily the cholinergic neurons in the basal forebrain as well as cortico-cortical neurons, which are thought to contribute extensively to the cognitive decline in AD sufferers [9, 15].

The basal forebrain provides cholinergic innervation for the entire cerebral cortex including the neocortex, amygdala, hippocampus, and thalamus (Figure 1). The cholinergic projections reach hippocampus *via* the septohippocampal pathway, whereas hippocampal inputs to the basal forebrain are included in the fornix, the largest pathway of the limbic system [16]. The left and right fornix communicate through commissura fornicis. These anatomo-neurochemical connections between brain structures are involved in cognitive processes and are, actually, very important in both the pathogenesis and clinical feature of AD.

Cholinergic dysfunction has been linked to the following:

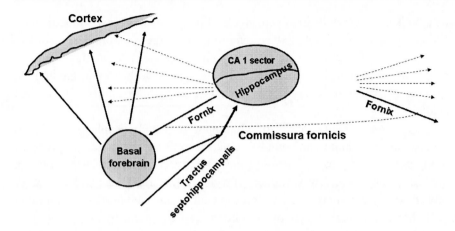

Figure 1. Neuro-anatomical connections between some brain structures involved in cholinergic transmission and cognitive processes in both the Alzheimer's disease and aluminium intoxication.

- deficits in the neurotransmitter acetylcholine,
- loss of the activity of choline acetyltransferase (ChAT, EC 2.3.1.6), which is a specific marker of cholinergic neurons since only these neurons contain this enzyme, and
- reduced acetylcholinesterase activity (AChE), which is impaired especially in the late stage of AD.

While biological role of ChAT lies in acetylcholine synthesis, AChE breaks down this neurotransmitter in the synaptic cleft by rapid hydrolysis that terminates nerve impulse transmissions at cholinergic synapses, and maintains pulsatile cholinergic stimulation [17]. Thus, AChE is a marker of cholinergic transmission. Considering all the aforementioned, it may be assumed that cholinergic system is a core focus of pharmacological intervention in AD [18].

ALUMINIUM AND BRAIN

Aluminium and Alzheimer's Disease

In spite of considerable evidence, a causative relationship between aluminium and brain pathology distinctive for Alzheimer's disease is still inconclusive and remains a highly debated subject within the scientific community [19]. The current state of knowledge suggests that aluminium metabolism is probably involved in the etiology, pathogenesis, precipitation and/or aggravation of AD, dialysis syndrome and other neurological disorders [10, 11, 20]. There is no doubt that aluminium has neurotoxic effects as revealed by biochemical, structural and functional disturbances in the brain, a number of which have been well documented in both human and animal studies [21].

Food is the main source of aluminum to which people are exposed because the aluminum compounds are added to many commercially-prepared products designed for ingestion (juices, dairy products, sweets, soybean products, baby food, etc.). Rather worryingly, the food that is prepared or preserved in aluminium dishes or foil can contain elevated levels of aluminium [22]. Moreover, high levels of aluminium can be found in many over-the-counter drugs, such as antacids, antidiarrhoeal drugs and antiperspirants.

Aluminium toxicity exhibits spatial selectivity in the brain. It affects brain regions involved in memory and learning [23]. This selectivity is expressed biochemically and neuroanatomically. It could partly be determined by the distribution of transferrin receptors (Tf–R) since aluminum is transported by transferrin, the iron–carrier protein that enters the brain by binding to Tf–R [24]. Some brain regions including the fronto–temporo–parietal cortex and hippocampus have been shown to exhibit a high density of Tf–R [25]. Therefore, neurotoxic effects of aluminum are predominantly manifested in the brain cortex and hippocampus providing neuroanatomical explanation for Alzheimer's type dementia that is developed under aluminum intoxication.

The pathological features of aluminium neurotoxicity can be the same or can resemble β–amyloid deposition and neurofibrillary tangles, which are also found in the same brain regions as in the AD patients [10, 11]. Furthermore, aluminium content in the brain of AD patients is two to three times higher than in the matched brains of non-AD sufferers [26]. Both the aforementioned pathologies (AD and aluminium neurointoxication) are also characterized by the loss of cholinergic innervation originating from the basal forebrain [27], and by memory deficits, as well [28].

Aluminium and Biochemical Changes

Aluminium and Oxidative Stress

Aluminum exerts multiple effects. One of them is strong prooxidant action despite the fact that it is not a transition metal. Its toxicity is manifested through the increased production of reactive species and the development of the oxidative stress, the condition in which the demand for reducing equivalents is so high that it exceeds the antioxidative capabilities [29, 30]. These findings are supported by the increased level of superoxide anion and nitric oxide in different brain structures (forebrain cortex, hippocampus, basal forebrain, striatum) after an acute application of aluminium chloride in the cornu ammonis region 1 (CA1) of the hippocampus in the rats [31, 32]. Moreover, aluminium readily binds to membrane phospholipids, which are some of the most vulnerable cellular components to oxidative stress. Namely, it makes them more prone to lipid peroxidation and facilitates their oxidative damage [33]. In accordance with these aluminium effects are the findings of increased lipid peroxidation in the rat brain after a single injection of aluminium chloride into the CA1 sector of the hippocampus not only early (three hours), but also 30 days after the injection [34]. Thus, intrahippocampal application of aluminum chloride exhibits both the acute as well as long-lasting damage of cell membrane.

Aluminium inhibits the production of nicotinamide adenine dinucleotide phosphate (NADPH), and also NADH, the donors of reducing equivalents [35]. That is the reason for inadequate regeneration of the reduced form of glutathione (GSH) from its oxidized species (GSSG) since this reaction is a NADPH-dependent:

$$GSSG + NADPH\ 2GSH + NADP^+$$
(GR = glutathione reductase).

The further depletion of GSH in NADPH deficit could be developed as the GSH could be used as a precursor for reducing equivalents [36, 35].

The insufficient production of NADPH brings about the reduction or even depletion of the antioxidant defense in the brain, thus facilitating the conditions for the occurrence of oxidative stress, i.e. the mitochondrial dysfunction is imminent in the case of aluminum overload. And *vice versa*: the sufficient production of NADPH is essential for the brain function, which is particularly susceptible to damage by reactive species due to the high energy requirements, the high oxygen consumption, the relative deficit of antioxidative defense system with low glutathione content, the high content of polyunsaturated fatty acids, which are especially prone to oxidation, and the high concentration of transition metals. Furthermore, the energy reserves of the brain are so small that a cascade of damage may be triggered even after a brief deprivation of either glucose or oxygen.

Aluminium and Glycolysis, Pentose Monophosphate Pathway, COX and the Production of Endogenous Energy (Figure 2)

Aluminium inhibits the glycolysis and the pentose monophosphate pathway of glucose metabolism, both of which take place in cytoplasm [36, 37]. The impaired glycolysis, which supplies cells with piruvate, is primarily related to the decreased activity of glucokinase, the enzyme that catalyzes the first reaction in glycolysis pathway, producing glucose-6-phosphate from glucose [38, 39].

The glucose-6-phosphate enters the glycolytic as well as the pentose monophosphate pathway. During glucose-6-phosphate oxidation, glucose-6-phosphate dehydrogenase (G6PDH), an enzyme of pentose monophosphate pathway reduces nicotinamide adenine dinucleotide phosphate (NADP) to the NADPH, the major donor of reductive equivalents for the reactions of reductive biosynthesis within cells:

$$\text{Glucose-6-phosphate} + \text{NADP}^+ \xrightarrow{\quad G6PDH \quad} \text{6-phosphogluconolactone} + \text{NADPH} + \text{H}^+.$$

In the rats intrahippocampally treated with aluminium chloride in the presented study, the activity of the G6PDH was impaired (Figure 2). This activity was reduced to 41% in the forebrain cortex, to 35% in the hippocampus and to 51% in the basal forebrain in comparison with the control group (Figure 2). These findings suggest the disruption of pentose monophosphate pathway, which leads to the impaired production of reductive equivalents in the form of NADPH.

Under physiological conditions the NADPH created in the cytosol should be transferred to the mitochondria to be included in the electron transport chain of oxidative phosphorylation. The energy released in electron flow through electron transport chain is used to transport (pump) hydrogen protons across the inner mitochondrial membrane into the intermembrane space producing an electrochemical proton gradient (proton motive force). The flow of protons from the intermembrane space back into the matrix through Complex V (ATP synthase) allows the complex to use the energy stored in the proton gradient to condense ADP with inorganic phosphate into ATP [40]. Thereby, a dysfunctional mitochondrial electron transport chain evoked by aluminium, including decreased supply of NADPH and reduced activity of COX, undoubtedly decreases ATP production and accelerates the generation of free radicals [23]. The aforementioned disturbances also exist in AD patients brain, which indicate additional similarities between AD and aluminum intoxication [41].

A number of studies have demonstrated that the neurotoxic activity of aluminum is accompanied by a reduction of COX activity [42]. Its activity is decreased in the rat forebrain cortex, hippocampus and basal forebrain after the application of aluminum chloride in the hippocampus. This happens as early as 10 minutes and also much later, i.e. three and 12 days after the application of this toxin, indicating the long-term toxic effects of aluminum, and their rapid development [43, 44, 31]. The value of COX activity in the forebrain cortex, hippocampus and basal forebrain of aluminium treated rats was only 14, 10 and 14 percent, respectively, compared to the control group (Figure 2).

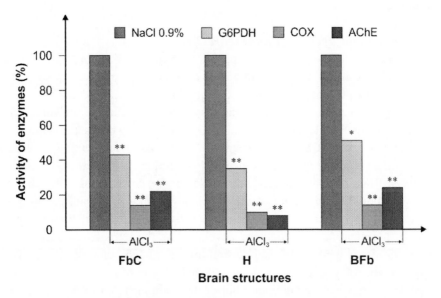

Figure 2. The activity of glucose-6-phosphate dehydrogenase (G6PDH), cytochrome *c* oxidase (COX) and acetylcholinesterase (AChE) in the brain of Wistar rats (n=9–12) intra-hippocampally treated with 0.9% NaCl and aluminium chloride (AlCl$_3$). The measurement unit for G6PDH is nM NADPH/h/mg prot., for COX is mg cit c/mg prot., and for AChE is mM acetylthiocholine/min./g prot. The values were expressed as percentages in comparison with the control group (NaCl 0.9%); 100% represented the value of the control group for every analyzed parameter. $p < 0.05$, $p < 0.01$ are the levels of statistical significance found versus 0.9% NaCl (*, **) (The differences between two percentages were calculated). The rats were sacrificed 12 days after treatments. The brain structures were ipsilateral to the injection site. FbC: forebrain cortex; H: hippocampus; BFb: basal forebrain.

During the aluminium intoxication the metabolic pathways in the Krebs cycle are insufficient, as well. This comes from multiple reasons, including the insufficient supply of acetyl-CoA and the inhibition of the aconitase activity [45].The Krebs cycle is a cyclic aerobic pathway that occurs in the mitochondrial matrix in eukaryotic cells and is composed of the final series of chemical reactions of carbohydrates, proteins, and fatty acids that produce energy and reducing equivalents (ATP, NADH, FADH2). The NADH generated by the Krebs cycle is fed into the oxidative phosphorylation (electron transport pathway) that is impaired under aluminium overload. This decrease in the reducing equivalents generation as well as the decrease developed under the harmful effects of aluminum on the pentose monophosphate pathway unavoidably lead to the reduction of COX activity (Figure 2)

Aluminium and Acetylcholine (Figure 2)

Compared to the control group, the activity of AChE in the forebrain cortex, hippocampus and basal forebrain of aluminium treated rats was only 22, 8 and 24 percent, respectively (Figure 2). This indicated the deficit of cholinergic transmission in which the disturbances in glucose utilization and piruvate generation under the aluminium toxicity as well as the supply of choline and acetyl-CoA are considered to be essential, as the substrate concentrations in the cholinergic neurons determine the rate of acetylcholine syntesis. Thus, the disturbances that lead to the decrease of acetylcholine synthesis could be the result of the deficiency of any of the aforementioned components, together with the decreased activity of ChAT in the destroyed cholinergic neurons that might be developed as the retrograde degeneration after the intrahippocampal application of aluminium chloride [46]. This sequence of events might suggest the reduced activity of AChE not only in the hippocampus, where aluminium chloride was administered in our study, but also in the basal forebrain, and in the forebrain cortex. Indeed, in the absence of the substrate, AChE activity is expected to be reduced after the aluminum administration, whether oral or in the hippocampal CA1 sector [39, 31, 47, 48].

Glycolysis is the principal source of acetyl-CoA that is yielded from piruvate as the end product derived during the 10 steps of glucose metabolism in the glycolytic process. Pyruvate is a precursor of acetyl-CoA, which feeds the Krebs cycle, also known as the citric acid cycle and the tricarboxylic acid cycle (TCA cycle). Prior to entering the Krebs cycle, pyruvate must be converted into acetyl-CoA in the pyruvate dehydrogenase reaction, which, in fact, is inhibited by aluminium [49]. The reduced generation of pyruvate that occurres under the aluminum overload as well as the inhibition of pyruvate dehydrogenase inevitably lead to the decreased production of acetyl-CoA and consequtively acetylcholine, as it is indicated by the decreased AChE activity (Figure 2).

THE INVOLVEMENT OF CYTOCHROME *C* OXIDASE IN ALUMINIUM NEUROTOXICITY

Material and Methods

The Aim of the Study

The similarity between neuropathological, neurochemical and cognitive findings in AD sufferers and aluminium overload has already been established. Bearing this in mind, the aim of the study that is now presented was to determine the biochemical effects in the specific brain structures induced by aluminum under experimental conditions, after aluminum chloride ($AlCl_3$) intrahippocampal administration to rats. Moreover, it was also of interest to investigate whether aluminium neurotoxicity is followed by clinical manifestations. In order to examine this, the animals were subjected to the behavioral testing. In addition, a possibility of protection against neurotoxic effects of aluminum by G6PDH and by green tea leaf extract (GTLE) was investigated.

Animals and Experimental Design

The research was performed on the male albino rats of Wistar strain 12 weeks old at the beginning of the experiments. While being in total anesthesia induced by intraperitoneal injection of thiopental sodium (Specia, Paris, 40 mg/kg body weight), the test substances were given in the volume of 0.01 ml. They were injected into the CA1 region of the hippocampus using a stereotaxic frame for small animals (La Precision Cinematographique, Paris). The injection position, determined relative to the lambda suture, defined from its center, was: 3.1 mm dorsally, 4.3 mm laterally and 2.5 mm ventrally (from the skull surface) [50].

Treatments

Four groups of rats (n = 9-12 in each) were treated. The first one received saline (0.9% NaCl, control), the second one AlCl₃ (Sigma-Aldrich, USA) dissolved in sterile de-ionized water, administered at 3.7 x 10^4 g/kg body weight. The third group received G6PDH (2500 U/ml; Sigma-Aldrich, USA), while the fourth one received freshly prepared GTLE just before AlCl₃. The rats were randomly submitted to treatments and behavioral testing.

After a 6-day recovery period, the rats were submitted to behavioral testing during five consecutive days. Thereafter, on the 12th day of the applied treatments, they were sacrificed by decapitation. The heads were immediately frozen in liquid nitrogen and stored at −70° C until the brain samples were prepared for biochemical analysis.

The GTLE Preparation

10 ml boiled de-ionized water was added to 0.5g of commercially available dried green tea leaves (Žid Trade, Belgrade). The resulting extract was filtered 30 minutes later through standard Whatman laboratory filter paper and cooled to room temperature before use.

Behavioral Testing

The ability of rats to learn and retain memory was evaluated by the two-way active avoidance (AA) task apparatus (Automatic Reflex Conditioner 7501, Ugo Basile, Milano, Italy). The AA task response was based on the daily blocks of 50 sessions (cycles). Each cycle lasted 30 seconds. An adaptation period of 5 minutes preceded the trial session. During each cycle the rat was exposed to an auditory stimulus [broadband noise of 68 dB (conditioned stimulus, CS), lasting seven seconds] followed by an aversive one (foot shock, 3 mA, delivered from the metallic grid floor of the shuttle box, lasting three seconds; unconditioned stimulus, US) and a period of 20 seconds without any stimulus. The CS was terminated if the rat made a crossing response to the other half of the box (AA response, the correct reaction), which prevented the US. If no response was obtained, the US was given.

Biochemical Analysis

Biochemical parameters were determined in the crude mitochondrial fractions from the forebrain cortex, hippocampus and basal forebrain ipsilateral to the injection site [51]. The activity of glucose-6-phosphate dehydrogenase (G6PDH. EC 1.1.1.49), cytochrome c oxidase (COX, EC

1.9.3.1) and acetylcholinesterase (AChE, EC 3.1.1.7) was assayed according to the methods of Bergmayer [52], Hess and Pope [53] and Ellman et al. [54], respectively.

Statistics

The biochemical parameters data were given as mean ± SD and were compared by the Student's t-tests, while for the AA task data (mean ± SE) the Kruskal-Wallis and Mann-Whitney U tests were applied. When the data were given as percentages, the differences between two percentages were calculated. The differences between experimental groups were considered significant when $p < 0.05$.

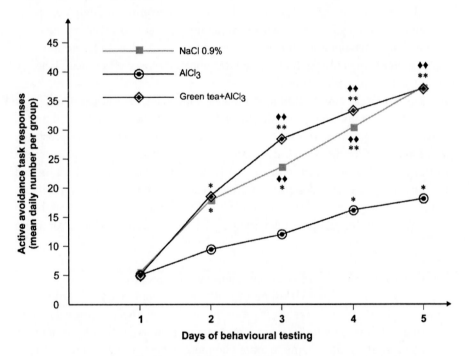

Figure 3. The effects of intra-hippocampal injections of 0.9% NaCl, aluminium chloride (AlCl$_3$) and green tea leaf extract administered prior to AlCl3 on two-way active avoidance tasks in Wistar rats (n=9–12).
The mean daily score of active avoidance responses per group was depicted. $p < 0.05$, $p < 0.01$ indicate statistical significance when basal (first test day) values were compared with the same treatments over the next 4 days (*, **, Kruskal–Wallis test) and with AlCl$_3$-treated rats ($\blacklozenge$, $\blacklozenge\blacklozenge$, Mann–Whitney U test).

Results and Discussion

Behavioral Testing and Biochemical Analysis after Aluminium Chloride Treatment

Active Avoidance (AA) Task, COX, AChE

In comparison to the control group, aluminium treated rats showed a decreased learning and memory ability as it was seen on the basis of the reduced acquisition of AA task (Figure 3). That was followed by the decreased activity of three enzymes, G6PDH, COX and AChE, in all the examined brain structures (Figures 2, 4, 5).

The complexity of acquisition of AA tasks requires a high degree of attention, the recognition of the aversive stimulus, spatial orientation, memory acquisition, consolidation and other brain processes. It has to be pointed out that different transmitters like glutamate, dopamine as well as acetylcholine participate in these processes.

The forebrain cortex, limbic structures, hippocampus and basal forebrain are of special importance for the understanding of the developed cognitive deficit. The projections from the caudal part of basal forebrain to the neocortex are responsible for the processes of attention, whereas the projections from the rostral part to the hippocampus are involved in the regulation of learning and memory [27]. Serious cognitive deficits resulting from the basal forebrain injury, including impairments in memory and learning, could be attributable to the loss of both corticopetal cholinergic projections from the basal forebrain and hippocampal cholinergic inputs to this brain region [55]. Accordingly, the metabolism of acetylcholine must be considered both in terms of normal learning and memory and in terms of aluminum neurotoxicity.

The synthesis of acetylcholine depends on the availability of choline and acetyl-CoA [56]. Choline is supplied to the cholinergic nerve terminals either by acetylcholine hydrolysis or by metabolism of choline-containing compounds. It is the reuptake into cholinergic nerves via a high affinity transport system (sodium-choline cotransport) that is indirectly coupled to the energy stored by the Na/K pump ATPase. For acetylcholine production, ChAT combines choline with acetate derived from acetyl-CoA. Apart from being the cells primary energy precursor, cholinergic neuron cytoplasmatic compartment requires an additional acetyl-CoA for the synthesis of the acetylcholine. Just because of these facts, the parts of the brain with cholinergic innervations are especially vulnerable to energy deficit. A knock-on effect of the reduced cholinergic transmission in the brain is the decreased learning and memory ability. Thus, three main parts of cellular function must be taken into consideration while examining the causes of altered acetylcholine synthesis under aluminium neurotoxicity post intrahippocampal application of aluminium chloride. These are the decreased production of substrates, reducing equivalents and endogenous energy. All these phenomena primarily result from the impaired glycolysis, pentose phosphate pathway and respiratory chain, with consequently disrupted cell energy metabolism. Such considerations are imposed since the sharp fall of the activity of three enzymes, G6PDH, COX and AChE, means that aluminium strongly interfered with them. Furthermore, the resulting biochemical disturbances were clinically manifested as the impaired acquisition of AA avoidance task performed in the two-way active avoidance shuttle box.

Potentially Protective Substances in the Aluminium Neurotoxicity

Aluminium Neurotoxicity and G6PDH

Having in mind that aluminum reduces the activity of G6PGH (Figure 2), it was presumed that giving this enzyme could decrease the toxic effects of aluminum. The expectations proved to be correct because the G6PDH supplementation exhibited neuroprotective effects in the aluminium neurotoxicity. That could be seen through the increased activity of COX when G6PDH was applied into the CA1 sector of the hippocampus before aluminium chloride. Furthermore, the pretreatment with G6PDH protected the COX activity altogether, as this activity was reverted to the control values in all the three examined brain structures, without significant difference between the control and G6PDH pretreated rats. The increased activity of COX was not unexpected and surprising, since G6PDH has a direct effect on the NADPH production. This means that other positive effects of this pretreatment could be reasonably expected. They could primarily be related to the decreased oxidative stress and improved energy production, and thus to the improvement of the energy-dependent processes. The analysis of the results we obtained is still in progress, and not yet completed.

Aluminium Neurotoxicity and Green Tea

The plant *Camellia sinensis L* is one of a major sources of dietary aluminium. The leaves accumulate and store this metal during their growth because aluminum is a cofactor for polyphenol biosynthesis. Despite being consumed in large amounts, the beverage made of plant *Camellia sinensis L*, which is popular worldwide and is traditionally consumed by some societies

(China, India, Far East and other parts of Asia) as green, black and oolong tea, has never been found to be neurotoxic. Furthermore, numerous previous and recent data suggest that green tea consumption may have favorable effects on human health, particularly with respect to its potential for preventing/treating stroke [57], coronary artery disease, diabetes mellitus [58] and some malignancies [59]. In addition, a huge number of studies demonstrated green tea consumption to be beneficial for cognitive functions [60, 61, 62]. Moreover, green tea was shown to prevent memory impairment induced by beta amyloid in animals [63, 64].

Active Avoidance Task (AA)

The application of GTLE before aluminium chloride in the CA1 part of the hippocampus opposed neurotoxicity of aluminium. From the clinical standpoint, GTLE completely prevented the effects of aluminum on the AA tasks (Figure 3). In other words, GTLE disabled the influence of aluminum on cognitive functions on which the acquisition of the AA tasks depends.

Our findings of the restored aluminium-evoked decrease of acquisition of AA task with GTLE pretreatment are in accordance with recently published studies in which it is suggested that green tea consumption may be neuroprotective and may prevent dementia, at least in animal models [65, 66]. Also, green tea application in animals was found by Haque et al. to improve some aspects of learning and memory [67].

The Activity of COX

The clinical improvement induced by GTLE pretreatment may be supported by the obtained biochemical changes. Namely, under the influence of GTLE, the deterioration of the activitiy of two enzymes, COX and AChE, was not as prominent in all the three examined brain structures as when only aluminum was applied (Figures 4 and 5). Although this activity did not reach the existing values in the control group, the increment was significantly higher in all the structures in comparison with the group which received aluminum chloride only, with the exception of the activity of COX in the hippocampus. It is likely that the obtained effects on the activity of COX and AChE were sufficient to prevent deleterious effects of aluminium on AA tasks.

The increment of the COX activity in the GTLE pretreated rats was the biggest in the basal forebrain and was 92% higher than the values in the aluminium treated rats. In the forebrain cortex and hippocampus these values were 57% and 32% higher, respectively.

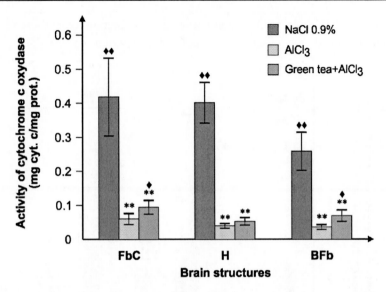

Figure 4. Activity of cytochrome c oxidase (COX) in the brain of Wistar rats (n=9–12) intra-hippocampally treated with 0.9% NaCl, aluminium chloride ($AlCl_3$) and green tea leaf extract administered prior to $AlCl_3$.
The values were expressed as mean ± SD. $p < 0.05$, $p < 0.01$ are the levels of statistical significance found versus 0.9% NaCl (*, **) and versus $AlCl_3$-treated rats (♦, ♦♦) (Student's t-test). The rats were sacrificed 12 days after treatments. The brain structures were ipsilateral to the injection site. FbC: forebrain cortex; H: hippocampus; BFb: basal forebrain.

The Activity of AChE

A far greater impact of GTLE was demonstrated on the activity of AChE. In comparison with the aluminium treated rats, these values were more than 90% higher in the forebrain cortex and basal forebrain, while in the hippocampus that value was even 400% higher. It should be noted that the hippocampus is essential for a range of memory functions, including the acquisition of spatial reference memory tasks, the recollection of the learning episode, etc. The hippocampal damage disrupts the connections of the hippocampus with other brain regions involved in the processes of learning and memory. Among the three sectors of the hippocampus (CA1, CA2 and CA3), the most vulnerable is the CA1. It was the one into which the substances examined in the presented study were administered. The hippocampal and cortical cholinergic transmission damage under the influence of aluminum was supported by the results of Platt and coworkers [68]. They registered the loss of acetylcholine-esterase bearing neurons after intraventricular application of aluminium for five successive days in these regions. Their findings emphasized the selective vulnerability of these regions to aluminium and its toxic effects on cholinergic function.

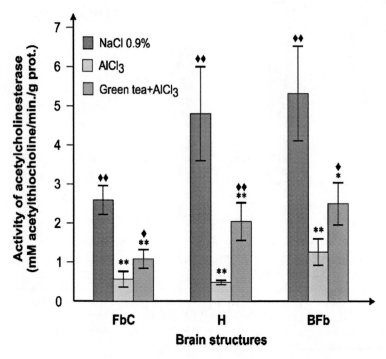

Figure 5. Activity of acetylcholinesterase (AChE) in the brain of Wistar rats (n=9–12) intra-hippocampally treated with 0.9% NaCl, aluminium chloride (AlCl₃) and green tea leaf extract administered prior to AlCl₃.
The values were expressed as mean ± SD. p<0.05, p<0.01 are the levels of statistical significance found versus 0.9% NaCl (*, **) and versus AlCl₃-treated rats (♦, ♦♦) (Student's t-test). The rats were sacrificed 12 days after treatments. The brain structures were ipsilateral to the injection site. FbC: forebrain cortex; H: hippocampus; BFb: basal forebrain.

A less prominent decrease in the activity of both enzymes, COX and AChE, in GTLE pretreated animals could be attributed to its strong antioxidant effects. It is the polyphenols and their derivatives that produce the beneficial effects ascribed to green tea. Among numerous polyphenols, (-) epigallocatechin gallate (EGCG), the major constituent of dry weight of green tea leaves, is the one which demonstrates the strongest biological activity [69, 31]. Indeed, complex and multi-faceted pharmacological properties of green tea have already been established [69, 70]. Namely, green tea, an excellent source of natural antioxidants, has both direct and indirect effects. The direct ones are achieved by strong scavenging of free radicals. On the other hand, its indirect effects account for the activation of antioxidant enzymes and other endogenous antioxidants [71].

Apart from its influence on free radicals, GTLE could exert neuroprotection independent of its classical antioxidant activity since it possesses potent metal-chelating properties [72]. Its polyphenols chelate transition metal ions such as iron and copper, which are capable of stimulating free radical formation. This is of special importance when it is known that iron is elevated in parallel with aluminium overload in the brain [24, 73]. Therefore, the protective effect of GTLE on the oxidative stress in the brain exposed to aluminium is multi-faceted and might be related to its scavenging ability on the free radicals, indirect antioxidative effects and its chelating ability.

Green tea can also antagonize toxic effects of aluminium on ATP synthesis. In our study, GTLE reduced the harmful effects of aluminum on the activity of COX, which is an indirect indicator of the mitochondrial complex V activity. COX activity precedes ATP synthesis and, therefore, any reduction of this enzyme would decrease ATP (energy) generation. Bearing in mind that ATP is necessary for maintaining all metabolic pathways examined in our study, conditions for a vicious cycle could be established if the COX activity is disturbed in any way, and, *vice versa,* if mitochondrial function is preserved. The results obtained by Srividhya et al. [74] are those that support the latter statement. In fact, they registered the protective effects of the EGCG toward mitochondrial function in the brain of aging rats. EGCG exhibited antioxidative effects, leading to the increased activity not only of the Complex IV of the respiratory chain, but also the previous three complexes. In addition, it improved the activity of a number of the Krebs cycle enzymes. One of them is aconitase whose activity is reduced by aluminum, as has already been mentioned [45]. Srividhya et al. [74] suggest that the improvement of the respiratory chain function and the Krebs cycle could be due to the antioxidant effects of the EGCG.

Furthermore, green tea influences intracellular calcium homeostasis in the opposite direction of aluminium. The dysregulation of calcium homeostasis is involved not only in the aluminium neurotoxicity but also in the pathophysiology of AD. Calcium is accumulating in the mitochondrial matrix in the presence of aluminium overload [49]. Because of that, the mitochondrial membrane proton gradient produced during oxidative phosphorylation collapses and triggers mitochondrial dysfunction [10, 11]. In the absence of a proton-motive force in the mitochondria, the reaction of ATP synthesis will run from right to left causing ATP hydrolysis, instead of producing ATP. Contrary to aluminium, the pharmacologically active constituents of green tea can inhibit calcium ion influx despite the high production of reactive species, thus protecting cells from the toxic effects of these species [75, 76].

The presented study has shown that green tea had strong effects against aluminium neurotoxicity developed after administration of aluminium chloride in the CA1 region of hippocampus. GTLE pretreatment reduced the harmful effects of aluminum on two enzymes, COX and AChE, in the forebrain cortex, hippocampus and basal forebrain to some extent. Taking into account the localization of these enzymes within the cell and their actions in the cell metabolism, we demonstrated that GTLE, most likely through the EGCG (biologically the most active constituent of green tea), protects mitochondrial and cholinergic function. These effects were clinically very clearly expressed in improved learning and memory abilities as the acquisition of AA task was completely normalized by the pretreatment with GTLE, despite the aluminium overload.

CONCLUSION

The neurotoxicity of aluminum chloride applied in the CA1 of the hippocampus of the adult male Wistar rats could be developed in the same parts of the brain which are usually damaged in AD. According to the presented results, aluminium damages glycolysis and pentose monophosphate pathway as well as mitochondrial function with the damage of the respiratory chain function. Cholinergic malfunction was also registered. Clinically, the decreased acquisition of AA task, indicating impaired cognitive functions, was found in these rats, as well.

The protective effects against aluminum overload were obtained with the application of G6PDH as well as GTLE prior to aluminium chloride. That was clearly demonstrated biochemically and clinically. When compared to the rats treated with aluminium only, the activity of COX was increased in both groups which had been given pretreatment. Similar findings concerning AChE activity were registered in the GTLE pretreated rats. Moreover, these rats even showed clinical improvement, i.e. the pathological findings of AA task induced by aluminum were even reverted to the values of the control group. All this suggests that COX is of great importance in the neurotoxicity of the acute aluminum overload shown in the forebrain cortex, hippocampus and basal forebrain of rats. Furthermore, according to these findings, COX undoubtedly has a significant role in the activities of the potentially protective substances, such as G6PDH and GTLE, when aluminium toxicity is concerned.

ACKNOWLEDGMENTS

This research was supported by the Ministry of Science of the Republic of Serbia (contract number 175058) and the Ministry of Defense of the Republic of Serbia (contract number MMA/06-10/B.3).

Our thanks to the publisher of the Phytotherapy Research journal who permitted us to use some of the results we had already published there.

REFERENCES

[1]   Maurer I, Zierz S, Möller HJ. A selective defect of cytochrome c oxidase is present in brain of Alzheimer disease patients. *Neurobiol Aging.* 2000; 21:455-62.

[2]   Hirai K, Aliev G, Nunomura A, Fujioka H, Russell RL, Atwood CS, et al. Mitochondrial abnormalities in Alzheimer's disease. *J Neurosci.* 2001; 21:3017-23.

[3]   Manczak M, Park BS, Jung Y, Reddy PH. Differential expression of oxidative phosphorylation genes in patients with Alzheimer's disease: implications for early mitochondrial dysfunction and oxidative damage. *Neuromolecular Med.* 2004; 5:147-62.

[4]   Pérez-Gracia E, Torrejón-Escribano B, Ferrer I. Dystrophic neurites of senile plaques in Alzheimer's disease are deficient in cytochrome c oxidase. *Acta Neuropathol.* 2008; 116:261-8.

[5]   Luques L, Shoham S, Weinstock M. Chronic brain cytochrome oxidase inhibition selectively alters hippocampal cholinergic innervation and impairs memory: prevention by ladostigil. *Exp Neurol.* 2007; 206:209-19.

[6]   Wenk GL. Neuropathologic changes in Alzheimer's disease: potential targets for treatment. *J Clin Psychiatry.* 2006; 67 Suppl 3:3-7.

[7]   Du H, Guo L, Yan SS. Synaptic mitochondrial pathology in Alzheimer's disease. *Antioxid Redox Signal.* 2012; 16:1467-75.

[8]   Swerdlow RH. Pathogenesis of Alzheimer's disease. *Clin Interv Aging.* 2007; 2:347-59.

[9]   Armstrong RA. What causes alzheimer's disease? *Folia Neuropathol.* 2013; 51:169-88.

[10]   Exley C, Esiri MM. Severe cerebral congophilic angiopathy coincident with increased brain aluminium in a resident of Camelford, Cornwall, UK. *J Neurol Neurosurg Psychiatry.* 2006; 77:877–9.

[11]   Tomljenovic L. Aluminum and Alzheimer's disease: after a century of controversy, is there a plausible link? *J Alzheimers Dis.* 2011; 23:567–98.

[12]   Yan MH, Wang X, Zhu X. Mitochondrial defects and oxidative stress in Alzheimer disease and Parkinson disease. *Free Radic Biol Med.* 2013; 62:90-101.

[13]   Bishop NA, Lu T, Yankner BA. Neural mechanisms of ageing and cognitive decline. *Nature.* 2010; 464:529-35.

[14]   Swerdlow RH, Burns JM, Khan SM. The Alzheimer's disease mitochondrial cascade hypothesis. *J Alzheimers Dis.* 2010; 20 (Suppl 2):S265-79.

[15]   Bartus RT, Dean RL, Pontecorvo MJ, Flicker C. The cholinergic hypothesis: a historical overview, current perspective, and future directions. *Ann N Y Acad Sci.* 1985; 444:332-58.

[16]   Mesulam MM. Some cholinergic themes related to AD: synaptology of the nucleus basalis, location of m2 receptors, interactions with amyloid metabolism and perturbations of cortical plasticity. *J Physiol Paris.* 1998; 92:293-8.

[17]   Massoulie J. The origin of the molecular diversity and functional anchoring of cholinesterases. *Neurosignals.* 2002; 11:130-43.

[18]   Dani JA, De Biasi M, Liang Y, Peterson J, Zhang L, Zhang T, et al. Potential applications of nicotinic ligands in the laboratory and clinic. *Bioorg Med Chem Lett.* 2000; 14:1837-9.

[19]   Frisardi V, Solfrizzi V, Capurso C, Kehoe PG, Imbimbo BP, Santamato A, et al. Aluminum in the diet and Alzheimer's disease: from current epidemiology to possible disease-modifying treatment. *J Alzheimers Dis.* 2010; 20:17-30.

[20]   Walton JR. Aluminum involvement in the progression of Alzheimer's disease. *J Alzheimers Dis.* 2013; 35:7-43.

[21]   Yokel RA. The toxicology of aluminum in the brain: a review. *Neurotoxicology.* 2000; 21: 813-8.

[22] Meiri H, Banin E, Roll M. Aluminium ingestion--is related to dementia. *Rev Environ Health.* 1991; 9:191-205.

[23] Swegert CV, Dave KR, Katyare SS. Effect of aluminium–induced Alzheimer like condition on oxidative energy metabolism in rat liver, brain in heart mitochondria. *Mech Ageing Dev.* 1999; 112:27-42.

[24] Ward RJ, Zhang Y, Crichton RR. Aluminium toxicity and iron homeostasis. *J Inorg Biochem.* 2001; 87:9-14.

[25] Edwardson JA, Candy JM, Ince PG, McArthur FK, Morris CM, Oakley AE, et al. Aluminium accumulation, beta-amyloid deposition and neurofibrillary changes in the central nervous system. *Ciba Found Symp.* 1992; 169:165-79.

[26] Walton JR. Aluminum disruption of calcium homeostasis and signal transduction resembles change that occurs in aging and Alzheimer's disease. *J Alzheimers Dis.* 2012; 29:255-73.

[27] Baxter MG, Chiba AA. Cognitive functions of the basal forebrain. *Curr Opinion Neurobiol.* 1999; 9:178–83.

[28] Bierer LM, Haroutunian V, Gabriel S, Knott PJ, Carlin LS, Purohit DP, et al. Neurochemical correlates of dementia severity in Alzheimer's disease: relative importance of the cholinergic deficits. *J Neurochem.* 1995; 64:749-60.

[29] Flora SJ, Mehta A, Satsangi K, Kannan GM, Gupta M. Aluminum-induced oxidative stress in rat brain: response to combined administration of citric acid and HEDTA. *Comp Biochem Physiol C Toxicol Pharmacol.* 2003; 134:319-28.

[30] Becaria A, Bondy SC, Campbell A. Aluminum and copper interact in the promotion of oxidative but not inflammatory events: implications for Alzheimer's disease. *J Alzheimers Dis.* 2003; 5:31-8

[31] Jelenković A, Jovanović MD, Stevanović I, Petronijević N, Bokonjić D, Zivković J, et al. Influence of the green tea leaf extract on neurotoxicity of aluminium chloride in rats. *Phytother Res.* 2013 Mar 11. doi: 10.1002/ptr.4962.

[32] Stevanović ID, Jovanović MD, Colić M, Jelenković A, Bokonjić D, Ninković M, Stojanović I. N-nitro-L-arginine methyl ester influence on aluminium toxicity in the brain. *Folia Neuropathol.* 2011; 49:219-29.

[33] Verstraeten SV, Nogueira LV, Schreier S, Oteiza PI. Effect of trivalent metal ions on phase separation and membrane lipid packing: role in lipid peroxidation. *Arch Biochem Biophys.* 1997; 338:121-7.

[34] Stevanović ID, Jovanović MD, Jelenković A, Colić M, Stojanović I, Ninković M. Effects of L-NAME, a non-specific nitric oxide synthase

inhibitor, on AlCl3-induced toxicity in the rat forebrain cortex. *J Vet Sci.* 2009; 10:15-22.

[35] Cho SW, Joshi JG. Inactivation of glucose-6-phosphate dehydrogenase isozymes from human and pig brain by aluminum. *J Neurochem.* 1989; 53:616-21.

[36] Lai JC, Blass JP. Inhibition of brain glycolysis by aluminum: *J Neurochem.* 1984; 42:438-46.

[37] Cho S, Joshi JG. Effect of long-term feeding of aluminium chloride on hexokinase and glucose-6-phosphate dehydrogenase in the brain. *Toxicology.* 1988; 48:61-9.

[38] Singla N, Dhawan DK. Regulatory role of zinc during aluminium-induced altered carbohydrate metabolism in rat brain. *J Neurosci Res.* 2012; 90:698-705.

[39] Nehru B, Bhalla P, Garg A. Evidence for centrophenoxine as a protective drug in aluminium induced behavioral and biochemical alteration in rat brain. *Cell Biochem.* 2006; 290:33-42.

[40] Horton RH, Moran LA, Ochs RS, Rawn DJ, Scrimgeour GK, editors. *Principles of biochemistry.* Prentice-Hall: London, Sydney, Toronto, Mexico, New Delhi, Tokyo, Singapore, Rio de Janeiro; 1996.

[41] Bigl M, Brückner MK, Arendt T, Bigl V, Eschrich K. Activities of key glycolytic enzymes in the brains of patients with Alzheimer's disease. *J Neural Transm.* 1999; 106:499-511.

[42] Mohan N, Alleyne T, Adogwa A. The effects of ingested aluminium on brain cytochrome oxidase activity. *West Indian Med J.* 2009; 58:422-7.

[43] Stevanović ID, Jovanović MD, Colić M, Ninković M, Jelenković A, Mihajlović R. Cytochrome C oxidase activity and nitric oxide synthase in the rat brain following aluminium intracerebral application. *Folia Neuropathol. 2013*; 51:140-6.

[44] Jovanović MD, Ninković M, Malicević Z, Mihajlović R, Mićić D, Vasiljević I, et al. Cytochrome C oxidase activity and total glutathione content in experimental model of intracerebral aluminum overload. *Vojnosanit Pregl.* 2000; 57:265-70.

[45] Zatta P, Lain E, Cagnolini C. Effects of aluminum on activity of Krebs cycle enzymes and glutamate dehydrogenase in rat brain homogenate. *Eur J Biochem.* 2000; 267:3049-55.

[46] Smith G. Animal models of Alzheimer\s disease: experimental cholinergic denervation. *Brain Res.* 1988; 13:103-18.

[47] Mićić DV, Petronijević ND. Acetylcholinesterase activity in the Mongolian gerbil brain after acute poisoning with aluminium. *J Alzheimer's Disease.* 2000; 2:1–6.

[48] Stevanović ID, Jovanović MD, Colić M, Jelenković A, Bokonjić D, Ninković M. Nitric oxide synthase inhibitors protect cholinergic neurons against AlCl3 excitotoxicity in the rat brain. *Brain Res Bull.* 2010; 81:641-6.

[49] Szutowicz A, Bielarczyk H, Kisielevski Y, Jankowska A, Madziar B, Tomaszewicz M. Effects of aluminum and calcium on acetyl-CoA metabolism in rat brain mitochondria. *J Neurochem.* 1998; 71:2447-53.

[50] Konig JFR, Klippel RA. *The Rat Brain. A stereotaxic atlas of the forebrain and lower parts of the brain stem.* The Williams and Wilkins Company: Baltimore; 1963.

[51] Gurd JW, Jones LR, Mahler HR, Moore WJ. Isolation and partial characterization of rat brain synaptic plasma membranes. *J Neurochem.* 1974; 22:281-90.

[52] Bergmayer H. *Methods of enzymatic analysis.* New York: Academic Press; 1974.

[53] Hess HH, Pope A. Intralaminar distribution of cytochrome c oxidase activity in human isocortex. *J Neurochem.* 1960; 5:207–17.

[54] Ellman GL, Courtney KD, Andres V Jr, Feather-Stone RM. A new and rapid colorimetric determination of acetylcholinesterase activity. *Biochem Pharmacol.* 1961; 7:88-95.

[55] Hasselmo ME, Schnell E. Laminar selectivity of the cholinergic suppression of synaptic transmission in rat hippocampal region CA1: computational modeling and brain slice physiology. *J Neurosci.* 1994; 14:3898-914.

[56] Oda Y. Choline acetyltransferase: the structure, distribution and pathologic changes in the central nervous system. *Pathol Int.* 2000; 49:921–37.

[57] Arab L, Liu W, Elashoff D. Green and black tea consumption and risk of stroke: a meta-analysis. *Stroke.* 2009; 40:1786-92.

[58] Chacko SM, Thambi PT, Kuttan R, Nishigaki I.Beneficial effects of green tea: a literature review. *Chin Med.* 2010; 6:5-13.

[59] Ogunleye AA., Xue F, Michels KB. Green tea consumption and breast cancer risk or recurrence: a meta-analysis. *Breast Cancer Res Treat.* 2010; 119:477-84.

[60] Feng L, Gwee X, Kua EH, Ng TP. Cognitive function and tea consumption in community dwelling older Chinese in Singapore. *J Nutr Health Aging.* 2010; 14:433-8.

[61] Kakuda T. Neuroprotective effects of theanine and its preventive effects on cognitive dysfunction. *Pharmacol Res.* 2011; 64:162-8.

[62] Park SK, Jung IC, Lee WK, Lee YS, Park HK, Go HJ, et al. A combination of green tea extract and l-theanine improves memory and attention in subjects with mild cognitive impairment: a double-blind placebo-controlled study. *J Med Food.* 2011; 14:334-43.

[63] Haque AM, Hashimoto M, Katakura M, Hara Y, Shido O. Green tea catechins prevent cognitive deficits caused by Abeta1-40 in rats. *J Nutr Biochem.* 2008; 19:619-26.

[64] Rezai-Zadeh K, Arendash GW, Hou H, Fernandez F, Jensen M, Runfeldt M, et al. Green tea epigallocatechin-3-gallate (EGCG) reduces beta-amyloid mediated cognitive impairment and modulates tau pathology in Alzheimer transgenic mice. *Brain Res.* 2008; 1214:177-87.

[65] Mandel S, Weinreb O, Amit T, Youdim MB. Cell signaling pathways in the neuroprotective actions of the green tea polyphenol (-)-epigallocatechin-3-gallate: implications for neurodegenerative diseases. *J Neurochem.* 2004; 88:1555-69.

[66] Unno K, Takabayashi F, Yoshida H, Choba D, Fukutomi R, Kikunaga N, et al. Daily consumption of green tea catechin delays memory regression in aged mice. *Biogerontology.* 2007; 8:89-95.

[67] Haque AM, Hashimoto M, Katakura M, Tanabe Y, Hara Y, Shido O. Long-term administration of green tea catechins improves spatial cognition learning ability in rats. *J Nutr.* 2006; 136:1043-7.

[68] Platt B, Fiddler G, Riedel G, Henderson Z. Aluminium toxicity in the rat brain: histochemical and immunocytochemical evidence. *Brain Res Bull.* 2001; 55:257-67.

[69] Mandel SA, Amit T, Weinreb O, Youdim MB. Understanding the broad-spectrum neuroprotective action profile of green tea polyphenols in aging and neurodegenerative diseases. *J Alzheimers Dis.* 2011; 25:187-208.

[70] Nakagawa T, Yokozawa T. Direct scavenging of nitric oxide and superoxide by green tea. *Food Chem Toxicol.* 2002; 40:1745-50.

[71] Fu Y, Zheng S, Lu SC, Chen A. Epigallocatechin-3-gallate inhibits growth of activated hepatic stellate cells by enhancing the capacity of glutathione synthesis. *Mol Pharmacol.* 2008; 73:1465-73.

[72] Guo Q, Zhao B, Li M, Shen S, Xin W. Studies on protective mechanisms of four components of green tea polyphenols against lipid peroxidation in synaptosomes. *Biochim Biophys Acta.* 1996; 1304:210-22.

[73] Domingo JL. Aluminum and other metals in Alzheimer's disease: a review of potential therapy with chelating agents. *J Alzheimers Dis.* 2006; 10:331-41.

[74] Srividhya R, Zarkovic K, Stroser M, Waeg G, Zarkovic N, Kalaiselvi P. Mitochondrial alterations in aging rat brain: effective role of (-)-epigallo catechin gallate. *Int J Dev Neurosci.* 2009 ; 27:223-31.

[75] Ishige K, Schubert D, Sagara Y. Flavonoids protect neuronal cells from oxidative stress by three distinct mechanisms. *Free Radic Biol Med.* 2001; 30:433–46.

[76] Chen L, Yang X, Jiao H, Zhao B. Tea catechins protect against lead-induced ROS formation, mitochondrial dysfunction, and calcium dysregulation in PC12 cells. *Chem Res Toxicol.* 2003; 16:1155-61.

INDEX

D

E

S